A VETERINARY GUIDE
TO THE PARASITES
OF REPTILES

Fig. 23. *Culex* sp. Female laying egg raft. (Photo courtesy of Susan E. Ellis).

Fig. 119. *Ixodes ricinus* parasitizing the viviparous lizard, *Lacerta vivipara*.
(Photo courtesy of Rudolf Malkmus).

A VETERINARY GUIDE TO THE PARASITES OF REPTILES

Volume 2 Arthropods (Excluding Mites)

SUSAN M. BARNARD, B.S.
Department of Herpetology
Zoo Atlanta

and

LANCE A. DURDEN, Ph.D.
Institute of Arthropodology and Parasitology
Georgia Southern University

KRIEGER PUBLISHING COMPANY
MALABAR, FLORIDA
2000

 PUBLISHER'S NOTE

A Veterinary Guide to the Parasites of Reptiles

was conceived as a continuing series. We are anxious to have contributing experts contact us in order to participate in future volumes covering the remaining parasite groups: trematodes, nematodes, acanthocephalids, pentastomids, leeches, and pseudoparasites.

Krieger Publishing Company

Original Edition 2000

Printed and Published by
KRIEGER PUBLISHING COMPANY
KRIEGER DRIVE
MALABAR, FLORIDA 32950

FROM A DECLARATION OF PRINCIPLES JOINTLY ADOPTED BY A COMMITTEE OF THE AMERICAN BAR ASSOCIATION AND A COMMITTEE OF PUBLISHERS: This publication is designed to provide accurate and authoritative information in regard to the subject matter covered. It is sold with the understanding that the publisher is not engaged in rendering legal, accounting, or other professional service. If legal advice or other expert assistance is required, the services of a competent professional person should be sought.

The Library of Congress has catalogued Volume 1 of this title as follows:

Library of Congress Cataloging-in-Publication Data

Barnard, Susan M.
    A veterinary guide to the parasites of reptiles/Susan M. Barnard and Steve J. Upton.
      p.   cm.
    Includes bibliographical references and index.
    Contents: v. 1. Protozoa
    ISBN 0–89464–832–2 (acid-free)
    1. Reptiles—Parasites. 2. Veterinary parasitology. I. Upton, Steve J. II. Title.
SF997.5.R4B37   1993
639.3′9—dc20
                         93–20082
                         CIP

      Contents: v. 2. Arthropods (excluding mites)
      Susan M. Barnard and Lance A. Durden
      ISBN 0–89464–908–6 (acid-free)

10 9 8 7 6 5 4 3 2

ACKNOWLEDGMENTS

We appreciate the kind assistance and support from the following individuals and organizations:

David G. Cook, Jay R. Georgi, Connie Waterstradt Haynes, Thomas G. Hollinger, James E. Keirans, Jeffrey R. Muenster, Kathleen O. Muller, Tamara A. Romaine, and Nixon Wilson.

American Association of Zoo Keepers, Society for the Study of Amphibians and Reptiles, and the Jonesboro and Morrow Branches of the Clayton County, Georgia, Library System.

We also express our deepest appreciation to the individuals and zoological institutions who contributed material for examination.

Illustrations and photographs are by the authors unless otherwise credited.

We dedicate this book to
Nixon Wilson
for his many years of friendship
and contributions to parasitology.

CONTENTS

INTRODUCTION

Arthropods comprise the largest phylum in the animal kingdom. There are about one million described species. They include insects, spiders, scorpions, mites, ticks, millipedes, centipedes, and crustaceans such as lobsters and shrimps. These diverse animals are dioecious, bilaterally symmetrical, have segmented bodies bearing jointed appendages, and possess a chitinous exoskeleton. Depending on the group, their mouthparts are adapted for biting, chewing, or sucking.

Although most arthropods are free-living, those that are parasitic may be found on or within a host. Furthermore, they often serve as intermediate hosts in parasitic life cycles, and some also serve as vectors or reservoirs of disease agents.

All groups of ectoparasitic arthropods affecting reptiles, except mites, are treated in this volume. Our reasons for excluding parasitic mites are largely two-fold. First, we desired to keep the book to a manageable size and second, the vast majority of parasitic mites are tiny or exploit specialized niches, and are likely to be overlooked by all but the most diligent herpetologists. Therefore, reptile mites (chiggers, pterygosomatids, lung mites, cloaca mites, etc.) will be treated in a separate volume of this series.

CHAPTER 1

ORDER: HEMIPTERA (TRUE BUGS)

In the insect order Hemiptera (true bugs), only members in the family Reduviidae, subfamily Triatominae, are blood-feeders of reptiles (Frank, 1981) and other vertebrates, especially mammals. Vernacular names include "cone-nose bugs" because of the shape of their heads, and "kissing bugs" because of the habit some species have of biting the lips of sleeping people. Triatomine bugs are important vectors of human pathogens. *Panstrongylus megistus* (Fig. 1) and *Triatoma sanguisuga* (Fig. 2) are two of the most important vectors of *Trypanosoma cruzi,* the causative agent of Chagas' disease (Schofield, 1994). Although Ryckman (1954) showed that the alligator lizard (*Gerrhonotus multicarinatus webbii*) was a suitable laboratory host for *T. cruzi,* reptiles do not appear to be involved in the epidemiology of Chagas' disease. The family Reduviidae includes over four thousand species, while the subfamily Triatominae includes 116 species.

Triatomine bugs are large, measuring 1.5–2.0 cm long, and some are brightly colored. The bodies of triatomines are generally oval in shape. Adults possess a three-jointed, short proboscis which is usually curved and fits into a groove on the sternum when not in use. Antennae are four-segmented, and both compound eyes and ocelli are present. Adults have one pair of well-formed wings and a pair of leathery wing covers called hemielytra.

Females deposit relatively large, smooth, barrel-shaped eggs on the ground, on trees, in crevices of buildings, or in animal cages either in clusters or singly. Depending on the species, each female deposits from a few dozen to over 500 eggs. The incubation period is species-dependent, and also varies according to ambient temperature. Hatching usually occurs after 8–30 days, and emerging nymphs are wingless. Most triatomine species pass through five nymphal instars, taking a blood meal between each molt. The time between molts is approximately 40–50 days. The life cycle of triatomine bugs takes a year or more to complete in nature.

Triatomine bugs are most diverse in the New World (especially the Neotropical region) where 104 species are known. Five species, however, are known from India, seven from southeast Asia, and one from Africa. Triatomines are often non-

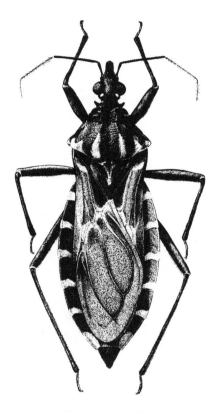

Fig. 1. *Panstronglyus megistus.* (Reproduced from Lent and Wygodzinsky, 1979. Courtesy of the American Museum of Natural History.)

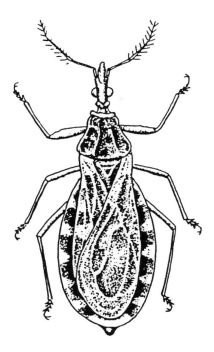

Fig. 2. *Triatoma sanguisuga.* (Reproduced from Scott and Borom, 1961).

specific feeders. Many species feed on any available vertebrate including reptiles, especially iguanas in the Neotropics (Schofield and Dolling, 1993). *Hepatozoon* (formerly *Haemogregarina*) *triatomae,* a protozoan parasite of the South American lizards, *Tupinambis teguixin* and *Tropidurus torquatus* has been shown to be transmitted by *Triatoma rubrovaria* (Osimani, 1942; Smith 1996).

CHAPTER 2

ORDER: DIPTERA (FLIES)

Of the approximately one million described arthropods, about 120,000 are dipterans (true flies). Dipterans are differentiated from other insects by their wings; they possess one pair of membranous forewings. Their hindwings are reduced to stalklike attachments (halteres). Dipteran mouthparts are developed for various feeding modes, particularly sucking or piercing. Figures 3–7 depict generalized diagrams of fly morphology. Fly genera reported to feed on or infest reptiles are summarized below. Asterisked genera parasitize reptiles as larvae (maggots) causing myiasis, whereas other genera feed on reptile blood as adults.

Class: Insecta
  Order: Diptera (Flies)
    Family: Calliphoridae (Blow Flies)
      Genus: *Calliphora**
            *Cochliomyia**
            *Phaenicia**
    Family: Ceratopogonidae (Biting Midges)
      Genus: *Culicoides*
    Family: Culicidae (Mosquitoes)
      Genus: *Aedeomyia*
            Aedes
            Coquilletidia
            Culex
            Culiseta
            Deinocerites
            Mansonia
            Psorophora
            Uranotaenia
    Family: Cuterebridae (Rabbit and Rodent Bot Flies)
      Genus: *Cuterebra**

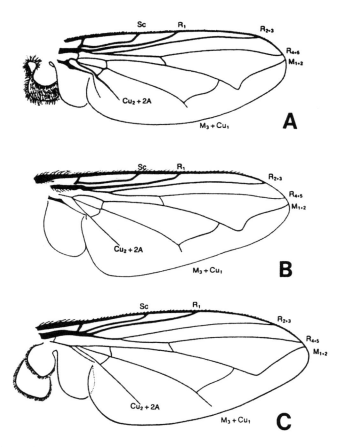

Fig. 3. General wing venation of three Diptera. **A.** Wing of *Calliphora*; **B.** Wing of *Cochliomyia*; **C.** Wing of *Phaenicia*. **Legend:** Sc (sub-costa); R_1 (first branch of radial vein); R_{2+3} (second and third branches of radial vein); R_{4+5} (fourth and fifth branches of radial vein); M_{1+2} (first and second branches of media vein); $M_3 + Cu_1$ (third branch of media vein and first branch of cubitus vein); $Cu_2 + 2A$ (second branch of cubitus vein and second anal vein). (Reproduced from Gorham, 1991).

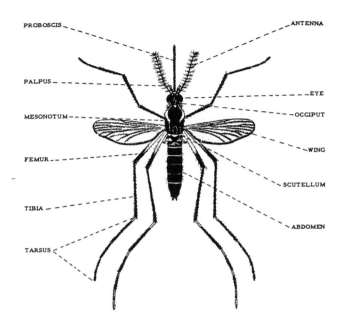

MOSQUITO DIAGRAM – ADULT FEMALE AEDES
Chester J. Stojanovich and Harold George Scott

Fig. 4. Basic morphology of an adult mosquito (*Aedes* sp). (Courtesy of U.S. Department of Health, Education, and Welfare, Public Health Service, Communicable Disease Center, 1966).

Family: Glossinidae (Tsetse Flies)
  Genus: *Glossina*
Family: Psychodidae (Sand Flies)
  Genus: *Lutzomyia*
       Phlebotomus
       Sergentomyia
Family: Sarcophagidae (Flesh Flies)
  Genus: *Anolisomyia**
       *Blaesoxipha**
       *Cistudinomyia**
       *Eumacronychia**
       *Metoposarcophaga**
Family: Tabanidae (Horse and Deer Flies)
  Genus: *Chrysops*
       Hybomitra
       Tabanus

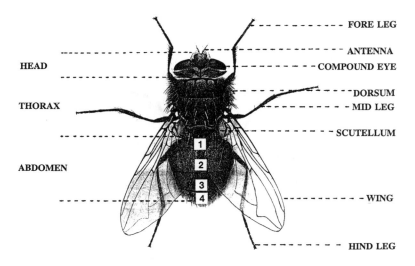

Fig. 5. Basic morphology of an adult fly of the suborder Cyclorrhapha
(*Calliphora* sp.). (Courtesy of the Department of Agriculture and
Agri-Food; reproduced with permission of the Minister of Public
Works and Government Services Canada, 1997).

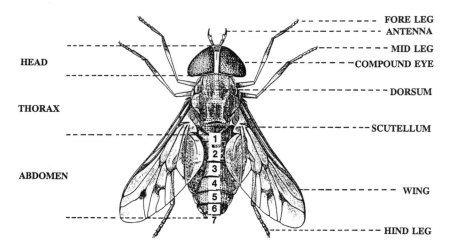

Fig. 6. Basic morphology of an adult fly of the suborder (Brachycera (*Tabanus*
sp.). (Reproduced from Schwardt and Hall, 1930.).

A key to myiasis-causing fly larvae that parasitize reptiles is given in Chapter 5, Raising myiasis-producing flies and larval identification. The following key can be used for identifying adult flies that feed on reptiles.

Key to genera of adult Diptera (flies) feeding on reptiles

1a	Antennae with 6 or more segments and usually long and/or plumose; legs usually long and thin	5
1b	Antennae with 3 segments; robust flies usually with stout legs	2
2a (1b)	Third antennal segment with an elaborate plumose branch (= arista); Africa (Glossinidae)	*Glossina*
	(tsetse flies).	
2b	Third antennal segment unbranched (Tabanidae)	3
3a (2b)	Hind tibiae with a pair of apical spurs; wings patterned	*Chrysops*
	(deer flies).	
3b	Hind tibiae lacking apical spurs; wings not patterned	4
4a (3b)	Top of head with a distinct ocellar tubercle	*Hybomitra*
	(horse flies)	
4b	Top of head lacking an ocellar tubercle	*Tabanus*
	(horse flies)	
5a (1a)	Wings short, broadly oval, pointed at tip, densely hairy and held rooflike over body at rest (Psychodidae - sand flies)	6
5b	Wings usually long and narrow; if broad, never pointed at tip; wings never densely hairy but may have minute sparse scales or hairs; wings held flat over body at rest	8
6a (5a)	New World sand flies feeding on reptiles	*Lutzomyia*
6b	Old World sand flies feeding on reptiles	7
7a (6b)	Abdominal tergites 2–6 with numerous erect setae arising from large round sockets	*Phlebotomus*
7b	Abdominal tergites 2–6 with horizontal (recumbent) setae arising from small oval sockets	*Sergentomyia*
8a (5b)	Costal vein terminating before wing tip; proboscis short; tiny flies ($\leq$ 3mm) Ceratopogonidae - no-see-ums, punkies)	*Culicoides, Leptoconops, & Forcipomyia*
8b	Costal vein continuing around wing tip; proboscis long; minute scales along wing veins and margins (Culicidae - mosquitoes)	9
9a (8b)	Antennae short with tuft of scales on first segment; thorax lacking prespiracular scales or setae; mid and hind femora with large tufts of scales	*Aedeomyia*
9b	Lacking the above combination of characters	10
10a (9b)	Wing cell R_2 shorter than vein R_{2+3}; thorax with iridescent blue stripes	*Uranotaenia*

10b	Wing cell R_2 at least as long as vein R_{2+3}; thorax lacking iridescent blue stripes 11	
11a (10b)	Postspiracular thoracic setae present 12	
11b	Postspiracular thoracic setae absent. 14	
12a (11a)	Apex of abdomen rounded in dorsal view; most scales on dorsal wing surface very broad . . . . *Mansonia*	
12b	Apex of abdomen tapering to a point in dorsal view; abdominal segment VII much narrower than segment VI; dorsal wing scales long and slender on veins R_s and M 13	
13a (12b)	Prespiracular thoracic setae present; pale, transverse bands or lateral spots, if present, always apical on abdominal terga. . . . . *Psorophora*	
13b	Prespiracular thoracic setae absent; pale, transverse bands or lateral spots, if present, always apical on abdominal terga. . . . . *Aedes* (in part).	
14a (10b)	Prespiracular thoracic setae present . . . . *Culiseta*	
14b	Prespiracular thoracic setae absent 15	
15a (14b)	Most wing scales on dorsal surface very broad. . . . . . . *Coquilletidia*	
15b	Wing scales on dorsal surface long and narrow 16	
16a (15b)	Antennae longer than proboscis . . . . *Deinocerites*	
16b	Antennae shorter than, or equal in length to, proboscis 17	
17a (16b)	Abdomen tapering to a point in dorsal view; basolateral patches of silvery scales present on terga . . . . *Aedes* (in part).	
17b	Abdomen bluntly rounded at apex in dorsal view; baso- or apicolateral patches of pale white or dull yellow scales present on terga . . . . *Culex*	

FAMILY: CALLIPHORIDAE (BLOW FLIES)

Blow flies are relatively large, and their bodies are metallic green, blue, violet, or copper. They possess plumose antennae. Hypo- and pteropleural bristles are present. A posterior-most posthumeral bristle is present, located more ventrally than the presutural bristle. The edges of the second ventral abdominal sclerite overlie the ventral edges of the corresponding dorsal sclerites.

Most blow fly larvae feed on carrion, but several species are parasitic in the larval stages (called maggots; Fig. 7), causing myiasis. Many species can feed on either carrion or live hosts (facultative myiasis) while a few are exclusively parasitic (obligate myiasis). Adults can transmit pathogens on their mouthparts and feet; however, they do not feed on blood. Depending on the species, larvae develop on carcasses, excreta, or in wounds. While a few species of myiasis-causing calliphorids are host-specific, most will feed on a variety of vertebrates. Particularly parasitic on reptiles are the genera presented below.

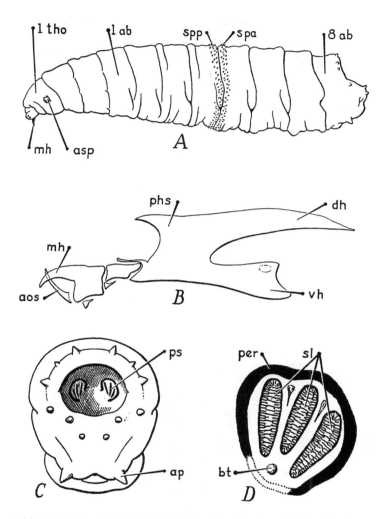

Fig. 7. Mature larva of a muscoid fly. **A.** Lateral view; **B.** Cephalopharyngeal skeleton; **C.** Posterior view; **D.** Posterior spiracle. **Legend:** aos (accessory oral sclerite); ap (anal protruberance); asp (anterior spiracle); bt (button); dh (dorsal horn); mh (mouth hooks); per (peritreme); phs (pharyngeal sclerite); ps (posterior spiracle); sl (respiratory slits); spa (spines along anterior margin); spp (spines along posterior margin); vh (ventral horn); 1ab (first abdominal segment); 1tho (first thoracic or prothoracic segment); 8ab (anal segments or 8th abdominal segment). (Reproduced from James, 1947).

I. *Calliphora* spp. (Fig. 8)

Also known as bluebottle flies because their bodies have a metallic blue sheen, these insects are distributed worldwide. Myiasis-producing, calliphorid flies can be either facultative or obligatory parasites. Those flies whose larvae are free-living, such as members in the genus *Calliphora,* are facultative because their larvae can subsist on a wide variety of materials. Such food sources include overripe fruit, other decaying vegetable matter, and fresh or tainted meat. They occasionally gain access to a living vertebrate, developing temporarily in wounds.

Description

Adult: size ranges from 8–14 mm long; wingspan approximately 25 mm; 4th wing vein sharply angled (see Fig. 4); eyes red; thorax bluish gray with indistinct, longitudinal, darker blue stripes; abdomen paler blue than thorax, with whitish pubescence on anterior half of each segment.

Larva: body of mature larva white to yellowish in color and measuring approximately 7 mm long; posterior spiracles (Fig. 126, Chapter 5) with complete peritreme, within which is situated the

Fig. 8. A bluebottle fly, *Calliphora* sp. (Courtesy of the Department of Agriculture and Agri-Food; reproduced with permission of the Minister of Public Works and Government Services Canada, 1997).

	button (Fig. 7d); inner margin of peritreme (Fig. 7d) between slits, with or without scallops; accessory oral hooks present.
Host(s)	Various non-aquatic reptiles.
Host location	Body surface, especially on tail, around cloaca, and under carapace; virtually anywhere on host's body where wounds exist.
Life cycle	Eggs that are deposited on living vertebrates are usually laid around animal's natural orifices; eggs hatch in 8–24 hours; larval period lasts 4–9 days; flies pupate in soil, and adults emerge in 10–17 days.
Host acquisition	By direct contact with larvae, or by eggs being directly deposited on the animal.
Symptoms	Not always apparent, particularly for immature larvae; cyst-like subcutaneous lesions; secondary infection or death can occur if not diagnosed.
Diagnosis	By recognition of small "breathing" holes (through which spiracular plates at posterior end of maggots may be seen) in animal's skin, or by egg deposition on animal (Fig. 9a).
Treatment	See Appendix I. Prevention is by screening windows and cages. Fecal material should always be removed as soon as possible. When myiasis-producing flies are known to be a problem, frequently check animals for attached eggs (Fig. 9a) or fly larvae (Fig. 9b).

II. *Cochliomyia* spp. (syn. *Callitroga*)

Also known as the screwworms, members in this genus range throughout North and South America, and are occasionally introduced to other parts of the world. *Cochliomyia hominivorax,* however, has been eradicated from mainland U.S.A. Adult flies are metallic dull to bright green, or greenish-blue in color. They are medium-sized. Their heads (including the palps), and usually the antennae, are orange to yellow. All have three distinct longitudinal black stripes on the thorax. Four species cause myiasis, *C. hominivorax* (syn. *C. americana*), *C. minima, C. macellaria* and *C. aldrichi. Cochliomyia* larvae are primarily obligate parasites, living only on vertebrates and not on decaying vegetable matter. However, some species, such as *C. macellaria,* can subsist on carrion including dead flesh around wounds in live hosts.

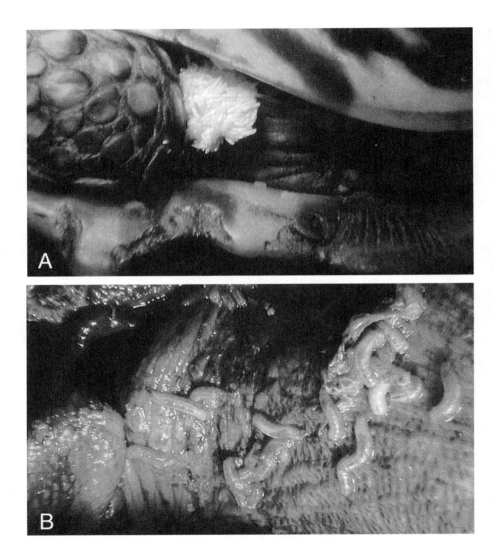

Fig. 9. **A.** Freshly deposited fly eggs on the skin of a box turtle, *Terrapene carolina*; **B.** Newly hatched fly maggots feeding on a tortoise. (Reproduced with permission from Frye, 1991).

Description

Adult: *Cochliomyia hominivorax* (Fig. 10), the "primary screwworm," body measures 8 - 10 mm long; bluish to bluish-green in color; black setae on lower and upper parafrontals; basicostal scale black; occiput of female usually reddish-orange to brown; feeds primarily on healthy tissue. *Cochliomyia macellaria* (Fig. 11), the "secondary screwworm," body measures 6–9 mm long; green in color with orange head; setae on lower portion of parafrontals yellow and fine in texture; mid-dorsal longitudinal stripe of thorax not extended over scutellum (see Fig. 4 for mosquito); fourth abdominal segment strongly pollinose laterally; feeds primarily in wounds and on carrion.

Larva: Mature *C. hominivorax* body (Fig. 128a, Chapter 5) measures approximately 17 mm long; segments banded with large, robust spines; tracheal trunks leading from posterior spiracles pigmented. Mature *C. macellaria* (Fig. 128b, Chapter 5) body also measures 17 mm long; spines smaller than in *C. hominivorax*; tracheal trunks leading from posterior spiracles not pigmented in second and third instars. Feeds primarily in wounds.

Host(s)

Various non-aquatic reptiles.

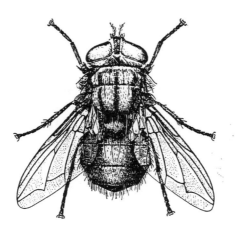

Fig. 10. *Cochliomyia hominivorax*. Female. (Reproduced from James, 1947).

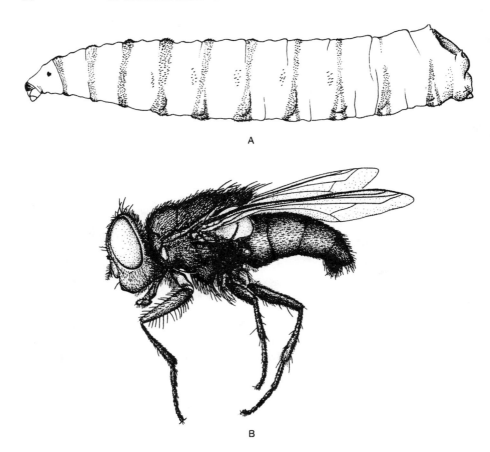

Fig. 11. Secondary screwworm, *Cochliomyia macellaria*. **A.** Larva; **B.** Adult.
(Reproduced from Gorham, 1991).

Host location	Body surface, especially on tail, around cloaca, and under carapace; virtually anywhere on host where wounds exist.
Life cycle	*Cochliomyia hominivorax* lays 10–400 eggs in a shinglelike mass, tightly glued to the dry edge or surface of an animal's 2- to 10-day old wounds, on tick-feeding sites, near scabs, or on blood clots; eggs hatch in 11–21 hours, at which time the gregarious larvae begin feeding, producing a deep, pocketlike injury; larvae mature in 4–8 days, drop to the ground and pupate in

soil; depending on species, pupal stage varies from 7–54 days under environmental conditions such as found in Texas - average life cycle in summer in Dallas is about 24 days.

Cochliomyia macellaria lays from 40 to approximately 1,000 eggs in a yellowish, loosely cemented mass; under favorable conditions, eggs may hatch in 4 hours; larvae mature in 6–20 days, then leave the food source to pupate in soil; larvae of *C. macellaria* do not form a pocketlike injury as seen with *C. hominivorax*.

Host acquisition
By direct contact with larvae, or by eggs being directly deposited on the animal.

Symptoms
Not always apparent; cyst-like, subcutaneous lesions; secondary infection or death can occur if not diagnosed.

Diagnosis
By recognition of small spiracular plates ("breathing holes") in wound in animal's skin (Fig. 125, Chapter 5), or by egg deposition on animal (Fig. 9a).

Treatment
See Appendix I. Prevention is by screening windows and cages. Fecal material should always be removed as soon as possible. When myiasis-producing flies are known to be a problem, check animals frequently for egg deposits.

III. Other calliphorid spp. causing myiasis in reptiles

Larvae of *Phaenicia* spp. (syn. *Lucilia* spp.) can also cause facultative myiasis in many species of reptiles. *Phaenicia sericata* larvae (Fig. 127, Chapter 5), which cause "sheep strike" in many parts of the world, can also cause myiasis in reptiles. *Phaenicia coeruleviridis* can cause a serious, potentially fatal infection, called "traumatic myiasis," in the North American eastern box turtle, *Terrapene carolina* (Abercrombie, 1977; Baumgartner, 1988). Larvae of *Calliphora stygia* cause myiasis in the green gecko, *Naultinus elegans,* in Australia (Zumpt, 1965).

FAMILY: CERATOPOGONIDAE (BITING MIDGES, NO-SEE-UMS, PUNKIES)

These insects have small bodies, ranging from 0.6–3.0 mm in length, and they are sparsely covered with setae. Biting midges have broad wings with few veins that are not all parallel. Their antennae are long, and their proboscis is short. Members of the genus *Culicoides* have been implicated in the transmission of protozoa to reptiles (Frank, 1981; Lainson et al., 1974), and are vectors of pathogenic nematodes and viruses to humans and livestock (Wirth and Hubert, 1989). Also, the lizard parasite *Plasmodium agamae* undergoes cyclical development in *Culicoides nebeculosus* in the laboratory (Petit et al., 1983), although this appears to be an abnormal insect host.

Most species of ceratopogonids feed on birds or mammals but a few species feed on reptiles. For example, *Culicoides testudinalis* feeds on turtles in North America (Wirth and Hubert, 1962), *Leptoconops minutus* and an undetermined *Leptoconops* sp. feed on lizards in Kazakhstan (Auezova et al., 1990), an undetermined *Forcipomyia* sp. feeds on iguanas in Costa Rica (Borkent, 1995a), *Culicoides phlebotomus* feeds on leatherback turtles (Borkent, 1995b), and *Leptoconops californiensis* and an undetermined *Leptoconops* sp. feed on lizards in Mexico and Southern California (Mullens et al., 1997). Also see host/parasite in Appendix III.

Culicoides spp. (Figs. 12, 13)

Number	Approximately 1,000 described species comprise this genus.
Description	Adult: ocelli absent; antenna of female with 14–15 segments; well-defined humeral pits on thorax; median veins on speckled wings forked and connected to anterior veins by cross-veins (see wing venation in Fig. 3); thickened costal wing

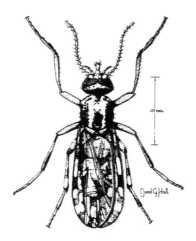

Fig. 12. *Culicoides dovei*. Female. (Reproduced with permission from Dove et al., 1932; copyrighted by the Entomological Society of America).

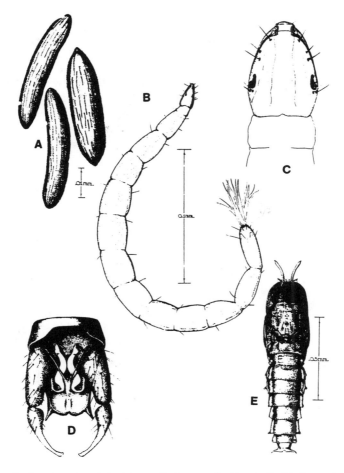

Fig. 13. *Culicoides dovei*. **A.** Eggs; **B.** Larva; **C.** Head; **D.** Male genitalia; **E.** Pupa. (Reproduced with permission from Dove et al., 1932; copyrighted by the Entomological Society of America).

vein ends ½ to ¾ along wing surface length; 1–3 mm long (can pass through ordinary window screening).

Pupa (Fig. 13e): resembles butterfly chrysalis; brown, 2 respiratory trumpets present; anchors at shallow water surface, or in crevices of manure or rotting vegetation.

Larva (Fig. 13b): when hatching, wormlike in shape, whitish in color with small head; 3 tho-

	racic and 9 abdominal segments; retractile, fila-mentous gills protruding from last abdominal segment; aquatic or semi-aquatic; swims in an eel-like fashion.
Host(s)	Many vertebrates; although some are strictly reptile, bird, or mammal feeders, most species are not host-specific.
Host location	Body surface. *Culicoides* spp. may go undetected because of their small size and fleeting association with the host.
Life cycle	Eggs laid in mass on algae or decaying vegetation often near brackish or fresh water; pupate in water, on surface of wet mud, moist vegetation, or algae.
Host acquisition	Attracted to host by respiratory carbon dioxide (CO_2) and/or movement. Adult *Culicoides* spp. fly to host.
Symptoms	Heavy infestations can cause blood loss and stress in small reptiles (Frye 1991).
Diagnosis	By observation of organisms on host or in caging.
Treatment	Place dichlorvos-impregnated pest strips in affected animal areas; eliminate standing water; regularly change water in reptile enclosures (in zoos this includes stock tanks and pools). Prevention is difficult as members in this genus can pass through ordinary mosquito screening.

FAMILY: CULICIDAE (MOSQUITOES)

More than 3,000 species of mosquitoes have been described worldwide. The mosquito body is slight with a long, slender abdomen and proboscis. Mosquitoes possess narrow, fringed wings. These insects have large eyes relative to their total head size, and most measure 2.5–6.0 mm in length (Darsie and Ward, 1981). Of the parasitic species, only the females suck blood. Natural symbionts of mosquitoes include certain protozoa and nematodes. A generalized life cycle is presented in Figure 17. They breed in moist soil or primarily standing water, depending on the species. Females usually lay their eggs on water or on floating vegetation. Some mosquito species lay their eggs in fresh rain water, others in saltwater or in areas subjected to flooding.

Mosquitoes are known or suspected to be vectors of viruses, protozoa, and filarial nematodes infecting reptiles. Certain reptile-feeding mosquitoes may be important vectors of the causative agents of malaria and viral encephalitis/encephalomyelitis in reptiles. With respect to the latter, some reptiles exhibit prolonged viremias, particularly for western equine encephalomyelitis (WEE), eastern equine encephalomyelitis (EEE), Japanese encephalitis (JE), and Venezuelan equine encephalomyelitis (VEE) viruses, and they may be efficient reservoirs for these zoonotic pathogens (Burton et al., 1966).

Several species of the protozoan genus *Hepatozoon* (Apicomplexa: Adeleina) that parasitize lizards and snakes in various parts of the world have also been detected in mosquitoes. Some of these *Hepatozoon* species have been shown to undergo developmental cycles in their mosquito hosts which have been implicated as vectors of these protozoans to reptiles. Transmission of *Hepatozoon* to reptiles in some cases is known to be via ingestion of infected mosquitoes. Transmission by mosquitoes during blood-feeding has not yet been demonstrated but may occur. In his review paper, Smith (1996) cites the following cases of lizard and snake associated species of *Hepatozoon* being present in both reptiles and mosquitoes:

1. *H. breinli* in Australian *Varanus* spp. lizards and in *Culex fatigans* mosquitoes.
2. *H. gracilis* in the North African lizard *Mabuya quinquetaeniata* and in *Culex pipiens* mosquitoes.
3. *H. mesnili* in the Old World gecko *Gecko veticillatus* and in the mosquitoes *Aedes albopictus* and *Culex fatigans*.
4. *H. aegypti* in the snake *Spalerosophis diamema* and in the mosquito *Culex pipiens*.
5. *H. domerguei* in the lizards *Lacerta* spp. and *Oplurus sebae,* in the snakes *Lioheterodon modestus, Madagascarophis colubrina,* and *Python sebae;* and in the mosquitoes *Anopheles stephensi* and *Culex fatigans* in Madagascar.
6. *H. fusifex* in the Neotropical snake *Boa constrictor* and in the mosquitoes *Aedes togoi* and *Culex tarsalis*.
7. *H. matruhensis* in the North African snake *Psammophis schokari* and in the mosquito *Culex pipiens*.
8. *H. mehlhorni* in the North African viper *Echis carinatus* and in the mosquito *Culex pipiens*.
9. *H. mocassini* in the cottonmouth *Agkistrodon piscivorus* and in the mosquito *Aedes aegypti* in North America.
10. *H. najae* in African *Naja* spp. snakes and in *Culex pipiens* mosquitoes.
11. *H. rarefaciens* in the New World snakes *Drymarchon corais, Boa constrictor,* and *Pituophis catenifer* and in the mosquitoes *Aedes sierrensis, Anopheles albimanus,* and *Culex tarsalis*.
12. *H. seurati* in North African *Cerastes* spp. snakes and in *Culex pipiens* mosquitoes.

13. *H. sipedon* in the North American water snake *Nerodia sipedon,* and garter snake *Thamnophis sirtalis* and in mosquitoes belonging to the genus *Culex.* Smith et al. (1994) list these mosquitoes as *Culex pipiens* and *Culex territans.*

McIver (1968) reported that culicid feeding behavior is cued by temperature, humidity, odor, carbon dioxide concentration, and visual stimuli. While many species of mosquitoes prefer mammals or birds as hosts, most will feed on reptile blood if given the chance. A few mosquito groups, however, preferentially feed on poikilothermic vertebrates including reptiles. Representatives of reptile-feeding mosquitoes occur in several genera, notably *Aedeomyia, Aedes, Coquilletidia, Culiseta, Culex, Deinocerites, Mansonia, Psorphora* and *Uranotaenia.*

I. *Aedes* spp. (Figs. 14–16)

Aedes spp. are distributed worldwide from the polar regions to the tropics. They are also found at high elevations in mountains. Some *Aedes* spp. may function as vectors of protozoa (e.g., *Hepatozoon* spp.) and viruses to reptiles (Frank, 1981). Klein et al. (1988) demonstrated transmission of the sporozoite protozoan *Schellackia occidentalis* to eastern fence lizards, *Sceloporus undulatus,* when these lizards ingested *Aedes aegypti* mosquitoes that had previously fed on infected lizards. Many

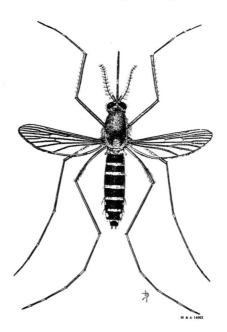

Fig. 14. *Aedes* sp. Adult female. (Reproduced from King et al., 1960).

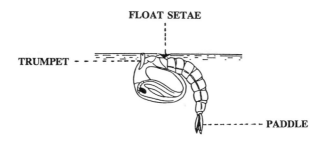

Fig. 15. *Aedes* sp. Pupa. (Reproduced from Littig and Stojanovich, 1965).

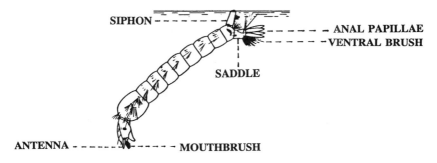

Fig. 16. *Aedes* sp. Larva. (Reproduced from Littig and Stojanovich, 1965).

species also serve as vectors for pathogens which cause human diseases such as elephantiasis from filarial nematodes, and yellow fever, dengue, and encephalitis from viruses.

Description   Adult female: scutellum (Fig. 4) with 3 lobes, each bristled, but with bare areas between lobes; abdomen covered with scales, pointed with long cerci; claws toothed; bristles present posterior to spiracles; pulvilli absent or hairlike.

Pupa (Fig. 15): one pair of respiratory trumpets present dorsally on cephalothorax; paddlelike flaps at end of abdomen; hang from water surface by trumpets.

Larva (Fig. 16): siphon prominent with 1 pair of posteroventral hair tufts; pecten usually distinct; hang vertically or diagonally from water surface.

Host(s)   All major groups of vertebrates including reptiles, especially turtles (Carpenter, 1941; DeFoliart,

1967; Hayes, 1965; Nolan, et al., 1965). The following *Aedes* spp. are known to feed on reptiles:

Ae. aegypti - mainly a mammal-feeder, but will also feed on turtles and lizards. This mosquito is distributed across most of the warmer regions of the world. Some researchers have allowed *Ae. aegypti* to feed on reptiles to obtain small blood samples as a laboratory technique (Frank, 1981; Yuill, 1969).

Ae. atlanticus - feeds on reptiles, birds, and mammals in the southeastern United States (Irby and Apperson, 1988).

Ae. angustivittatus - feeds on reptiles in Panama (Christensen et al., 1996).

Ae. canadensis - feeds on many vertebrates including reptiles (especially turtles) throughout much of North America (Irby and Apperson, 1988; Means, 1968; Wright and DeFoliart, 1970).

Ae. cinereus - feeds on snapping turtles, birds, and mammals in Wisconsin (Wright and DeFoliart, 1970).

Ae. hendersoni - feeds on mammals and reptiles in North Carolina (Irby and Apperson, 1988).

Ae. sticticus - mainly feeds on mammals, but also on reptiles and birds in Wisconsin (Wright and DeFoliart, 1970).

Ae. taeniorhynchus - feeds on many vertebrates including lizards in Panama (Christensen et al., 1996).

Ae. triseriatus - feeds on many vertebrates including reptiles (Irby and Apperson, 1988; Wright and DeFoliart, 1970) in North America.

Ae. trivittatus - feeds on turtles, snakes, birds, and mammals in Wisconsin (Wright and DeFoliart, 1970).

Ae. vexans - feeds on reptiles, birds, and mammals in North America (Irby and Apperson, 1988; Wright and DeFoliart, 1970).

Host location   Skin.

Life cycle (Fig. 17)   Depending on species, they breed in tidal areas along seacoasts, wooded areas, in floodwaters, melted snow, and open plains; eggs are rela-

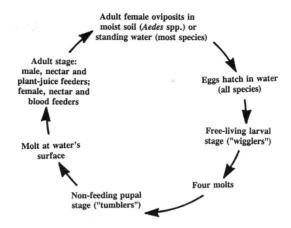

Fig. 17. Generalized life cycle of mosquitoes.

	tively resistant to drying, and can lie dormant for several years; eggs are laid in places where water becomes plentiful by rain, melting snow, or rising tides.
Host acquisition	By direct contact with female seeking host for blood meal.
Symptoms	Heavy infestations can cause blood loss and stress in small reptiles (Frye, 1991).
Diagnosis	By demonstration of organism on body surface or cage environment.
Treatment	Place dichlorvos-impregnated pest strips in affected animal areas; screen all windows and doors; eliminate standing water, and regularly change water in reptile enclosures (in zoos this includes stock tanks and pools).

II. *Culex* spp. (Figs. 18–23)

Culex spp. are the most widespread of the mosquitoes, and often the most annoying. Marshall (1938) reported that *C. molestus* is the species most commonly encountered by humans in North America, and it transmits pathogens such as viruses that cause western (WEE) and eastern (EEE) equine encephalomyelitis. Henderson and Senior (1961), however, reported *C. tarsalis* as being the primary arthropod vector of these viruses, and Thomas et al. (1958) suggested that reptiles may play a role in the overwintering and summer maintenance of WEE virus. This was demonstrated in snakes by Gebhardt et al. (1964). Under laboratory conditions, *Plasmodium flori-*

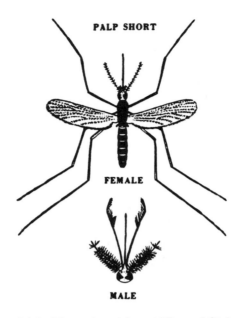

Fig. 18. *Culex* sp. Adult. (Reproduced from Littig and Stojanovich, 1965).

Fig. 19. *Culex* sp. Adult. (Photo courtesy of Susan E. Ellis).

dense was successfully transmitted to the green anole (*Anolis carolinensis*) from feeding on infected *Cx. erraticus* (Klein et al., 1987). In the laboratory, it was shown that *Culex* spp. transmitted the protozoa *Hepatozoon fusifex, H. rarefaciens,* and *H. domerguei* which are pathogenic to several snakes and lizards. Transmission apparently can occur either via feeding by infected mosquitoes or by host ingestion of infected mosquitoes (Booden et al., 1970; Chao and Ball, 1969). In Brazil, *Culex pipiens* was found to transmit another protozoan, *Saurocytozoon tupinambi,* to reptiles (Lainson and Shaw, 1969). Klein et al. (1988) demonstrated transmission of the sporozoite protozoans *Schellackia golvani* and *S. occidentalis* to the Carolina anole, *Anolis carolinensis,* and the eastern fence lizard, *Sceloporus undulatus,* respectively, when these lizards ingested *Culex erraticus* mosquitoes that had previously fed on infected lizards. Other *Culex* spp. can transmit encephalitide viruses to reptiles (Frank, 1981).

Description	Adult female: scutellum and abdomen as in *Aedes* except apex of abdomen broadly rounded in dorsal view.
	Pupa (Fig. 20): similar to those of *Aedes* spp.
	Larva (Fig. 21): similar to those of *Aedes* spp. but usually with a long, slender siphon with many hair tufts; saddle completely encircling abdominal segment X.
Host(s)	Snakes, lizards and turtles (Boreham and Snow, 1973; Christopher and Reuben, 1971; Gebhardt et al., 1966; Henderson and Senior, 1961; O'Connor, 1966). *Culex* spp. that feed on reptiles are as follows:
	Cx. aitkeni - reptiles in Panama (Tempelis and Galindo, 1975).
	Cx. amazonensis - reptiles in Panama (Christensen et al., 1996; Tempelis and Galindo, 1975).
	Cx. apanastasis - reptiles in Panama (Tempelis and Galindo, 1975).
	Cx. conspirator - lizards and crocodilians in Panama (Christensen et al., 1996).
	Cx. decens - usually bird-feeder in Europe, but will feed on reptiles (Boreham and Snow, 1973).
	Cx. declarator - lizards and crocodilians in Panama (Christensen et al., 1996).
	Cx. dunni - prefers reptiles, especially lizards and turtles, over other vertebrates in Central America (Christensen et al., 1996; Tempelis and Galindo, 1975).

Fig. 20. *Culex* sp. Pupa. (Reproduced from Littig and Stojanovich, 1965).

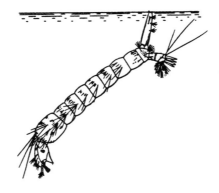

Fig. 21. *Culex* sp. Larva. (Reproduced from Littig and Stojanovich, 1965).

Cx. egcymon - prefers reptiles, especially lizards, over other vertebrates in Central America (Christensen et al., 1996; Tempelis and Galindo, 1975).

Cx. elevator - prefers lizards over other vertebrates (Christensen et al., 1996; Tempelis and Galindo, 1975).

Cx. epanastasis - all reptilian groups in Panama (Christensen et al., 1996).

Cx. erraticus - prefers mammals and/or birds in North America and beyond, but will feed on several species of reptiles (Irby and Apperson, 1988; Means, 1968; Wright and DeFoliart, 1970). In Panama, Christensen et al., (1996) showed that lizards are the most important reptilian hosts.

Cx. invidiosus - usually bird-feeder in Europe, but will feed on reptiles (Boreham and Snow, 1973).

Cx. nigripalpis - lizards and crocodilians in Panama (Christensen et al., 1996).

Cx. peccator - almost exclusively on snakes and

frogs in North Carolina (Irby and Apperson, 1988).

Cx. pipiens - prefers mammals and/or birds in North America and beyond, but will feed on several species of reptiles (Irby and Apperson, 1988; Means, 1968; Wright and DeFoliart, 1970).

Cx. quinquefasciatus - prefers mammals and/or birds in North America and beyond, but will feed on several species of reptiles (Irby and Apperson, 1988; Means, 1968; Wright and DeFoliart, 1970).

Cx. restuans - prefers mammals and/or birds in North America and beyond, but will feed on several species of reptiles (Irby and Apperson, 1988; Means, 1968; Wright and DeFoliart, 1970).

Cx. spissipes - lizards in Panama (Christensen et al., 1996).

Cx. taeniopus - reptiles in Panama, especially lizards (Christensen et al., 1996).

Cx. tecmarsis - prefers reptiles over other vertebrates (Tempelis and Galindo, 1975).

Cx. territans - feeds almost exclusively on reptiles and amphibians in North America (Harris et al., 1969; Irby and Apperson, 1988; Means, 1968).

Host location Skin.

Life cycle (Fig. 17) Selected breeding sites include almost any water-filled container, garden pools stocked with aquatic plants, and slow-flowing polluted streams; 100–400 eggs laid vertically in clusters or "rafts" (Figs. 22, 23) with anterior ends toward the water; hatching occurs in 1–3 days, depending on temperature; larvae emerge from large end of egg where a tiny pore (micropyle) exists; larvae develop rapidly in warm weather,

Fig. 22. *Culex* sp. Egg raft. (Reproduced from Littig and Stojanovich, 1965).

Fig. 23. *Culex* sp. Female laying egg raft. (Photo courtesy of Susan E. Ellis).

	with pupal stage being reached in 7–10 days; pupal stage usually lasts for only 2–3 days.
Host acquisition	By direct contact with female seeking host for blood meal.
Symptoms	Heavy infestations can cause blood loss and stress in small reptiles (Frye, 1991).
Diagnosis	By demonstration of organism on body surface or cage environment.
Treatment	Place dichlorvos-impregnated pest strips in affected animal areas; screen all windows and doors; eliminate standing water, and regularly change water in reptile enclosures (in zoos this includes stock tanks and pools).

III. *Deinocerites* spp. (Fig. 24)

Members of the genus *Deinocerites* are distributed tropically, including peninsular Florida, living in water along the shore. In 1923, Dyar first described these mosquitoes from crab holes. The adult mosquitoes rest in the upper dry part of the holes. Apparently, they fly out when the crabs approach in order to prevent being overwhelmed in the water by the entrance of the crabs.

Fig. 24. *Deinocerites* sp. Head of female. **A**. Antenna; **B**. Proboscis. (Reproduced from Pratt and Stojanovich, 1965).

Description	Adult female: antennae (Fig. 24a) longer than proboscis (Fig. 24b); dorsal wing scales long and straight; postspiracular setae absent; scutellum as in *Aedes* and *Culex*; maxillary palps shorter than proboscis.
	Pupa: similar to those of *Aedes* and *Culex* (see Figs. 15, 20).
	Larva: similar to those of *Aedes* and *Culex* (see Figs. 17, 21). Head capsule widest near level of antennal attachment; abdominal segment X with dorsal and ventral sclerotized plates.
Host(s)	Most vertebrates, occasionally including snakes and lizards (Edman, 1974; Tempelis and Galindo, 1970).
Host location	Body surface.
Life cycle (Fig. 17)	Breeding occurs inside land crab holes in coastal areas with brackish or salt water habitats (King et al., 1960).
Transmission	By direct contact with female seeking host for blood meal.
Symptoms	Heavy infestations can cause blood loss and stress in small reptiles (Frye, 1991).
Diagnosis	By demonstration of organism on body surface or cage environment.
Treatment	Place dichlorvos-impregnated pest strips in affected animal areas; screen all windows and doors; eliminate standing water, and regularly change water in reptile enclosures (in zoos this includes stock tanks and pools).

IV. Other mosquitoes that feed on reptiles

Aedeomyia squamipennis is known to feed on lizards and amphibians in Panama (Christensen et al., 1996).

Coquilletidia perturbans is a general vertebrate feeder that will sometimes feed on reptiles, especially turtles (Wright and DeFoliart, 1970). This North American mosquito is an epizootic vector of eastern equine encephalomyelitis (EEE) virus. *Coquilletidia nigricans* and *Cq. venezuelensis* both feed on reptiles and amphibians in Panama (Christensen et al., 1996).

Culiseta melanura feeds mainly on passerine birds but will also feed on reptile blood (Irby and Apperson, 1988; Means, 1968). This mosquito is the main enzootic vector of EEE virus in North America.

Mansonia dyeri is known to feed on reptiles, especially lizards and snakes in Panama (Christensen et al., 1996).

Psorophora spp. fed on reptiles, in addition to mammals (one species also fed on birds) in a study in North Carolina by Irby and Apperson (1988).

Uranotaenia sapphirina fed exclusively on snakes in a study in North Carolina (Irby and Apperson, 1988). Also, both *Ur. apicalis* and *Ur. lowii* are known to feed on reptiles in Panama (Christensen et al., 1996).

FAMILY: CUTEREBRIDAE (RABBIT AND RODENT BOT FLIES)

As indicated by their vernacular name, larvae of these flies do not typically cause myiasis in reptiles. There is, however, a report of accidental myiasis in a Grand Canyon rattlesnake, *Crotalus viridis abyssus,* caused by an undetermined *Cuterebra* sp. (Fig. 25; also see Fig. 129, Chapter 5) (Garrigues, 1965). The family Cuterebridae occurs in the New World (Sabrosky, 1986).

Fig. 25. *Cuterebra* sp. Adult. (Specimen courtesy of Nixon Wilson; photo courtesy of Rick E. Perry).

FAMILY: GLOSSINIDAE (TSETSE FLIES)

Tsetse flies feed primarily on hosts confined to their habitat. For example, open savanna-dwellers prey on hoofed stock, and those living in rain forests feed on monitor lizards, crocodiles, and other animals living or visiting water. These flies transmit protozoa, such as trypanosomes, to reptiles. For example, Hoare (1931) described the life cycle and transmission by tsetse flies of the crocodile parasite, *Trypanosoma grayi*. Of the six currently recognized protozan parasites belonging to the genus *Hepatozoon* that infect crocodilians, at least one of these, *H. pettiti*, has been shown to be transmitted by tsetse flies, *Glossina palpalis* (Hoare, 1932; Smith, 1996).

Glossina spp.

Members of this genus are currently limited to the African continent, south of the Tropic of Cancer. *G. palpalis* (Fig. 26), for example, is a waterside species of west and central African forests and the surrounding savanna woodlands. There are 22 recognized *Glossina* species, and several are important vectors of the agents of trypanosomiasis, causing sleeping sickness in humans and nagana in livestock. Both sexes are hematophagous. Several *Glossina* spp., especially those in the *G. palpalis* species group, feed readily on reptiles, particularly monitor lizards (*Varanus* spp.), snakes, tortoises, and crocodiles (Frank, 1981).

Description   Adult: narrow-bodied; 6–14 mm long; proboscis long and held horizontally; yellowish to dark

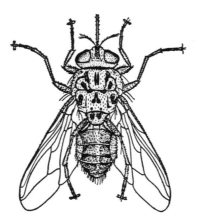

Fig. 26. *Glossina palpalis.* Female. (Reproduced with permission from Matheson, 1950; courtesy of Cornell University Press).

brown in color, but thorax sometimes dull greenish and marked with inconspicuous stripes or spots; discal wing cell shaped like a meat cleaver (called the cleaver or hatchet cell); palps nearly as long as bayonetlike proboscis; rays of antennal arista laterally branched. Female viviparous; wings crossed scissorlike at rest and extending well beyond the tip of the abdomen.

Pupa (puparium): ovoid; 6–7 mm long; brownish-black in color; two posterior lobes.

Larva: fourth instar, oval in shape, off-white to pale yellow in color; measures 7 mm long; movement by longitudinal, peristaltic contractions.

Host(s)   Many vertebrates including reptiles. *Glossina palpalis* and *G. tachinoides* often feed on crocodiles, varanid lizards, and other reptiles (Askew, 1971; Cheng, 1973; Frank, 1981; Newstead et al., 1924); 93% of the *G. fuscipes* tested in Uganda had fed on monitor lizards (*Varanus* spp.), 6% on snakes, and 0.6% on tortoises (Frank, 1981). Clausen et al. (1998) found that 4 of 119 (3.4%) *G. fusca* and 2 of 828 (0.25%) *G. longipennis* tested from various parts of Africa had fed on non-specified reptiles. They further found that 13 (0.8%) and 151 (9.7%) of 1563 *G. palpalis* tested had fed on crocodiles and monitor lizards, respectively; 20 (1.5%) and 527 (40.5%) of 1301 *G. fuscipes* tested had fed on crocodiles and monitor lizards, respectively; 29 (1.1%) and 337 (12.6%) of 2680 *G. tachinoides* tested had fed on crocodiles and monitor lizards, respectively; 3 (0.04%) and 10 (0.14%) of 7,085 *G. morsitans* tested had fed on crocodiles and monitor lizards respectively; 1 (0.35%) and 26 (9.2%) of 283 *G. longipalpis* tested had fed on crocodiles and monitor lizards, respectively; and that 7 (0.6%) of 1236 *G. pallidipes* tested had fed on monitor lizards.

Host location   Skin.

Life cycle (Fig. 27)   Fourth instar mature larvae deposited singly by gravid female, at the base of shrubs and other vegetation in damp loose soil, at intervals of

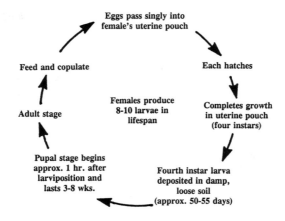

Eggs pass singly into
female's uterine pouch

Each hatches

Feed and copulate

Completes growth
in uterine pouch
(four instars)

Adult stage

Females produce
8-10 larvae in
lifespan

Pupal stage begins
approx. 1 hr. after
larviposition and
lasts 3-8 wks.

Fourth instar larva
deposited in damp,
loose soil
(approx. 50-55 days)

Fig. 27. Generalized life cycle of *Glossina* spp.

	10–12 days; each female deposits 8–10 larvae in life span; larvae burrow into soil and pupate approximately one hour after larviposition; pupal period 3–8 weeks, depending on species.
Host acquisition	By adults attracted to host for feeding or larviposition.
Symptoms	Heavy infestations can cause blood loss and stress in small reptiles (Frye, 1991).
Diagnosis	By demonstration of organism on body surface or cage environment.
Treatment	Prevention is by screening windows and cages, and by avoiding the use of non-sterilized substrate for caging in endemic regions. Also see Appendix I.

FAMILY: PSYCHODIDAE (SAND FLIES, MOTH FLIES)

Only the sand flies (subfamily Phlebotominae) are blood-feeders in this family, and some of these feed on reptiles. Members in the sand fly genus *Phlebotomus* are found primarily in the southern region of the temperate part of the Old World. Those in the genus *Sergentomyia* are found in the Old World tropics, and *Lutzomyia* spp. inhabit the New World tropics and subtropics. Characterized by hairy, moth-like bodies, these flies have long slender antennae, mouthparts, and legs. Their wings are broad and have 9–11 long, parallel veins with cross-veins only at the bases. Two or three of the longitudinal veins are forked. Small flies, they rarely measure over 5 mm in length. Ocelli are absent. Only females are blood-sucking; males are nonparasitic and feed mainly on plant nectar.

Although sand flies are distributed throughout the subtropics and tropics world-wide, they are limited to areas that support their breeding requirements and need for blood. Sand flies are rarely found more than 100–200 meters from their breeding grounds. They breed in dark humid places such as caves, animal burrows, rocky crevices, between stones, and in dense vegetation. Eggs are ovoid and elongate with elaborate chorionic sculpturing; there are 4 larval instars, and pupae are attached to the substrate by the molted skin of the last larval instar.

Sand flies have been reported to transmit protozoa such as *Leishmania* (Adler, 1964; Southgate, 1967), *Plasmodium* (Ayala and Lee, 1970), *Schellackia* (Klein et al., 1988) and haemogregarines (Ayala, 1970a). They may also transmit arboviruses (Doherty et al., 1971, 1973).

I. *Lutzomyia* spp. (Fig. 28)

Several species of *Lutzomyia* feed on mammals. In California, Chaniotis (1967) demonstrated that *L. californica*, *L. stewarti* and *L. vexator* (all reported as belonging to the genus *Phlebotomus* in his paper) readily feed on reptiles. Klein et al.

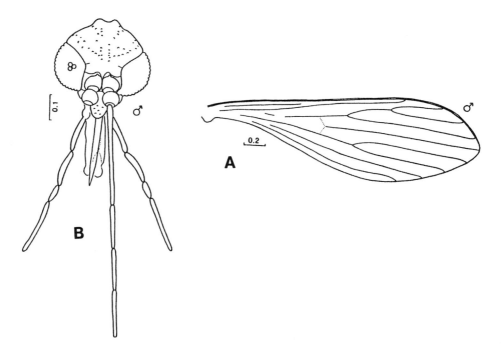

Fig. 28. *Lutzomyia guatemalensis.* Male. **A.** Wing; **B.** Head. (Porter and Young, 1986; reproduced with permission from Bishop Museum Press, Honolulu, Hawaii).

(1988) demonstrated transmission of the sporozoite protozoan *Schellackia golvani* to Carolina anoles, *Anolis carolinensis,* when the anoles ingested *Lutzomyia vexator* sand flies that had fed previously on infected anoles. These authors also demonstrated transmission of *Schellackia occidentalis* to eastern fence lizards, *Sceloporus undulatus,* when these lizards fed on infected *L. vexator* (Klein et al; 1988).

Description	Adults: wings distinctly pointed (Fig. 28a); mouthparts at least half as long as head (Fig. 28b); interocular suture incomplete; male style with 1–6 large spines; female cibarium with one row of posterior teeth; anterior teeth usually present.
	Pupa: abdomen well differentiated from thorax; terminal abdominal segment with 4 short spines (2 dorsal, 2 ventral); thoracic respiratory organs tubelike and conspicuously elevated; legs not extending beyond apices of wingbuds.
	Larva: wormlike, with well-sclerotized head capsule, without differentiation of segments into distinct thorax and abdomen; all or some of the dorsal segments with sclerotized straplike, narrow bands; most segmented with abundant, short setae.
Host(s)	Lizards (Smith, 1973).
Host location	Skin.
Life cycle	Most breed in forested, humid regions of North, Central and South America. Some *Lutzomyia* spp. can transmit protozoa such as *Leishmania* spp. Ayala and Lee (1970) and Klein et al. (1987) incriminated *L. vexator* and *L. stewarti* as vectors of a saurian malaria, *Plasmodium mexicanum.*
Host acquisition	By direct contact with female seeking host for blood meal.
Symptoms	Heavy infestations can cause blood loss and stress in small reptiles (Frye, 1991).
Diagnosis	By demonstration of organism on body surface or cage environment.
Treatment	Prevention is by removal of dense vegetation around outdoor enclosures, filling in cracks in walls of buildings, and by screening windows and cages. Fecal material should always be removed from animal enclosures as soon as possible.

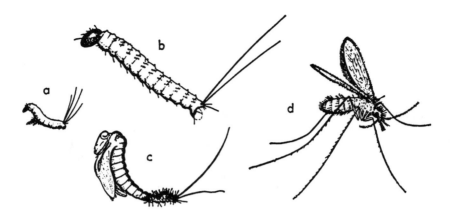

Fig. 29. *Phlebotomus papatasi*. **A.** Larva, first instar; **B.** Larva; **C.** Pupa
with larval skin attached; **D.** Female in resting position. (After Byam
and Archibald, 1921–1923).

II. *Phlebotomus* spp. (Fig. 29)

Although most *Phlebotomus* spp. feed on mammals, several feed frequently or predominantly on reptiles (Lane, 1993). Species that feed on both mammals and reptiles include *P. caucasicus, P. chinensis, P. papatasi* (Fig. 29d), and *P. sergenti* (Frank, 1981). In Kenya, *P. martini* feeds on lizards (Ngumbi et al., 1992). *Phlebotomus* spp. can transmit protozoa such as *Haemogregarina* spp., *Hepatozoon* spp., and *Leishmania* spp. It is also thought that *Phlebotomus* spp. may transmit viruses, such as Charleville virus, to reptiles (Ayala, 1970a,b; Frank, 1981).

Description	Adults: wings pointed; abdominal tergites lacking posterior processes; abdominal tergites 2–6 with many erect setae. Female pharynx armed with scalelike teeth; cibarium usually lacking teeth and pigmentation. Male style with 3–5 large spines.
	Pupa (Fig. 29c): similar to that of *Lutzomyia*.
	Larva (Fig. 29a,b): similar to that of *Lutzomyia*; when hatching, resembles a small caterpillar; feeds on dried leaves and feces.
Host(s)	Various vertebrates including reptiles (Smith, 1973). Also see discussion above.
Host location	Skin.
Life cycle	*P. papatasi* lays 40–60 eggs at one time.

Host acquisition	By direct contact with female seeking host for blood meal.
Symptoms	Heavy infestations can cause blood loss and stress in small reptiles (Frye, 1991).
Diagnosis	By demonstration of organism on body surface or cage environment.
Treatment	Prevention is by removal of dense vegetation around outdoor enclosures, filling in cracks in walls of buildings, and by screening windows and cages. Fecal material should always be removed from animal enclosures as soon as possible.

III. *Sergentomyia* spp. (Fig. 30)

This is a large genus with many species found in diverse habitats throughout the Old World. Although a few species feed on mammals, reptilian hosts are more typical. Some *Sergentomyia* spp. are vectors of *Sauroleishmania* spp. protozoa which are pathogenic to several reptiles (Adler, 1964; Belova, 1971; Belova and Bogdanov, 1968; Garnham, 1971; Lane, 1993; Mohiuddin, 1959; Wilson and Southgate, 1979).

Description	Adults: wings pointed (Fig. 30d); abdominal tergites without posterior processes; abdominal tergites 2–6 with horizontal setae; female cibarium (Fig. 30c) with teeth and pigment patch; male style with 4–6 stout spines.
	Pupa: similar to that of *Lutzomyia*.
	Larva: similar to that of *Lutzomyia*.
Host(s)	Predominantly reptiles (Lane, 1993; Smith, 1973). In Kenya, Ngumbi et al. (1992) recorded blood meals from lizards in both *S. antennata* and *S. schwetzi*.
Host location	Body surface.
Life cycle	Females lay small groups of eggs in decaying organic matter on which the larvae feed. The larval period lasts for 2–10 weeks.
Host acquisition	By direct contact with female seeking host for blood meal.
Symptoms	Heavy infestations can cause blood loss and stress in small reptiles (Frye, 1991).

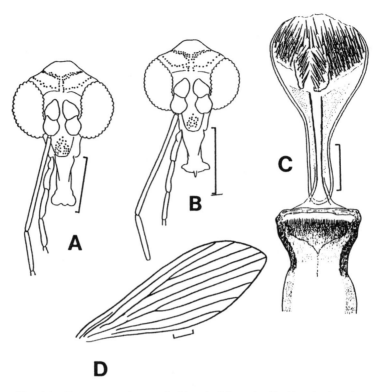

Fig. 30. *Sergentomyia* sp. **A.** Head of female; **B.** Head of male;
C. Cibarium and pharynx of female; **D.** Wing of female.
(Reproduced with permission from Laurence and Quate, 1967).

Diagnosis	By demonstration of organism on body surface or cage environment.
Treatment	Prevention is by removal of dense vegetation around outdoor enclosures, filling in cracks in walls of buildings, and by screening windows and cages. Fecal material should always be removed from animal enclosures as soon as possible.

FAMILY: SARCOPHAGIDAE (FLESH FLIES) (FIG. 31)

Flesh flies have gray or silvery bodies, and the sides of their heads are hairy. They possess plumose antennae, compound eyes, and a long proboscis. Palps are rudimentary. Vein M_{1+2} (shown in Fig. 3 for calliphorid flies) has an angular bend

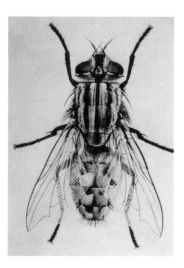

Fig. 31. Flesh fly, *Sarcophaga* sp. (Photo courtesy of Rhonda D. Pinckney).

and ends well before the wing apex. Maggots of sarcophagid flies are distinguished from calliphorid larvae by a girdle of minute spines on each abdominal segment. Additionally, they have well-developed, curved mouthparts. Posterior respiratory (= stigmal) plates are located in a deep cavity, with three slits on each that are vertically parallel.

Many flesh flies are parasitic in the larval stages (called maggots; see Figs. 33, 34) and cause myiasis. Adults can transmit pathogens on their mouthparts and feet. Larvae are primarily facultative parasites, developing on carcasses, excreta, and egg contents, but they also have been reported to develop in wounds and on healthy tissue. Graham-Jones (1961) reported that flesh flies often larviposit around the cloacae of chelonians. Frank (1981) reported the death of lizards in the genus *Hemidactylus* that had sarcophagid myiasis. These maggots penetrate the healthy skin of lizards to feed on their tissues and may ultimately kill them. Sarcophagids are worldwide in distribution. The four genera with members that are particularly parasitic on reptiles are presented below.

I. *Anolisimyia blakeae*

Description   Adult male: measures 6.8 mm long; head grayish, about 2/3 as long as high, with 2 postocular rows of black setae; antennae reddish with the apical half of third segment darkened; palps reddish; gray thorax with 3 dark stripes; gray abdomen with 4th segment reddish; genital segments yellowish and medium-sized; wings hyaline with dark brown veins; reddish legs including the coxae, and bases of tarsi darkened apically.

Adult female: measures 6.0 mm long; body coloration as in male; genital segments reddish.

Puparium: Measures 6.0–6.5 mm long; dark brown in color, body shaped cylindrically; posterior spiracles set in a deep concavity.

Larva: not described in detail. Blake (1955) stated that mature larvae feeding on the green anolis lizard, *Anolis carolinensis*, were 8 mm long.

Host(s)   Green anole, *Anolis carolinensis* (Blake, 1955; Dodge, 1955; Gunter, 1958).

Host location   On skin or in dermis; also may burrow inside host to feed on internal organs, usually resulting in death of host.

Life cycle (Fig. 32)   Larviparous.

Host acquisition   By direct contact with larvae.

Symptoms   Dermal lesions containing maggots. These larvae may also feed internally, exiting through the host's skin just before pupation. In this situation, the dermis is often unaffected until the exit hole is formed.

Diagnosis   By identification of dermal lesions containing mag-

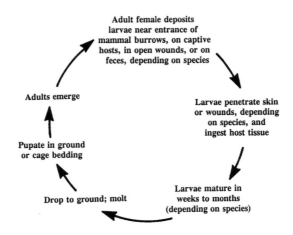

Fig. 32. Generalized life cycle of myiasis-producing flies.

gots, or by observation of maggots exiting from host.

Treatment

See Appendix I. Prevention is by screening windows and cages. Fecal material should always be removed as soon as possible. When myiasis-producing flies are known to be a problem, frequently check animals for egg deposits or larvae.

II. *Cistudinomyia cistudinus* (syn. *Sarcophaga cistudinus*) (Fig. 33)

Description

Adult male: parafrontal and parafacial setae gray and pollinose; parafacials with few inconspicuous setae; frontal stripe dark red and relatively broad; frontal bristles short, approximately 13 in number; ocellar bristles distinct with coarse setae on and behind ocellar triangle; antennae brownish black; arista short; palps and proboscis black; abdomen gray, pollinose, tessellated, with median dark stripe; fourth segment yellow in ground color; first and second segments with only lateral bristles; hypopygium small, retracted and first segment yellow with row of strong bristles along hind margin; posterior clasper slender and curved with blunt tip; anterior clasper stout at base with slender sharp tip curved downward; legs black; wings hyaline; no costal spine; third costal segment shorter than fifth; first vein bare; third vein with a few setae at base.

Adult female: similar to male; body measures 8–10 mm long; orbitals and outer verticals present; third antennal segment short and rounded; genital segments entirely yellow; no specialized larvipositor present; femur without comb, but with numerous small bristles.

First instar larva: body gray-white, slender, widest near middle and tapering, measuring 0.35 mm wide by 2.20 mm long - at time of molt measuring 4 mm long; 12 apparent segments, including cephalic; cephalopharyngeal skeleton measures 0.312–0.354 mm in length, and at widest point, 0.104–0.114 mm wide; external,

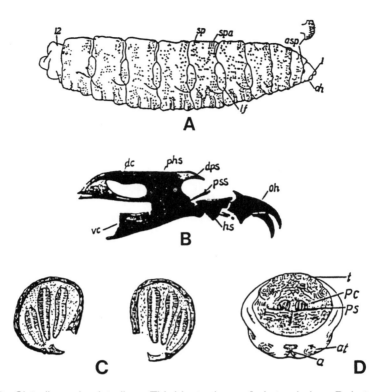

Fig. 33. *Cistudinomyia cistudinus.* Third instar larva. **A.** Lateral view; **B.** Lateral view of cephalopharyngeal sclerites; **C.** Posterior spiracles; **D.** Posterior view of 12th (or last) segment. **Legend:** a (anus); asp (anterior spiracles); at (anal tubercle); dc (dorsal cornu); dps (dorsopharyngeal sclerites); hs (hypostomal sclerites); lf (lateral fusiform area); oh (oral hooks); pc (posterior cavity); phs (pharyngeal sclerites); ps (posterior spiracle); pss (parastomal sclerites); sp (spines on posterior margin of segments); spa (spines on anterior margin of segments); t (tubercle on border of posterior cavity); vc (ventral cornu); 1 (first apparent or cephalic segment); 12 (twelfth segment). (Reproduced with permission from Knipling, 1937).

anterior spiracles absent; two posterior spiracles as pairs of slits opening into brownish pigmented spiracular atria that measure 120–200 μm; oral hooks paired with each divided into two points. Second instar larva: cephalopharyngeal skeleton measures 0.630 mm in length, and 0.175 mm wide; body measures 0.9–1.8 mm wide by 4.2–9.5 mm long; small anterior spiracles; posterior spiracles measure 0.115 mm wide by 0.145 mm long, each with two spiracular slits surrounded by incomplete ring or peritreme.

Third instar larva (Fig. 33a–d): cephalopharyngeal skeleton (Fig. 33b) measures 1.28 mm in length, body measures 2–4.5 mm wide by 10–15 mm long; two anterior spiracles (Fig. 33 c,d) present, one on each side of segment two; posterior spiracles measure 0.29 mm wide by 0.31 mm long.

Host(s)
Terrestrial and freshwater chelonians of the eastern United States (Connecticut, Florida, Georgia, Illinois, Kansas, Massachusetts, Mississippi, New Jersey, New York, North Carolina, Oklahoma, Texas, Virginia), and captive specimens having contact with the former (Aldrich, 1916; Baumgartner, 1988; Dodge, 1955; Emerton, 1904; Jackson et al., 1969; Kepner, 1912; King and Griffo, 1958; Knipling, 1937; Lawler, 1977; Packard, 1882; Peters, 1948; Rainey, 1953; Townsend, 1917; Wheeler, 1890).

Host location
Skin; larvae deposited on scar tissue and in wounds (e.g., wounds resulting from gopher tortoise ticks, *Amblyomma tuberculatum*).

Life cycle
At a mean ambient temperature of 76°F (24.4°C), the pre-larviposition period is 8–10 days; female larviposits approximately 120–140 larvae in wounds or on scar tissue; at a mean ambient temperature of 78°F (25.6°C), first instar larvae molt in 7–11 days; second instar larvae molt in approximately 7–9 days; the duration of third instar larvae is approximately 28–35 days; mature larvae pupate in approximately 18–36 hours at a mean ambient temperature of 78°F (25.6°C); at this temperature, duration of the pupal stage is approximately 18 days.

Host acquisition
By direct contact with larvae.

Symptoms
Not always apparent; cystlike subcutaneous lesions; death can occur if not diagnosed. Knipling (1937) reported that infested wounds may produce a dark discharge having an obnoxious odor.

Diagnosis   By recognition of small larval "breathing" hole(s) (Fig. 33c,d) in skin, or by larvae in wounds.

Treatment   See Appendix I. Prevention is by screening windows and cages. Fecal material should always be removed as soon as possible. When myiasis-producing flies are known to be a problem, check animals frequently for larvae in wounds. The neck and front legs of turtles are common sites for myiasis. Peters (1948) also gave an account of finding larvae anterior to the hind legs on both sides of two specimens of eastern box turtles, *Terrapene carolina*. One specimen had lost all control over its hind legs. A necropsy revealed that larvae had attacked lymph glands and affected muscular and nervous tissue.

III. *Eumacronychia nigricornis* (Fig. 34)

Description   Adult male: length 5.5–8 mm; thorax and scutellum black or gray; wings clear; 3rd vein setose halfway to small cross vein; abdomen subconical with 3 yellowish terminal segments, with shiny black cross bands; parafrontals with long, erect black bristly setae (Reinhard, 1965).

Adult female: similar to male except for genitalia and other sexual differences; 1st genital segment protruding to resemble an extra segment.

Larva: third instar (Fig. 34a–d) measures 5.0–11.3 mm long; body spinose; individual spines dark-tipped, and usually with 1–2 (occasionally up to 5) points; antennomaxillary complex of sensory structures on ventral aspect of segment; anterior spiracle with 5 or 6 processes (but may have 5 processes on one side and 6 on the other); mouth-hooks (Fig. 34b,c) on cephalopharyngeal skeleton (Fig. 34c) well developed; posterior spiracles (Fig. 34d) recessed in shallow depression.

Host(s)   Eggs of eastern fence lizard, *Sceloporus undulatus* (Mullen et al., 1984).

Host location   See Host(s) above.

Life cycle (Fig. 32)   Larviparous.

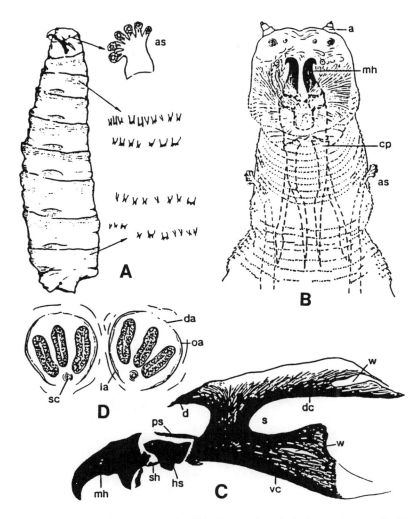

Fig. 34. *Eumacronychia nigricornis*. Third instar larva. **A.** Lateral view; **B.** Ventral view of larva; **C.** Lateral view of cephalopharyngeal skeleton; **D.** Posterior spiracles. **Legend:** a (antenna); as (anterior spiracle); cp (cephalopharyngeal skeleton); d (dorsal arch); da (dorsal arc); dc (dorsal cornu); hs (hypostomal sclerite); ia (inner arc); mh (mouth hook); oa (outer arc); ps (parastomal sclerite); s (sinus); sc (stigmatic scar); vc (ventral cornu); sh (subhypostomal sclerite); w (window). (Reproduced with permission from Mullen et al., 1984).

Host acquisition   By direct contact with larvae. Gravid female larviposits on the soil surface above an egg clutch. Larvae burrow rapidly and perforate intact egg shells to feed on the embryos inside. Because of this behavior, *E. nigricornis* may be considered a specialized predator of reptilian eggs, although the origins of such behavior are probably with parasitism (Mullen et al., 1984; Trauth and Mullen, 1990).

Symptoms   Unhatched egg clutches.

Diagnosis   By recognition of circular holes (Fig. 34d), with irregular margins, measuring 0.3–1.0 mm in diameter in host eggs.

Treatment   See Appendix I.

IV. *Metoposarcophaga importuna* (Fig. 35)

Description   Adults: body black with numerous black setae and bristles; head with gray stripe between the antennae and ocelli; eyes red; antennae black with tip of 2nd segment red dorsally; 3rd segment more than twice the length of the 2nd; four gray body stripes present; abdomen oval, with four rows of large irregular spots; tip of abdomen

Fig. 35. Hatching turtle egg of *Graptemys* sp. infested by fly larvae, *Metoposarcophaga importuna*. (Reproduced with permission from Vogt, 1981; courtesy of the American Society of Ichthyologists and Herpetologists).

	red; legs black with black bristles; wings with black veins and white scales with yellow borders; distal cross-vein curved inward basally, then straight to the apex, joining the wing border subterminally; proximal cross-vein with 2 slight curves, one outward, the other inward.
Host(s)	Diamondback terrapin, *Malaclemmys terrapin* (Aldrich, 1916): smooth, softshell turtle, *Trionyx muticus* (= *Apalone mutica*) and spiny softshell turtle, *Trionyx spiniferus* (= *Apalone spinifera*) (Muller, 1921); false map turtle, *Graptemys pseudogeographica* (Vogt, 1981).
Host location	In hatchlings, yolk plug.
Life cycle (Fig. 32)	Larviparous.
Host acquisition	Vogt (1981) reported that female flies target hatchling turtles (Fig. 35) (probably through olfaction); larviposit on sand over nest; maggots burrow down to hatching eggs and enter hatchlings through yolk plug. Baumgartner (1988) stated that, unlike *Eumacronychia* spp., maggots belonging to this genus cannot penetrate undamaged host eggs and suggested that the larvae attack turtle hatchlings as they begin to break out of their shells.
Symptoms	Presence of maggots in reptilian egg clutches.
Diagnosis	Presence of maggots in reptilian egg clutches.
Treatment	Prevention is by screening windows, cages, and incubators containing turtle eggs. In advanced cases of maggot infestation, it may be necessary to euthanize hatchlings. Also see Appendix I.

V. Other sarcophagid spp. that cause myiasis in reptiles

Anolisomyia rufianalis larvae cause lethal myiasis in *Anolis evermanni* and *Anolis stratulus* in the Caribbean region (Dominica and Puerto Rico) (Dial and Roughgarden, 1996).

Anolisomyia pallipes larvae caused myiasis in *Anolis* sp. lizards in Costa Rica (Lopes and Tibana, 1988).

Blaesoxipha plinthopyga larvae have been reported to cause myiasis and death in a whiptail lizard, *Cnemidophorus* sp. (Pape, 1994; Whitworth and Wangberg, 1985).

Cistudinomyia sp. larvae, probably belonging to an undescribed species, caused myiasis in a house gecko in Venezuela (de Marmels, 1994).

Eumacronychia sternalis larvae parasitize the eggs and hatchlings of the Pacific green sea turtle, *Chelonia mydas agassizi* (Lopes, 1982), in a manner similar to that described by Mullen et al. (1984) and Trauth and Mullen (1990) for *E. nigricornis* infesting *Sceloporus* eggs. Many of the 15 recognized species of *Eumacronychia* also parasitize other lizard and turtle eggs (Baumgartner, 1988).

FAMILY: TABANIDAE (HORSE AND DEER FLIES)

Adult horse and deer flies are associated with all major groups of vertebrates including reptiles, but only the female is hematophagous. Webb and Wells (1924) reported that a medium-sized tabanid took 8–10 minutes to feed, and consumed 0.125 cc of blood. Stone (1930) reported a blood intake of 0.20 cc. Thus, many flies feeding on a single animal can consume a significant volume of blood.

Tabanid flies are stout-bodied, with powerful, well-developed wings characterized by evenly distributed veins. They measure 7–35 mm in body length. Tabanids are often colored brown, black, orange, or metallic green. Their eyes are large, widely separated, and usually beautifully striped with gold, green, or purple. They usually possess short, trijointed antennae.

Horse and deer flies may serve as intermediate hosts for some protozoa, and some species can mechanically transmit various pathogens to humans such as those that cause tularemia, loiasis, and anthrax. The North American deer fly, *Chrysops callidus,* is a vector of the protozoan parasite *Haemoproteus metchnikovi* to freshwater turtles (DeGiusti et al; 1973).

I. *Chrysops* spp. (Fig. 36, 37)

Commonly known as deer flies, members of this genus are distributed worldwide.

Description   Adult (Fig. 36): relatively small, measuring 7–12 mm in length; proboscis soft, projecting downward; first and second segments of antennae long, without basal toothlike process on 3rd segment; wings (Fig. 37) with dark spots, patterns, or lines; hind tibiae with apical spurs; functional ocelli present and usually on a distinct tubercle; abdomen usually dark but sometimes green or yellow.

Pupa: brown in color and cylindrical in shape; elon-

Fig. 36. *Chrysops* sp. Adult. (After Francis and Mayne, 1922.)

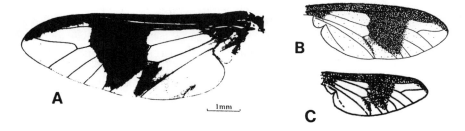

Fig. 37. *Chrysops callidus* wings. **A.** From Tennessee; **B.** From Arkansas; **C.** From West Virginia. (A, reproduced from Goodwin et al., 1985; B, reproduced from Schwardt and Hall, 1930; C, reproduced from Drees et al., 1980).

gate body with thoracic spiracles connected subcutaneously with a large prothoracic cavity; prothorax with a long aperture connected to the spiracle; combs absent on caudal abdominal segments.

Larva: less than 20 mm long when mature; newly hatched, cylindrical in shape, tapering at both ends, usually with longitudinal striations; abdominal segments each bearing one girdle of fleshy tubercles with setae; head retractile; spiracular fissure vertical. Larvae of this genus are chiefly saprophagous.

Egg: cylindrical, measuring 1–2.5 mm in length; light in color when first laid, turning dark later.

Host(s)	Most *Chrysops* spp. feed on several vertebrate species including reptiles. *Chrysops callidus* often feeds on the painted turtle, *Chrysemys picta,* in North America (De Giusti and Dobrzechowski, 1974).
Host location	Body surface; feeding occurs between scales on dorsum.
Life cycle (Fig. 38)	For *C. callidus*: 100–1000 eggs deposited in masses during summer or fall, neatly arranged in piles in mud, on logs, stems and leaves of aquatic plants, or on leaves of trees hanging over water; eggs adhered together with secretion; larvae hatch in 5–7 days during summer and either drop to water's substratum or burrow into mud; larvae pass through 4–9 instars by following spring; last instars migrate to dry ground and pupate; pupal stage lasts slightly over one week (Stone, 1930); emerging adults hide in foliage; females seek host upon which to feed.
Host acquisition	By direct contact with female seeking blood meal.
Symptoms	Large or bloody feeding lesions on skin surface.
Diagnosis	By demonstration of organism on body surface or in cage environment.
Treatment	Place dichlorvos-impregnated pest strips in affected animal areas; screen all windows and

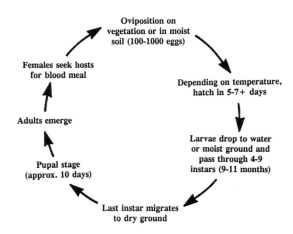

Fig. 38. Generalized life cycle of tabanid flies. (Adapted from Matheson, 1950).

doors; avoid the use of untreated soil or other substrates that may contain immature stages.

II. *Tabanus* spp. (Fig. 39)

Commonly known as horse flies, these large insects are distributed worldwide. The genus includes approximately 1,500 described species. In North America, *T. atratus* and *T. lineola* (Fig. 39) are commonly encountered species on reptiles.

Description   Adult: no apical spurs on hind tibiae; no functional ocelli on head; large in size (10–35 mm in length); 3rd antennal segment with a basal tooth-like process; wings without dark spots (although, in some, wings are entirely black or brown); abdomen gray or blackish.

Pupa: brown and robust; combs present on caudal abdominal segment; frontal bristles single; antenna short.

Larva: longer than 20 mm when mature; antennae with short terminal segment; dorsal and ventral body smooth, especially thorax; anal abdominal segment usually tapered. Larvae of this genus are chiefly carnivorous.

Host(s)   Crocodiles and sea turtles (Matheson, 1950).

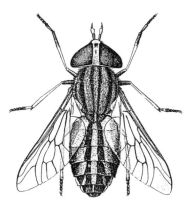

Fig. 39. Striped horsefly, *Tabanus lineola*. (Reproduced from Schwardt and Hall, 1930).

Host location	Body surface; feeding occurs between plates on dorsum.
Life cycle (Fig. 38)	See *Chrysops* above, except larvae are carnivorous (including being cannibalistic) rather than saprophagous.
Host acquisition	By direct contact with females seeking host for blood meal.
Symptoms	Large or bloody feeding lesions on skin surface.
Diagnosis	By demonstration of organism on body surface or in cage environment.
Treatment	Place dichlorvos-impregnated pest strips in affected animal areas; screen all windows and doors; avoid the use of untreated soil or other substrates that may contain immature stages.

III. Other horse flies that feed on reptiles

Hybomitra lasiophthalma is known to feed on many North American vertebrates including reptiles.

The feeding habits of most tabanids are poorly known and it is likely that members of some other genera also feed on reptile blood.

CHAPTER 3

ORDER: SIPHONAPTERA (FLEAS)

Although fleas are considered to parasitize exclusively endothermic vertebrates (mammals and birds), there are reports of these ectoparasites feeding on reptiles under captive conditions, such as in the laboratory. For example, Fox et al. (1966) reported that 33 of 43 *Xenopsylla cheopis,* the Oriental rat flea, and 12 of 18 *Ctenocephalides felis,* the cat flea, would feed on the Puerto Rican anole (*Anolis cristatellus*) when the lizard was offered as a host. Similarly, Jäth (1952) noted that *Ctenocephalides canis,* the dog flea, would feed on the emerald lizard (*Lacerta viridis*) and the viviparous lizard (*L. vivipara*), while Darskaya and Besedina (1961) and Kulakova (1964) reported that *Xenopsylla gerbilli* would feed on the blood of several species of Russian lizards (unspecified). Below is a general diagram of flea morphology (Fig. 40).

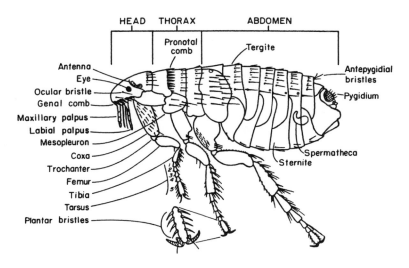

Fig. 40. Basic morphology of an adult flea. (Reproduced from Pratt, 1965).

CHAPTER 4

ORDER: PARASITIFORMES SUPERFAMILY: IXODOIDEA (TICKS)

Ticks have segmented bodies. These segments are not evident externally except in the legs and palps. Adults possess no antennae, and their head and thorax are fused into a cephalothorax. The anterior portion comprising the mouthparts and associated structures is termed the capitulum, while the larger posterior portion of the body is the idiosoma. The larvae possess three pairs of legs, and nymphs and adults have four pairs. The last segment of the first pair of legs has a sensory depression known as Haller's organ (Fig. 41), which is unique to ticks. All tick species have a hypostome (Fig. 42), which is usually toothed, on the capitulum. Nymphs resemble adults, but lack reproductive organs including the externally visible genital aperture. Figures 43 and 44 depict generalized diagrams of tick morphology.

Ticks have four stages in their life cycle: egg, larva, nymph, and adult. Depending on tick species, host availability, and environmental conditions, these stages may require from 6 weeks to 3 years to complete. Ticks in the family Ixodidae have one nymphal instar, but those in the family Argasidae may pass through as many as five with a molt at the end of each instar. Copulation occurs on the host in adult metastriate ticks (*Hyalomma, Amblyomma,* and *Aponomma* on reptiles), but prostriate ticks (*Ixodes* spp.) can mate successfully either on or off the host. Argasid ticks mate off the host. A blood meal is usually required for egg production. The engorged female drops to the ground, laying her eggs in soil, humus, leaf litter, or sand. Hatchling larvae possess 6 legs. Most climb onto low vegetation to wait for a host; a few quest from leaf litter or sand. After engorging, the 6-legged larva molts to an 8-legged nymph. Depending on the family, additional molts may occur on the same host, or multiple hosts may be used (e.g., argasid ticks) until the final adult tick stage is reached.

All ticks are blood-sucking parasites. To feed, ticks probe host skin with their pedipalps. Using sharp teeth on their chelicerae, they cut through it. The hypostome is then thrust into the wound while the tick uses its hypostomal teeth to

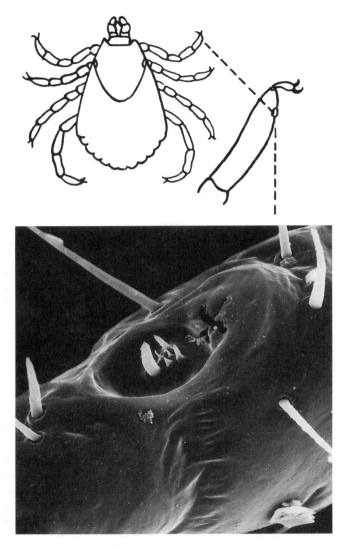

Fig. 41. Haller's organ. (Photo courtesy of the U.S. National Tick Collection).

help anchor it to its host. Salivary components including anticoagulants, enzymes, a cement plug, and, occasionally, toxins or pathogens, are liberated into the feeding site before blood and lymph from the wound are imbibed. Adult and nymphal soft ticks feed rapidly (usually in 30 minutes or less) and leave their host after engorging. Hard ticks and larval soft ticks remain on the host for several days and detach following full engorgement. However, because reptiles are

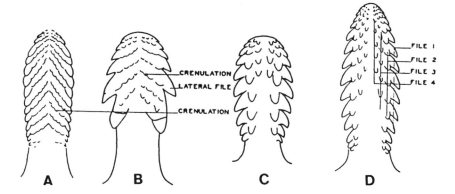

Fig. 42. Hypostome variation of *Ixodes* spp. **A, B, C.** Types of male hypostome; **D.** Female hypostome. Where hypostomal dentition is indistinct, tooth rows are referred to as "crenulations" (A and B). On each side of the hypostome midline, vertical rows of teeth are numbered from 1 (outer rows) upwards (D). (Reproduced with permission from Cooley and Kohls, 1945).

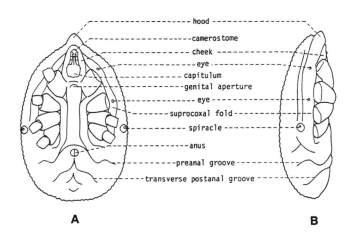

Fig. 43. Basic morphology of *Ornithodoros* spp. **A.** Ventral view; **B.** Lateral view. (Reproduced with permission from Yamaguti et al., 1971.

"cold-blooded," ticks feed more slowly on these hosts than on birds or mammals, and they may remain attached for weeks or months. Males of some hard ticks, especially *Ixodes* spp., take little or no host blood and therefore do not engorge dramatically.

Some reptile-feeding ticks may transmit pathogens to their hosts, but little information is available on this topic. It has been suggested that certain reptiles and

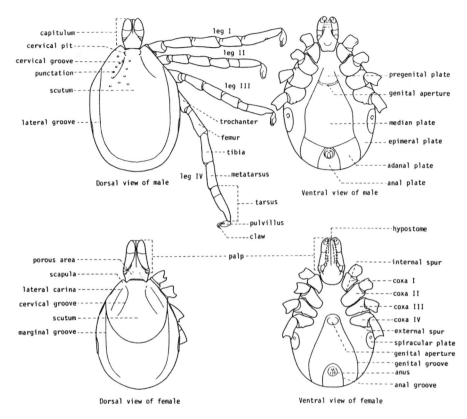

Fig. 44. Basic morphology of *Ixodes* sp. (Reproduced with permission from Yamaguti et al., 1971).

their ticks may be reservoirs and vectors, respectively, of *Coxiella burnetii,* the rickettsial agent that causes Q fever (Marchette, 1966). This pathogen has been detected in, or isolated from, both ticks and reptiles (Hoogstraal, 1985).

Of the ticks that parasitize reptiles, most occur on terrestrial chelonians, snakes, and lizards (Fig. 45) native to tropical, subtropical, and warm temperate regions. Tick genera with representatives parasitizing reptiles can be classified as follows:

Phylum: Arthropoda
   Class: Arachnida
      Subclass: Acari
         Order: Parasitiformes
            Suborder: Metastigmata

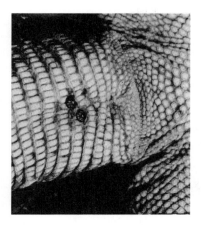

Fig. 45. Ticks on imported savanna monitor, *Varanus exanthematicus.*
(Photo courtesy of Murray E. Fowler).

Superfamily: Ixodoidea
    Family: Argasidae (Soft Ticks)
        Genus: *Argas*
                Ornithodoros
    Family: Ixodidae (Hard Ticks)
        Genus: *Amblyomma*
                Aponomma
                Dermacentor
                Haemaphysalis
                Hyalomma
                Ixodes

Key to genera of adult Ixodoidea (ticks) parasitizing reptiles

1a	Scutum present (covering entire dorsal surface of males); mouthparts and basis capituli apical 2
1b	Scutum absent; mouthparts and basis capituli ventral 7
2a (1a)	Anal groove distinct and curving anteriorly around anus; eyes and festoons absent. . . . . *Ixodes*
2b	Anal groove never extending anteriorly around anus, and sometimes indistinct; festoons present; eyes present or absent 3
3a (2b)	Eyes absent. 4
3b	Eyes present 5
4a (3a)	Scutum inornate (lacking color patterns); palps short and conical

	with segment 2 at least as broad as long and usually extended laterally . . . . *Haemaphysalis*
4b	Scutum ornate (with color patterns) or rarely inornate; palps long and subcylindrical, with segment 2 much longer than broad . . *Aponomma*
5a (3b)	Scutum inornate; festoons irregular and partially coalesced; males with distinct ventral plates; eyes orbited and bulging . . . . *Hyalomma*
5b	Scutum almost always ornate; festoons regular and not coalesced; males lacking ventral plates. 6
6a (5b)	Palps much longer than basis capituli, palpal segment 2 much longer than broad . . . . *Amblyomma*
6b	Palps short, about as long as basis capituli, palpal segment 2 about as long as broad . . . . *Dermacentor*
7a (1b)	Sutural line distinct around lateral body (Fig. 46). . . . . *Argas*
7b	Sutural line absent (Fig. 46) . . . . *Ornithodoros*

FAMILY: ARGASIDAE (SOFT TICKS)

These are leathery, soft-bodied ticks having a wrinkled, granulated, or mammillated integument. Protrusions on the dorsal walls of the leg segments, and the subapical dorsal protruberance, are important features in identifying argasid ticks to species. The scutum is absent in all stages. In nymphs and adults, the capitulum is situated subterminally and ventrally. In larvae, it is subterminal or terminal. The pedipalp segments are leglike and articulate freely in all stages. The eyes, if present, are located in supracoxal folds along the lateral body margin. Coxal glands, which are excretory organs, are present between the first and second leg coxae.

Balashov (1972) reported that sexual dimorphism in soft ticks is essentially confined to internal structures, although the sexes can be distinguished by observing the morphology of the external genital apertures. Adult females lay fewer than

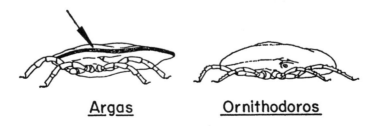

Argas   Ornithodoros

Fig. 46. Note that members of the genus *Argas* possess a distinct sutural line (arrow) around the lateral portion of the body; *Ornithodoros* ticks do not. (Reproduced with permission from Yamaguti et al., 1971).

1,000 eggs, ovipositing in their hiding places several times between feedings, and blood is required for egg production.

Only larval stages attach to the reptilian host for any length of time (2–5 days) and remain on the host until they molt to nymphs. Nymphs and adults spend most of their time off the host and crawl onto the host to feed rapidly (usually in less than an hour) when the reptile retreats to its burrow or den. They feed repeatedly, resting off the host between meals. Both sexes distend when engorged with blood.

Generally, argasid ticks are resistant to starvation. Many that live under desert conditions can endure long periods (several months or even years) between meals. During periods of inactivity, they typically remain motionless beneath sand or debris, often inside a cave or animal burrow.

The systematics of argasid ticks have been viewed differently by various authors. The most recent treatment is that of Klompen and Oliver (1993) who promoted new generic assignments for several soft ticks including some that parasitize reptiles. Although approximately 25 species of argasid ticks may feed on reptiles, only about 8 of these are considered to be true reptile parasites (Hoogstraal and Aeschlimann, 1982).

I. *Argas brumpti* (Fig. 47)

In Egypt and Kenya, *A. brumpti* and its lizard hosts have been found infected with the haemogregarine *Hepatozoon argantis* (Garnham, 1954; Hoogstraal and Kaiser, 1957).

Description

This large tick measures 15–20 mm long by 10 mm wide as an unfed adult female; body flattened with thin lateral margins; wrinkled integument interrupted by rounded areas pitted at top and armed with setae set in pits.

Adult male, female, and nymph: except for size variation and the presence or absence of genitalia, these stages are all morphologically similar. The body is flat, with nymphs and males occasionally having a slightly convex dorsum. Nymphs and males are smaller than females and average 7 mm long by 5 mm wide. Lateral body margins parallel with conical, anterior border (hood) and broadly rounded posterior margin; dorsal surface pitted by symmetrically arranged polygonal depressions bounded by coarse ridges and containing small discs; numerous short setae, especially along anterior margin; ventrally, camerostome

Fig. 47. *Argas brumpti*. Male, dorsal view. (Photo courtesy
of the U.S. National Tick Collection).

(see Fig. 43) deep and triangular, cheeks divergent posteriorly and connected behind the capitulum by a transverse fold immediately anterior to
the gentalia in adults; capitulum with thickened
base, palps tapering with articles 1 and 2 elongate and 3 and 4 short; hypostome elongate and
narrow with 2/2 dentition (see Fig. 42d) and
14–15 denticles per file; leg coxa I separate but
coxae II–IV contiguous.

Larva: body rounded with large, dorsal plate and
approximately 40 setae dorsally, 7 pairs of setae
ventrally but lacking posteromedian seta, 6 para-
capsular setae on tarsus I, 5 setae on palpal segment II, palpal segment II longer than other palpal segments; hypostome elongate and sharply
pointed with 2/2 dentition (see Fig. 42d) and
more than 20 denticles per file.

Host(s)   Larval and nymphal stages on various vertebrates
                           including lizards of North, South and East Africa

	(Frank, 1981; Hoogstraal, 1956, 1964; Theiler, 1962).
Host location	Body surface.
Life cycle (Fig. 48)	See Ticks Introduction, and Family Argasidae above.
Host acquisition	By direct contact with organism.
Symptoms	On rare occasions, anemia (Jacobson, 1986) and inanition in heavy infestations.
Diagnosis	By demonstration of organism on body surface or cage environment, especially in cracks and crevices. Examine ticks laterally in order to detect the characteristic sutural line (Fig. 46a) that separates the dorsal and ventral margins of the animal.
Treatment	See Appendix I.

II. Other *Argas* spp. affecting reptiles

Argas hoogstraali parasitizes three species of Madagascan lizards: *Oplurus fierinensis, O. grandidieri* and *O. quadrimaculatus*. This tick has not been recorded from other potential hosts and appears to be exclusively a reptile parasite (Uilenberg et al., 1979).

Argas transgariepinus feeds on many different vertebrate species, including reptiles, in North Africa (Hoogstraal and Aeschlimann, 1982).

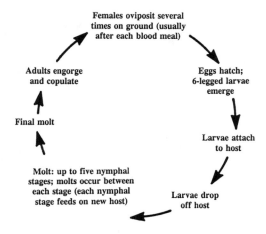

Fig. 48. Generalized life cycle of argasid ticks.

III. *Ornithodoros* spp.

Ornithodoros species are thick, leathery, rounded, and lack a sutural line between the dorsal and ventral surfaces (Fig. 46b) which is present in the genus *Argas*. The hypostome is variable but never scooplike. Non-engorged specimens are densely wrinkled, allowing for great distention when feeding. They commonly occur in caves, animal burrows, and campsites.

A. *Ornithodoros talaje* (Figs. 49, 50)

Ornithodoros talaje occurs in the central and southwestern United States, south to Argentina. There is also an unconfirmed record from Florida. Frank (1981) reported that *O. talaje* may transmit the filarial nematode, *Macdonaldius oscheri*, to snakes in the family Boidae.

Description   Adult: body oval and slightly pointed anteriorly; posterior border slightly flattened; sides nearly parallel; mammillae large, close, but not crowded; setae absent on dorsal and ventral sur-

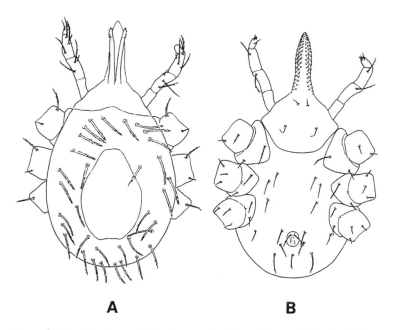

A   **B**

Fig. 49. *Ornithodoros talaje.* Larva. **A.** Dorsal view; **B.** Ventral view. (Reproduced with permission from Kohls et al., 1965; copyrighted by the Entomological Society of America).

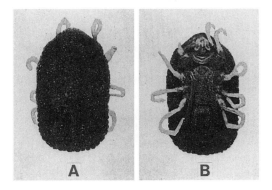

Fig. 50. *Ornithodoros talaje.* Adult. **A.** Dorsal view; **B.** Ventral view.
(Cooley and Kohls, 1944a; reproduced with permission
from American Midland Naturalist).

faces; hood small and in contact with cheeks, forming an enclosure covering the mouthparts; cheeks oval, large, and with irregular surface; females measure 4.20–7.25 mm long by 2.34– 4.60 mm wide, and males measure 3.36–5.80 mm long by 1.75–3.40 mm wide; capitulum wider than long with irregular transverse wrinkles and micromammillae; palps moderate in size; hypostome short (measures approximately 0.245 mm) with 2/2 dentition and with nearly parallel sides, notched apically; legs small, moderate in length with micromammillated surface; mild subapical dorsal protuberance on tarsus I, absent from all other tarsi; coxae I and II well separated, all others contiguous; genital opening between coxae I.

Nymph: essentially similar to the adult except genital pore absent; early instar nymphs distinctly smaller than adults.

Larva: unfed larva suboval in shape; basis capituli triangular in dorsal view; palps very long and slender; unengorged body measures 0.620–0.695 mm long including capitulum; dorsum with 16–17 pairs of setae; hypostome very long (approximately 0.21 mm) and slender; dentition 3/3 in anterior half then 2/2 posteriorly to base.

Host(s)   Rainbow boa, *Epicrates cenchria* (Dunn, 1933);

various reptiles in European zoological gardens (Frank, 1981); Galapagos marine iguana, *Amblyrhynchus cristatus* (Godsden and Guerra, 1991). *O. talaje* will feed on a wide variety of vertebrates, including rodents, ground-frequenting birds, reptiles, domestic animals, and humans (Kohls et al., 1965).

Host location	Body surface.
Life cycle	See Ticks Introduction, and Family Argasidae above.
Host acquisition	Via infestation from contaminated hosts or substrate containing resting nymphs or adults.
Symptoms	On rare occasions, anemia in heavy infestations (Jacobson, 1986).
Diagnosis	By demonstration of organism on body surface or cage environment.
Treatment	See Appendix I.

B. *Ornithodoros* (formerly *Argas*) *transversus* (Figs. 51–53)

Commonly called the minute Galapagos argasid, *O. transversus* was reassigned to the genus *Ornithodoros* by Klompen and Oliver (1993), partly because it lacks the sutural line between the dorsum and venter characteristic of the genus *Argas*. Morphologically, this tick is unique and shows several convergent traits with pterygosomatid mites (Hoogstraal et al., 1973).

Description	Adult female (Fig. 52 d,e): body 1.4–1.8 mm long by 2.1–2.8 mm broad and compressed antero-posteriorly; dorsal surface an irregular mosaic of flat, slightly elevated integument with irregularly depressed disclike areas; long, stout setae around entire body margin, except anterior margin which has short, spikelike setae; capitulum situated in a relatively deep camerostome; hypostome narrowly elongate with 2/2 dentition, approximately 6 small denticles in outer file and 3 slightly larger denticles in inner file; genital slit poorly defined, situated between coxae II and III.
	Adult male (Figs. 51, 52a–c): body 1.3–1.6 mm long by 2.2–2.6 mm broad and more compressed antero-posteriorly than female; dorsal surface as in female but with smaller, more regular mosaics, and with long stout setae (approx. 114) around entire body; capitulum as in female; hypostome

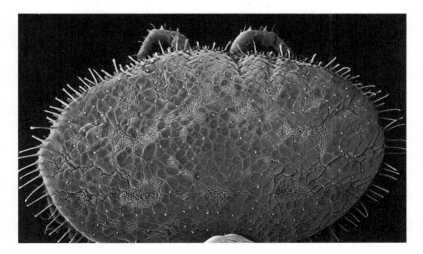

Fig. 51. *Ornithodoros transversus.* Male, dorsal view (also see Fig. 52a). (Photo courtesy of the U.S. National Tick Collection).

with 2/2 dentition with very small denticles in files of 6 or 7; genitalia between coxae II and III.

Nymph (Fig. 52 f,g): body size almost as large as adults, with similar outline; dorsal surface a mosaic of dense, irregularly defined elements much smaller than in adults; stout lateral body setae (68–76) essentially as in adults, but with length more variable and absent from anterior margin; capitulum situated in camerostome as in adult; hypostomal dentition 2/2 with 3–4 small denticles in outer file and 2 in inner file.

Larva (Fig. 53): very small; body (partially engorged) 0.326 mm long by 0.413 mm broad, antero-posteriorly compressed; integument finely folded unlike that of nymph and adults; dorsal plate absent; dorsal surface with 6 pairs of long, apically barbed setae, ventral surface with a cluster of approximately 30 short, blunt, nude setae in anal region, plus 1 slightly longer seta posterior to anus; hypostome arising from a small, median extension of the basis capituli, slender and bluntly rounded apically, hypostomal dentition 2/2 with 1 denticle in each file.

Host(s)   Galapagos giant tortoise, *Geochelone elephantopus.*

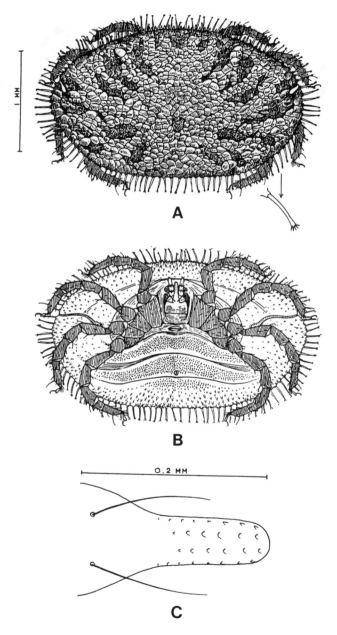

Fig. 52. *Ornithodoros transversus* (partially fed). **A.** Male, dorsal view; **B.** Male, ventral view; **C.** Hypostome of male, ventral view;

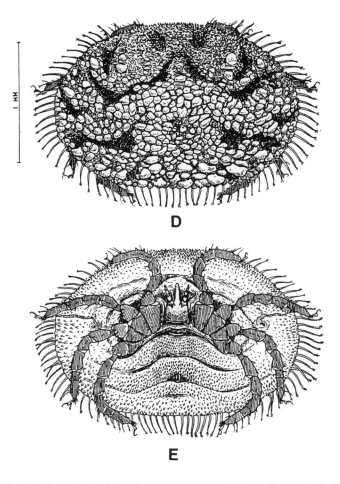

Fig. 52. Continued   **D.** Female, dorsal view; **E.** Female, ventral view;

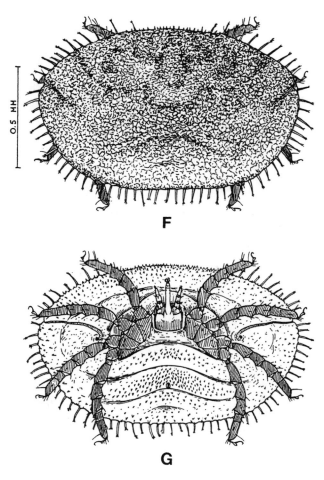

Fig. 52. Continued **F.** Nymph, dorsal view; **G.** Nymph, ventral view.
(Reproduced with permission from Hoogstraal et al., 1973; copyrighted
by the Entomological Society of America).

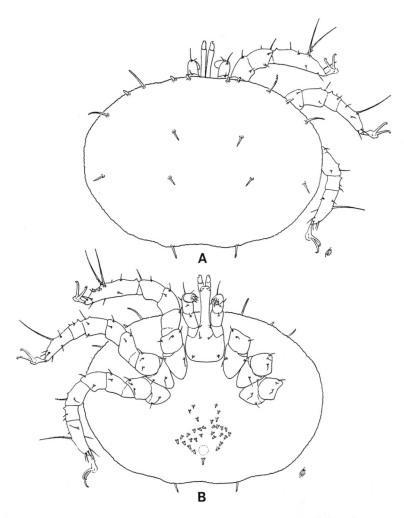

Fig. 53. *Ornithodoros transversus*. Larva. **A.** Dorsal view; **B.** Ventral view.
(Reproduced with permission from Hoogstraal and Kohls, 1966;
copyrighted by the Entomological Society of America).

Host location	Outer body surface, mainly on the plastron.
Life cycle	This is the only known tick that oviposits on the host so that all stages (egg, larva, nymph, and adults) are found on tortoises. Otherwise, the life cycle appears to be typical for argasids (Hoogstraal and Kohls, 1966; Hoogstraal et al., 1973; Oliver, 1989). MacFarland and Reeder (1974) described a form of symbiosis between Galapagos giant tortoises and Darwin's finches in which the finches groom ticks, including *O. transversus,* from the tortoises.
Host acquisition	By direct contact with organism or infested tortoises.
Symptoms	None reported.
Treatment	See Appendix I.

C. *Ornithodoros turicata* (Figs. 54, 55)

Ornithodoros turicata occurs primarily in the southwestern United States; however, it is also known from Florida and Mexico. *Ornithodoros turicata* is

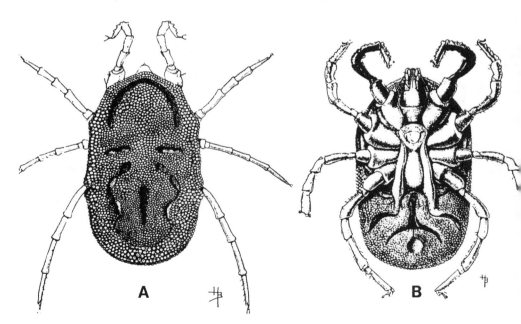

Fig. 54. *Ornithodoros turicata.* Female. **A.** Dorsal view; **B.** Ventral view. (Reproduced from Strickland et al., 1976).

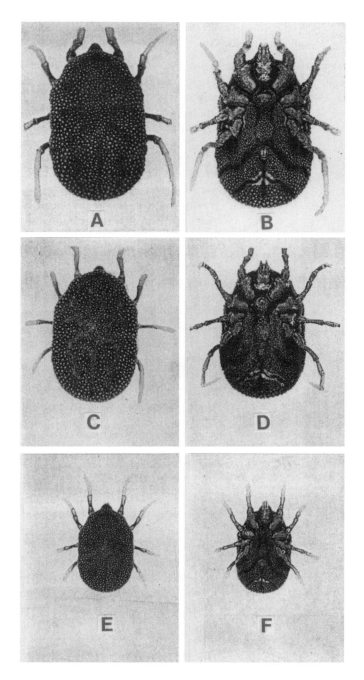

Fig. 55. *Ornithodoros turicata.* **A.** Female, dorsal view; **B.** Female, ventral view; **C.** Male, dorsal view; **D.** Male, ventral view; **E.** Fourth nymphal stage, dorsal view; **F.** Fourth nymphal stage ventral view. (Cooley and Kohls, 1944a; reproduced with permission from American Midland Naturalist).

sometimes called the "relapsing fever tick." Bites can cause inflammation, subcutaneous nodules, and itching in humans; this tick is a vector of *Borrelia turicatae,* a spirochete bacterium that causes relapsing fever, and it is a potential vector of the agent of leptospirosis. Wozniak and Telford (1991) stated that *O. turicata* is a potential vector of *Hepatozoon* spp. to snakes in Florida.

Description

Adult (Figs. 54, 55a–d): body oval, slightly wider posteriorly with anterior and posterior apices evenly rounded; mammillae large, relatively few in number and not crowded; large and prominent hood visible from above; cheeks absent; female measures 6.2–9.9 mm long by 4.6–6.8 mm wide, male measures 6.3–5.4 mm long by 3.3–4.0 mm wide; basis capitulum approximately as wide as long with irregular surface and a few spines in a group on each side; palps long with surface of all articles smooth; dentition 2/2; hypostome long with sides nearly parallel and rounded apically; legs with small, subapical, dorsal protuberance on tarsi I, II, and III, and nearly absent on tarsus IV; coxae prominent and progressively larger anteriorly; coxae I and II slightly separated, all other coxae contiguous; gential aperture between coxae I and II.

Nymph (Fig. 55 e,f): essentially similar to the adult except genital pore absent; early instar nymphs distinctly smaller than adults.

Larva: body oval, slightly wider posteriorly; mouthparts apical and visible from above; integument thin, striated, and with sparse setae arranged symmetrically; excluding mouthparts, unfed body measures 0.84 mm long by 0.57 mm wide; hypostome long (0.135 mm), with nearly parallel sides and rounded apically; dentition 2/2 with lateral denticles larger.

Host(s)

Many vertebrate species including the eastern box turtle, *Terrapene carolina* (Philip and Burgdorfer, 1961), ornate box turtle, *T. ornata* (Davis, 1936), desert tortoise, *Gopherus agassizi* (Harbinson, 1937; Ryckman and Kohls, 1962), gopher tortoise, *G. polyphemus* (Adeyeye and

Butler, 1989; Hubbard, 1894; Philip and Burgdorfer, 1961), Puerto Rican Boa, *Epicrates inornatus* (Abreu-Rodriguez and Moya, 1995), and rattlesnakes in the genera *Crotalus* and *Sistrurus* (Philip and Burgdorfer, 1961). Matheson (1950) reported that *O. turicata* is probably found on a wide variety of snakes and chelonians.

Host location — Body surface; postlarval stages are rapid feeders and may be overlooked because they leave the host after engorgement.

Life cycle (Fig. 48) — See Ticks Introduction, and Family Argasidae above.

Host acquisition — Via infestation from contaminated hosts or substrate containing resting nymphs or adults.

Symptoms — Anemia in heavy infestations (Jacobson, 1986).

Diagnosis — By demonstration of organism on body surface or cage environment.

Treatment — See Appendix I.

D. Other *Ornithodoros* spp. affecting reptiles

O. compactus infests tortoises of Africa (Cheng, 1973; Frank, 1981; Hoogstraal and Aeschlimann, 1982; van der Merwe, 1968; Walton, 1962). *O. compactus* has also been reported on the Greek tortoise, *Testudo graeca,* in a zoological garden in Hamburg, Germany (Walton, 1962).

O. darwini (Figs. 56, 57a–e) parasitizes the Galapagos marine iguana, *Amblyrhynchus cristatus,* and the Galapagos land iguanas, *Conolophus pallidus* and *C. subcristatus* (Keirans et al., 1980; Kohls et al., 1969).

O. erraticus (Figs. 58, 59) larval and nymphal stages occur on various reptiles of southern Europe, southeastern Asia, and northern Africa (Hoogstraal, 1956; Sonenshine et al., 1966; Theiler, 1962). Wassef et al. (1997) reported several specimens of *O. erraticus* from the desert monitor, *Varanus griseus,* in Oman. This tick inhabits primarily rodent burrows and is thought to feed principally on these mammals.

O. foleyi (Fig. 60) parasitizes various vertebrates including geckos and agamid lizards in Algeria, Libya, Egypt, and Niger (Hoogstraal and Kaiser, 1960a; Sonenshine et al., 1966). This tick is adapted to desert conditions, being found just beneath the surface of sand in small hillside caves. Two to 5 nymphal instars are required to reach adulthood. Eighty-two to 305 eggs are laid in batches. Larvae require 5–17 days to engorge (Hoogstraal and Kaiser, 1960a).

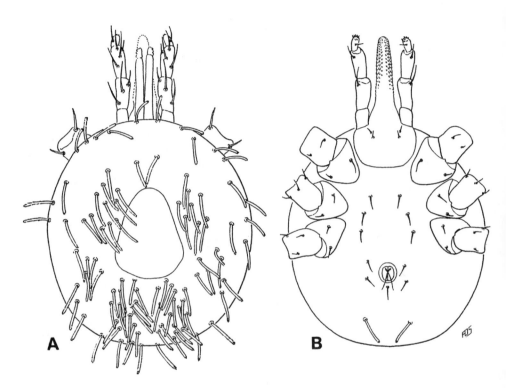

Fig. 56. *Ornithodoros darwini.* Larva. **A.** Dorsal view; **B.** Ventral view. (Reproduced with permission from Kohls et al., 1969).

Fig. 57. *Ornithodoros darwini*. **A.** Female, dorsal view; **B.** Female, ventral view; **C.** Capitulum of female; **D.** Male, ventral view; **E.** Larva, dorsal view. (Photos courtesy of the U.S. National Tick Collection).

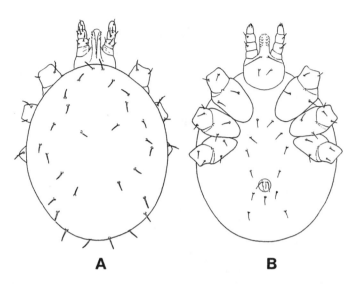

Fig. 58. *Ornithodoros erraticus*. Larva. **A.** Dorsal view; **B.** Ventral view. (Reproduced with permission from Sonenshine et al., 1966; copyrighted by the Entomological Society of America).

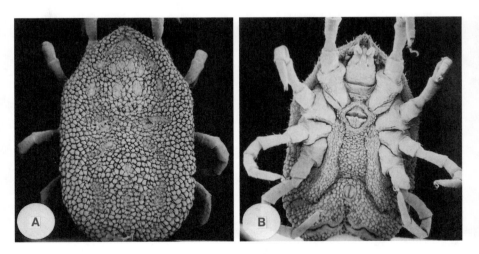

Fig. 59. *Ornithodoros erraticus*. Female. **A.** Dorsal view; **B.** Ventral view. (Photos courtesy of the U.S. National Tick Collection).

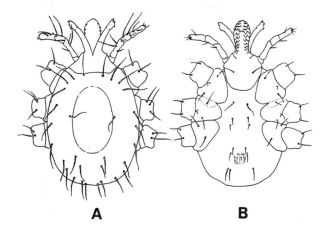

A   B

Fig. 60. *Ornithodoros foleyi.* Larva. **A.** Dorsal view; **B.** Ventral view. (Reproduced with permission from Sonenshine et al., 1966; copyrighted by the Entomological Society of America).

O. galapagensis (Figs. 61, 62 a–d) parasitizes the Galapagos marine iguana, *Amblyrhynchus cristatus,* the Galapagos lava lizard, *Tropidurus albemarlensis,* and the Galapagos land iguanas, *Conolophus pallidus* and *C. subcristatus* (Godsden and Guerra, 1991; Keirans et al., 1980; Kohls et al., 1969).

O. gurneyi has been recovered from the shingle-back skink, *Trachydosaurus (= Tiliqua) rugosus,* in Western Australia (Sharrad and King, 1981).

O. moubata (Fig. 63) adults and immatures were reported from a monitor lizard, *Varanus* sp., and tortoises in the genera *Homopus, Psammobates,* and *Testudo* (Theiler, 1962). This tick, however, parasitizes principally warthogs and other suids in Africa (Walton, 1962).

O. puertoricensis (Fig. 64 a–j) larvae have been recovered from 21 mammal species, one bird species, and two reptiles (*Iguana* sp. and an unidentified lizard) in the Caribbean region, Central America, and northern South America (Endris et al., 1989). There are no reptile host records for postlarval stages of this tick.

O. sonrai was reported from a Montpellier snake, *Malpolon moilensis,* in Oman by Papadopoulos et al. (1991), but Wassef et al. (1997) treated this record as doubtful.

O. tartakovskyi (Fig. 65) has been recovered from the burrows of tortoises, rodents, and hedgehogs throughout central Asia (Sonenshine et al., 1966; Vasil'eva, 1976). Preferred hosts are the gerbil, *Rhombomys opimus,* and the Horsfield's tortoise, *Testudo horsfieldii* (Sonenshine et al., 1966).

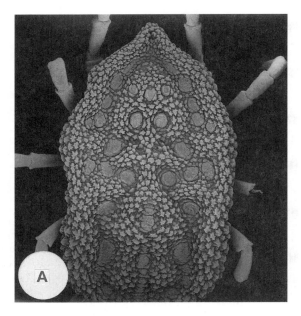

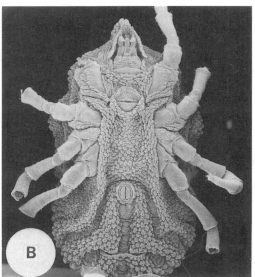

Fig. 61. *Ornithodoros galapagensis.* **A.** Female, dorsal view;
B. Female, ventral view;

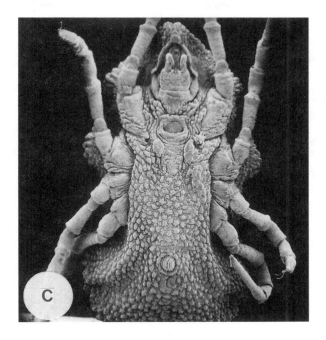

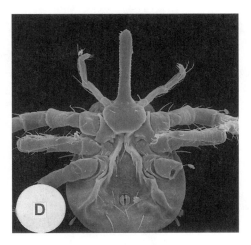

Fig. 61. Continued   **C.** Male, ventral view; **D.** Larva, ventral view.
(Photos courtesy of the U.S. National Tick Collection).

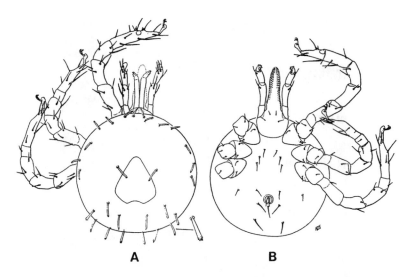

Fig. 62. *Ornithodoros galapagensis*. Larva. **A.** Dorsal view; **B.** Ventral view. (Reproduced with permission from Kohls et al., 1969).

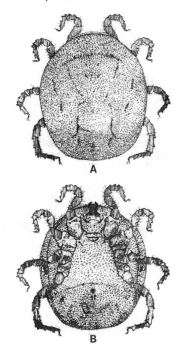

Fig. 63. *Ornithodoros moubata* (laboratory reared). Female.
A. Dorsal view; **B.** Ventral view. (Reproduced from Hoogstraal, 1956).

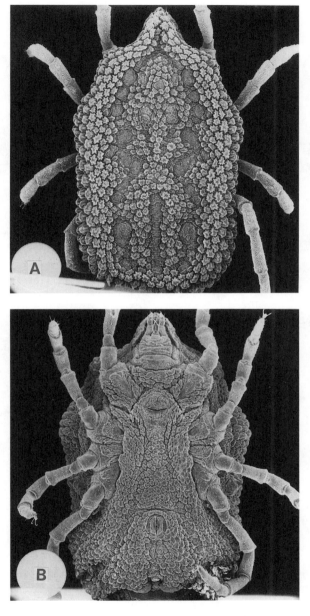

Fig. 64. *Ornithodoros puertoricensis.* **A.** Female, dorsal view; **B.** Female, ventral view;

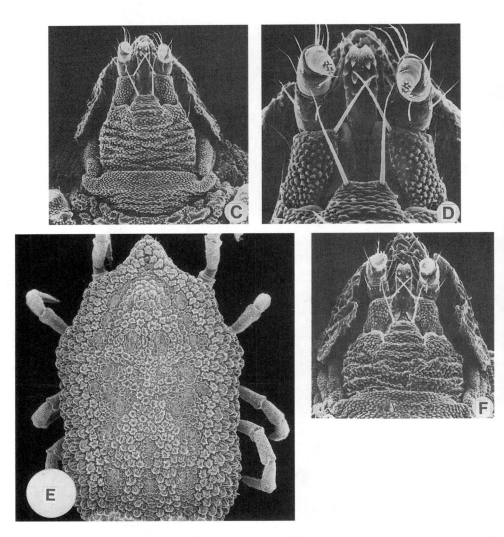

Fig. 64. Continued   **C.** Capitulum of female, ventral view; **D.** Hypostome and palpi of female; **E.** Male, dorsal view; **F.** Capitulum of male, ventral view;

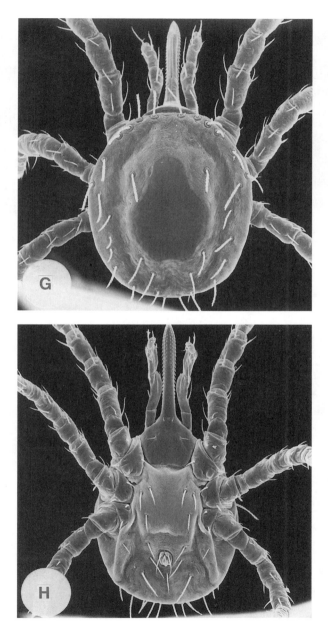

Fig. 64. Continued   **G.** Larva, dorsal view; **H.** Larva, ventral view;

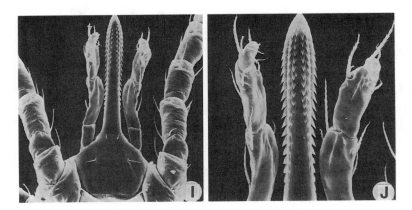

Fig. 64. Continued   **I.** Capitulum of larva, ventral view; **J.** Hypostome of larva. (G, H, courtesy of the U.S. National Tick Collection; A-F, I, J, reproduced with permission from Endris⸴et al., 1989).

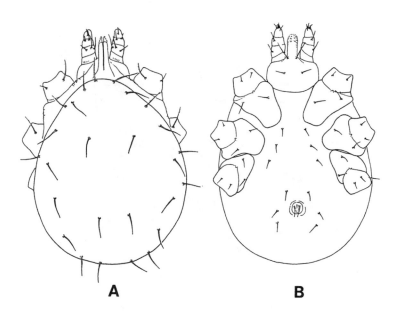

Fig. 65. *Ornithodoros tartakovskyi.* Larva. **A.** Dorsal view; **B.** Ventral view. (Reproduced with permission from Sonenshine et al., 1966; copyrighted by the Entomological Society of America).

FAMILY: IXODIDAE (HARD TICKS)

Ixodid ticks are ovoid and hard-bodied with a smooth or striated integument. A scutum is present in all stages. Ticks belonging to this family are markedly sexually dimorphic (Fig. 66). In adult males the scutum extends to the posterior margin of the body almost completely covering the dorsum. In adult females, larvae, and nymphs, it is limited to the anterior portion of the dorsum. Eyes are present in most genera and are located on the antero-lateral edges of the scutum in adults, nymphs, and larvae. Three genera that parasitize reptiles lack eyes: *Aponomma, Haemaphysalis,* and *Ixodes.* The gnathosoma (basis capituli) is anterior and visible from the dorsal aspect. Pedipalp segments have prominent chemosensory setae. Important diagnostic features of hard ticks are the shape, size, and cell composition of the spiracular plate, number and length of coxal spurs, number of rows and files of recurved teeth on the hypostome, shape of the basis capituli, and length and shape of the palps.

These ticks can be grouped together ecologically by the number of hosts they utilize. For example, one-host ticks engorge on the same animal throughout their life cycle. Two-host ticks utilize the same host during the larval and nymphal stages, but the adults engorge on new hosts. Members of the genus *Hyalomma* are two- or three-host ticks, some of which parasitize reptiles, especially as immature ticks. However, most ixodid ticks that parasitize reptiles are three-host ticks. Three-host ticks utilize a different host for each active stage of their life cycle (larva, nymph, adult).

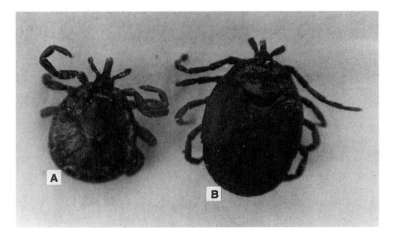

Fig. 66. *Amblyomma dissimile* from a yellow rat snake, *Elaphe obsoleta quadrivittata.* **A.** Male; **B.** Female. (Specimen courtesy of Nixon Wilson; photo courtesy of Rick E. Perry).

Females in this family lay their eggs in large masses in leaf litter, under stones, or soil clumps, or in cracks of wood near the ground. Eggs are laid in a single batch, numbering up to 18,000 depending on the species. The eggs are small in size and colored yellowish to dark brown. Incubation times vary according to ambient temperatures and diapause requirements. Hatchling larvae are sometimes called "seed ticks." They wait on vegetation until suitable hosts pass by. Mortality is high if they are unable to make contact with a suitable host (Hoogstraal, 1973). After a larval tick engorges on host blood, it molts and becomes a nymph; the nymph in turn engorges and molts to become an adult. Adults of *Ixodes* spp. can copulate either on the ground or on the host. Other ixodids, however, can only mate on the host after a blood meal has triggered certain hormonal changes in the female, and the cycle is once again repeated.

I. *Amblyomma* spp.

There are approximately 102 species of *Amblyomma,* most of which are restricted to the tropics (Keirans, 1992). Eight species are found in the southern United States.

These ticks are ornate, usually with dark scutal spots and stripes on a pale background. Legs are often banded, and eyes and festoons are present with the eyes located on the anterior scutal margin (Fig. 67). The hypostome and palps are long, and the second segment of the palps is much longer than broad and longer than each of the other segments. The basis capituli of *Amblyomma* spp. varies in shape, but is usually subquadrangular or subtriangular. Adanal plates are absent in males.

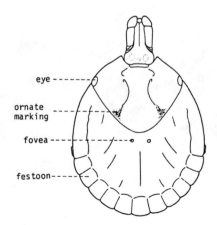

Fig. 67. Basic morphology of *Amblyomma* spp. (female, dorsal view). (Reproduced with permission from Yamaguti et al., 1971).

Amblyomma spp. larvae have 4-segmented palps and 2 marginal setae anterior to each sensilla sagittiformia (a circular pit on each side of the dorsolateral larval integument).

Some *Amblyomma* spp. can occasionally complete their life cycle on a single host, taking approximately one year; however, they usually utilize three hosts (see Fig. 73). Immature stages of many species will feed on almost any terrestrial vertebrate and, on reptiles, may be found alongside adults. Several *Amblyomma* spp. bite humans, and in parts of Africa, members of this genus often transmit *Cowdria ruminantium,* the causative agent of heartwater fever in ungulates (Walker, 1987).

A. *Amblyomma dissimile* (Figs. 66, 68–72)

Also known as the "iguana tick," the range of this tick extends from Florida, Mexico, and the West Indies to Argentina. It is the common reptile tick in Panama and in most of the rest of its range. Dunn (1918) found that 60% of snakes and 84% of iguanids examined were infested. In captivity, Fairchild (1943) noted that laboratory reptiles with heavy infestations died when ticks were not removed. For example, one snake harbored 1,800 ticks of all stages (Fairchild et al., 1966). Ball et al. (1969) reported the transmission of *Hepatozoon fusifex* to the common boa (*Boa constrictor*) from feeding *A. dissimile.*

Description

Adult female (Figs. 68a–d; 70g): body wide posteriorly, and measuring unfed, 3.6 mm long by 3.0 mm wide and engorged, up to 15 mm long by 9 mm wide; reddish brown in color; scutum (Fig. 68a) ornate with irregular spots anterolaterally, with large, pale spot medially and posteriorly; scutum measures 1.74–2.28 mm long by 2.10–2.58 mm wide; eyes large, flat and pale; capitulum with long, laterally compressed palps; hypostome (Fig. 68c) long, notched apically, dentition 3/3; legs with distinct apical, ventral spurs on tarsi II, III, and IV, faint on tarsus I; all coxae (Fig. 68b) with one short external spur, and coxae I, II, and III with very short internal spur; genital opening between coxae II.

Nymph (Fig. 70a-f): unengorged, body measures approximately 2.0 mm long by 1.5 mm wide; engorged, measures up to 5.0 mm long by 3.5 mm wide; body color various shades of brown;

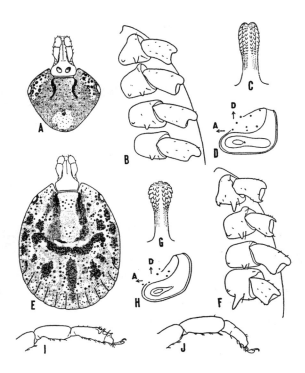

Fig. 68. *Amblyomma dissimile.* **A.** Scutum and capitulum of female;
B. Coxae of female; **C.** Hypostome of female; **D.** Spiracular plate of female;
E. Capitulum and scutum of male; **F.** Coxae of male; **G.** Hypostome of male;
H. Spiracular plate of male; **I.** Leg I of male; **J.** Leg IV of male.
(Reproduced with permission from Cooley and Kohls, 1944a;
courtesy of the Journal of Parasitology).

scutum (Fig. 70a) wider than long, measuring 0.66 mm long by 0.96 mm wide, and surface slightly irregular; hypostome (Fig. 70c) spatulate and rounded apically, dentition 3/3; two small spurs on coxa I, and one small spur on each of coxae II, III, and IV: spiracular plate measures 0.24 mm long by 0.18 mm wide, less sclerotized than in adults.

Larva (Fig. 71): body broadly oval, measuring unfed 0.680–0.746 mm long by 0.581–0.693 mm wide; 2 pairs of central dorsal setae, 8 pairs of marginal dorsals, 2 pairs of sternals, 2 pairs of

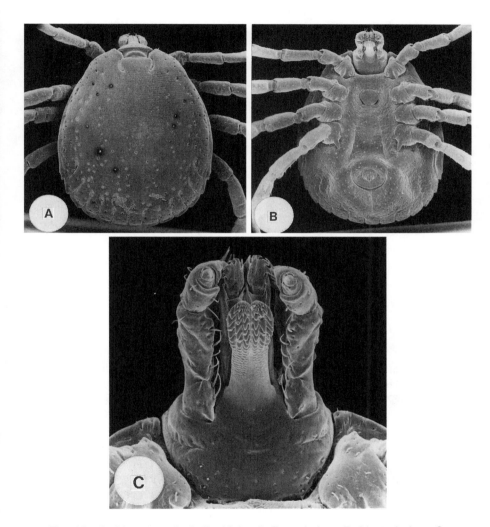

Fig. 69. *Amblyomma dissimile*. Male. **A.** Dorsal view; **B.** Ventral view; **C.** Capitulum, ventral view. (Photos courtesy of the U.S. National Tick Collection).

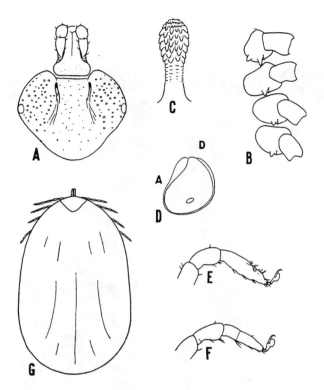

Fig. 70. *Amblyomma dissimile.* **A.** Capitulum and scutum of nymph;
B. Coxae of nymph; **C.** Hypostome of nymph; **D.** Spiracular plate of nymph;
E. Leg I of nymph; **F.** Leg IV of nymph; **G.** Engorged female.
(Reproduced with permission from Cooley and Kohls, 1944a;
courtesy of the Journal of Parasitology).

preanals, 4 pairs of premarginals, 5 pairs of marginal ventrals, and 1 pair of anal setae; 11 festoons, each separated by a prominent groove; leg coxa I with 2 spurs, coxae II and III each with 1 spur; capitulum subtriangular dorsally with rounded lateral edges, cornua absent; hypostomal dentition 2/2 with 8–9 principal denticles per file.

Host(s)   New World lizards and snakes. (Ball et al., 1969; Bequaert, 1932a; Calle et al., 1994; Cooley and Kohls, 1944b; Dinsmore, 1969; Dunn, 1918;

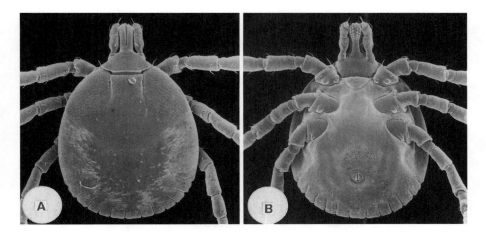

Fig. 71. *Amblyomma dissimile.* Larva. **A.** Dorsal view; **B.** Ventral view. (Photos courtesy of the U.S. National Tick Collection).

Durden et al., 1993; Fairchild et al., 1966; Jones et al., 1972; Kohls, 1969; Morel, 1967; Moreno and Bolanos, 1977; Robinson, 1926; Varma, 1973; Wilson and Kale, 1972).

Host location — Lizards, skin around body folds (Fig. 72); snakes, partially under scales.

Life cycle (Fig. 73) — Dunn (1918) reared *A. dissimile* in the laboratory. A rainbow boa, *Epicrates cenchria,* with a replete female tick was used for the life cycle experiment. Four days passed before the tick became engorged and dropped from the host. After a pre-oviposition period of 6 days, the tick oviposited daily for 35 days. The total number of eggs deposited was 9,254. The incubation period was 40 days. Newly hatched larvae were fed on a Central American boa, *Boa constrictor imperator,* for 11–18 days. The replete larvae molted to nymphs in approximately 11–15 days. The nymphs were then placed on a green vine snake, *Oxybelis fulgidus,* and were replete in 11 days. They molted to adults in 8–16 days. Also see family Ixodidae above.

Fig. 72. *Amblyomma dissimile* parasitizing the Mexican iguana, *Iguana i. rhinolopha.* (Photo of living animal by G. Nelson. Courtesy of Dr. Thomas Barbour. Reproduced from Psyche, 1932).

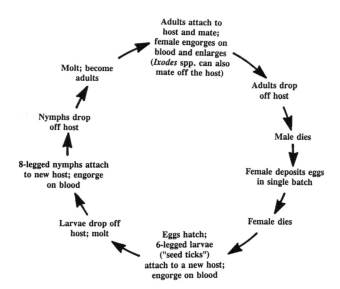

Fig. 73. Generalized life cycle of a 3-host ixodid tick (e.g., *Amblyomma dissimile*).

Host acquisition	By direct contact with organism.
Symptoms	Heavy infestations may cause skin irritation, trauma, and anemia, possibly resulting in death (Walker and Bezuidenhout, 1973).
Diagnosis	By demonstration of organism on body surface, or cage environment.
Treatment	See Appendix I.

B. *Amblyomma tuberculatum* (Figs. 74–75a–g, 76, 77)

Amblyomma tuberculatum is the largest tick native to the United States. Because of its size, large wounds cause scar tissue which may be invaded later by the flesh fly, *Cistudinomyia cistudinis,* for larviposition (Knipling, 1937).

Amblyomma tuberculatum is known as the "gopher tortoise tick," and all stages are found on this host throughout its range in the southeastern United States (Bishopp and Trembley, 1945). The larvae are also found on mammals and birds. Attached adult females require 40–74 days to fully engorge (Flynn, 1973).

Description	Adult female (Figs. 74a–d, i; 75a): body broad, oval, heavily sclerotized, and measuring 7.0–7.5 mm long in unfed specimens (increases to 18–24 mm engorged) by 5.5–6.0 mm wide; scutum (Fig. 74a) with cervical grooves deep and curved, ornate with dark brown pattern on a yellow-white background; eyes small, flat and pale; capitulum (Figs. 74a; 75d) with long palps measuring 2.3–2.6 mm long by 1.56 wide; hypostome (Fig. 74c) spatulate, measuring approximately 1.08 mm long; dentition 4/4; legs with apical, ventral spurs on all tarsi, and subapical, ventral spurs on tarsi II, III and IV; coxae (Fig. 74b) with 2 short, broad, flat spurs each; genital opening between posterior borders of coxae II.
	Adult male (Figs. 74e–h; 75b, c, e): body broad, oval, wider posteriorly, sides evenly rounded, and measuring 6.2 mm long by 5.5 mm wide; scutum (Fig. 74e) smooth, convex, with long cervical grooves, curved and deep anteriorly; marginal grooves absent, ornate with dark

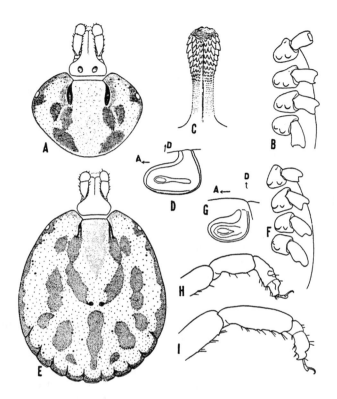

Fig. 74. *Amblyomma tuberculatum*. **A.** Capitulum and scutum of female; **B.** Coxae of female; **C.** Hypostome of female; **D.** Spiracular plate of female; **E.** Capitulum and scutum of male; **F.** Coxae of male; **G.** Spiracular plate of male; **H.** Leg I of male; **I.** Leg IV of female. (Reproduced with permission from Cooley and Kohls, 1944a; courtesy of the Journal of Parasitology).

brown spots on a yellow-white background; festoons short; capitulum (Figs. 74e; 75e) as in female, but shorter palps measuring 1.8 mm long by 1.23 mm wide; hypostome spatulate, slightly notched apically, and measuring 1.2 mm long; dentition 4/4; all tarsi with apical, ventral and subapical spurs; coxae with 2 short, broad spurs each; genital aperture between coxae II.

Nymph (Figs. 75f; 76a–d, g, h): engorged, measuring 8–10 mm in length; capitulum (Fig. 76a) measures 0.93 mm long; basis capituli subquadrate and convex, measuring 0.66 mm wide;

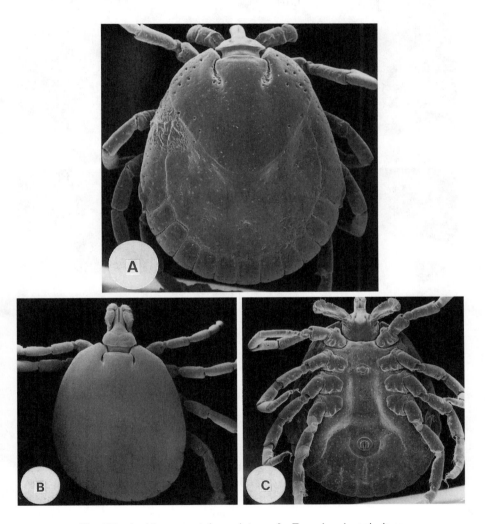

Fig. 75. *Amblyomma tuberculatum.* **A.** Female, dorsal view;
B. Male, dorsal view; **C.** Male, ventral view;

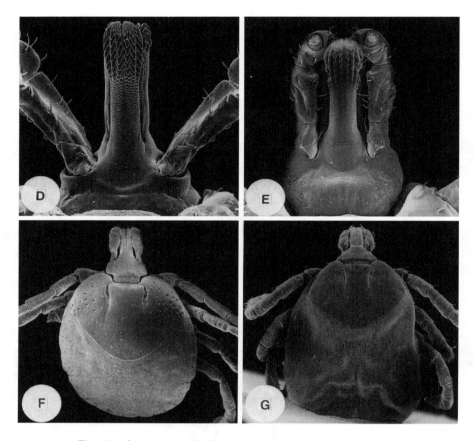

Fig. 75. Continued   **D.** Capitulum of female, ventral view;
E. Capitulum of male, ventral view; **F.** Nymph, dorsal view;
G. Larva, dorsal view. (Photos courtesy of the U.S. National Tick Collection).

palps long; scutum (Fig. 76a) with posterolateral margins slightly flattened; cervical grooves curved and deep, ornate, with dark brown markings on yellowish-white background; scutum surface pebbled, measuring 1.44 mm long by 1.74 mm wide; hypostome (Fig. 76c) measuring 0.36 mm long, and shaped as in adults; dentition 3/3; all tarsi with small, apical ventral spur; 2 broad, short, flat external spurs on coxae (Fig. 76b) I and II with small internal spurs present; 1 external spur each on coxae III and

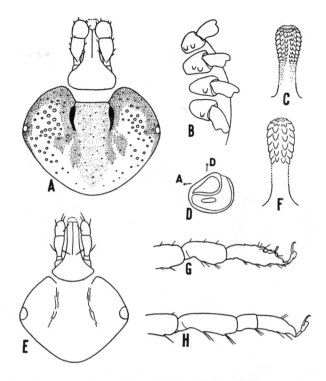

Fig. 76. *Amblyomma tuberculatum*. **A.** Capitulum and scutum of nymph; **B.** Coxae of nymph; **C.** Hypostome of nymph; **D.** Spiracular plate of nymph; **E.** Capitulum and scutum of larva; **F.** Hypostome of larva; **G.** Leg I of nymph; **H.** Leg IV of nymph. (Reproduced with permission from Cooley and Kohls, 1944a; courtesy of the Journal of Parasitology).

IV with no internal spurs; spiracular plate (Fig. 76d) heavily sclerotized, measuring 0.33 mm long by 0.33 mm wide.

Larva (Figs. 75g; 76e,f): scutum (Fig. 76e) measures 0.45 mm long by 0.57 mm wide, and with cervical grooves along 3/4 of length, which are deeper anteriorly; capitulum (Fig. 76e) subtriangular in shape, measuring 0.31 mm long with basis measuring 0.22 mm wide; hypostome (Fig. 76f) measures 0.19 mm long; dentition 2/2; 2 small spurs on coxa I and 1 small spur each on coxae II and III.

Host(s)

The gopher tortoise, *Gopherus polyphemus* (Fig. 77) (Cooley and Kohls, 1944b; Cooney and Hays, 1972; Morel, 1967; Wilson, 1966; Wilson and Kale, 1972) is the only host of adult *A. tuberculatum* in nature. The eastern fence lizard, *Sceloporus undulatus,* (Bishopp and Trembley,

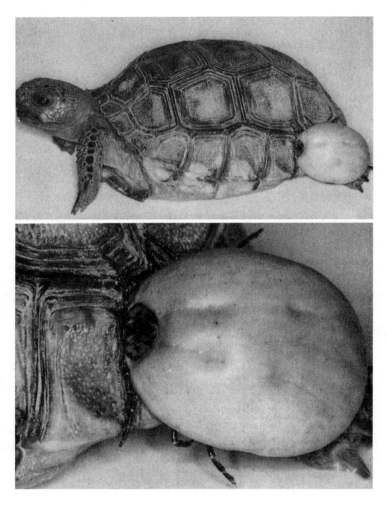

Fig. 77. *Amblyomma tuberculatum* attached in membrane between carapace scutes of the gopher tortoise, *Gopherus polyphemus.* (Photos by Jerry A. Payne. Reproduced with permission from the Entomological Society of America, 1997).

1945) can be parasitized by immature stages. Captive eastern box turtles, *Terrapene carolina,* have also been parasitized by these ticks. *Amblyomma tuberculatum* has never been recovered from wild box turtles. Immature stages, especially larvae, feed on a variety of reptiles, birds, and mammals.

Host location — Under scales around body folds, and along scale margins through the shell.

Life cycle (Fig. 73) — See Family Ixodidae above.

Host acquisition — By direct contact with organism.

Symptoms — Heavy infestations may cause anemia, possibly resulting in death (Walker and Bezuidenhout, 1973).

Diagnosis — By demonstration of organism on body surface or cage environment.

Treatment — See Appendix I.

C. Other *Amblyomma* spp. parasitizing reptiles.

Amblyomma sp. nymph was recovered from an Australian freshwater crocodile, *Crocodylus johnstoni,* in Queensland (Tucker, 1995). This is the only reliable record of an *Amblyomma* tick feeding on a crocodilian in nature.

A. *albolimbatum* parasitizes lizards and snakes of Australia. Its main host is the shingle-back skink, *Trachydosaurus* (= *Tiliqua*) *rugosus,* but other lizards and several species of snakes are also parasitized (Roberts, 1953, 1969, 1970; Sharrad and King, 1981; Smyth, 1973).

A. *albopictum* parasitizes reptiles in the genera *Cyclura, Iguana,* and *Epicrates* in the Caribbean region; however, it is mainly a parasite of iguanas (Cerny, 1969; Clifford and Kohls, 1962; Keirans, 1985; Morel, 1967).

A. *antillorum* (Fig. 78a–n) parasitizes iguanid lizards in the Caribbean region; most collections are from the rock iguana, *Iguana pinguis,* of the British Virgin Islands (Keirans, 1985; Kohls, 1969).

A. *boulengeri* parasitizes land iguanas and lava lizards, *Tropidurus* spp., on the Galapagos islands (Keirans et al., 1973).

A. *calabyi* parasitizes the parentie, *Varanus giganteus,* in Australia (Rendel, 1962; Roberts, 1963, 1970). Sharrad and King (1981) also recovered one specimen of this tick from a "*Varanus gouldii*-group" monitor in Western Australia.

A. *chabaudi* is a tortoise parasite from southern Madagascar. The principal host is the common spider tortoise, *Pyxis arachnoides,* but the flat-shelled spider tortoise, *Testudo* (= *Pyxis*) *planicauda,* and the radiated tortoise, *Tes-*

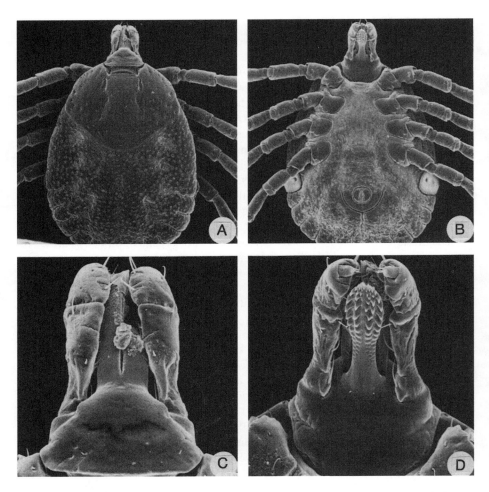

Fig. 78. *Amblyomma antillorum*. **A.** Nymph, dorsal view; **B.** Nymph, ventral view;
C. Capitulum of nymph, dorsal view; **D.** Capitulum of nymph, ventral view;

tudo (= *Geochelone*) *radiata,* are sometimes parasitized (Uilenberg et al., 1979).

A. clypeolatum (syns. *atrogenatum, zeylanicum*) parasitizes tortoises in India, Burma (= Myanmar) and Sri Lanka. The main host is the star tortoise, *Testudo* (= *Geochelone*) *elegans,* but other Asian tortoise species are also parasitized. Tortoises in zoos have been infested by this tick (Frazier and Keirans, 1990; Seneviratna, 1965).

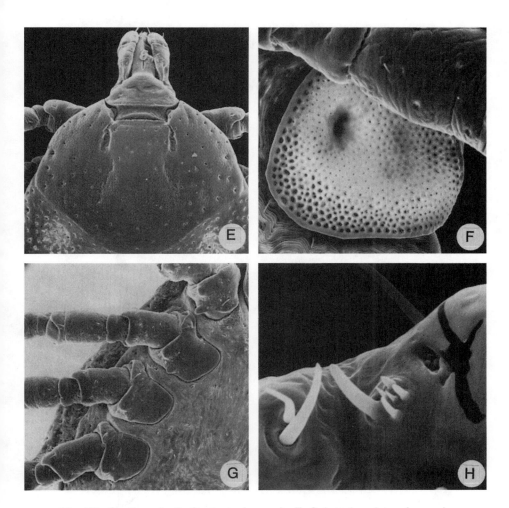

Fig. 78. Continued   **E.** Scutum of nymph; **F.** Spiracular plate of nymph;
G. Coxae I–IV of nymph; **H.** Haller's organ of nymph;

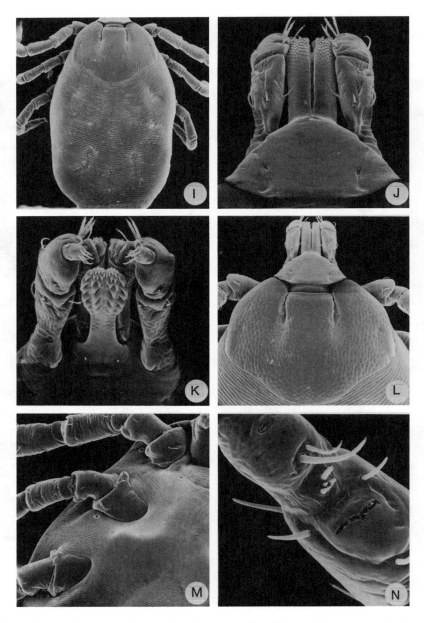

Fig. 78. Continued   **I.** Larva, dorsal view; **J.** Capitulum of larva, dorsal view;
K. Capitulum of larva, ventral view; **L.** Scutum of larva; **M.** Coxae I–IV of larva;
N. Haller's organ of larva. (Reproduced with permission from Keirans, 1985).

A. cordiferum has been reported mainly from the king cobra, *Ophiophagus hannah,* and the reticulated python, *Python reticulatus.* Immature stages apparently feed on rodents. In nature, this tick is known from Malaysia, Indonesia, Thailand, Taiwan and Western Samoa; there are also records from snakes in captivity (Anastos, 1950; Ho and Ismail, 1984; Lazell et al., 1991; Petney and Keirans, 1995; Robinson, 1926).

A. crassum is a parasite of land tortoises in South America. It has been collected from these hosts in Colombia, Peru, and Venezuela (Fairchild et al., 1966; Hoogstraal and Aeschlimann, 1982; Jones et al., 1972).

A. cruciferum (Fig. 79) is a parasite of iguanas in the genera *Iguana* and *Cyclura,* including the rock iguana (*I. pinguis*) and the rhinoceros iguana (*C. cornuta*). (Keirans, 1985; Keirans and Garris, 1986; Morel, 1967).

A. darwini (Fig. 80) is a parasite of the marine iguana, *Amblyrhynchus cristatus,* on the Galapagos islands (Bequaert, 1932b; Hoogstraal and Aeschlimann, 1982). Godsden and Guerra (1991) recovered this tick from marine iguanas on 7 of the Galapagos Islands; morphometric analyses showed fewer island to island differences in the ticks than in their hosts.

A. eburneum adults were reported from the Nile monitor, *Varanus niloticus,* by Theiler (1962). This tick, however, typically parasitizes large African mammals; records from reptiles are unusual (Walker, 1974).

A. falsomarmoreum parasitizes African reptiles, primarily tortoises, including the leopard tortoise (*Geochelone pardalis*), Bell's hinge-back tortoise (*Kinixys belliana*) and pancake tortoise (*Malacochersus tornieri*). *A. falsomarmoreum* was also reported from the savanna monitor (*Varanus exanthematicus*) (Hoffmann et al., 1970; Pegram, 1976; Theiler, 1962; Yeoman and Walker, 1967). This rare tick occurs in arid to semi-arid conditions, especially in parts of Uganda and Kenya (Matthysse and Colbo, 1987; Walker, 1974).

A. fulvum parasitizes the green anaconda, *Eunectes murinus,* in South America (Keirans, 1972).

A. fuscum is a poorly known species of questionable validity that has been recorded from snakes (especially the common boa constrictor, *Boa constrictor,* in Brazil and Colombia, and the indigo snake, *Drymarchon corais*) (Aragao, 1936; Hoogstraal and Aeschlimann, 1982; Robinson, 1926).

A. gemma was reported from an unspecified African tortoise (Yeoman and Walker, 1967), but records of this mammal tick parasitizing reptiles are atypical.

A. geoemydae (syns: *malayanum, caelaturum*) infests reptiles, especially chelonians, in the Oriental region, (e.g., Borneo, Burma [= Myanmar], India, Indonesia, Japan, Malaysia, Philippines, Singapore, Taiwan, Thailand, Vietnam) (Frazier and Keirans, 1990; Kohls, 1957; Kolonin, 1995; Maa and Kuo, 1966; Petney and Keirans, 1995; Wilson, 1966; Yamaguti et al., 1971). Some reported hosts include the Japanese pond turtle (*Clemmys* [= *Mauremys*] *japonica*),

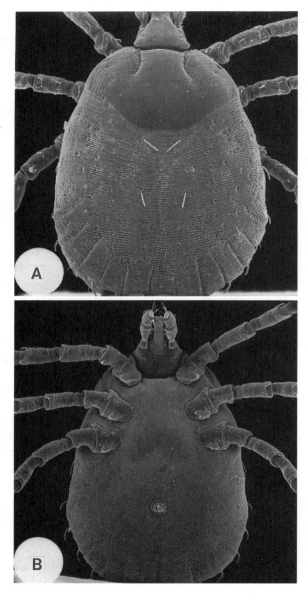

Fig. 79. *Amblyomma cruciferum.* Larva. **A.** Dorsal view;
B. Ventral view. (Photos courtesy of the U.S. National Tick Collection).

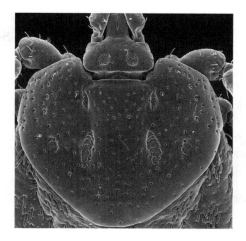

Fig. 80. *Amblyomma darwini*. Capitulum and scutum.
(Photo courtesy of the U.S. National Tick Collection).

southeast Asian box turtle (*Cuora amboinensis*), Asian leaf turtle (*Cyclemys dentata*), Reeve's turtle (*Chinemys reevesii*), spiny turtle (*Heosemys spinosa*), travancore tortoise (*Indotestudo travancorica* [= *forstenii*]), Indian black turtle (*Melanochelys trijuga*), and the water monitor (*Varanus salvator*). Immature stages of this tick also parasitize birds and mammals (Hoogstraal and Aeschlimann, 1982).

A. *glauerti* (Fig. 81a–o) parasitizes two species of Australian monitor lizards, *Varanus glebopalma* and *V. glauerti* (Keirans et al., 1994).

A. *goeldii* (syn., *ininii*) has been reported from snakes (including the common boa constrictor, *Boa constrictor,* and the African dwarf garter snake, *Elaps* (= *Homorelaps*) sp. toads, and anteaters (main hosts) in South America (Jones et al., 1972; Robinson, 1926).

A. *hainanense* was described from an unidentified snake from Hainan Island, People's Republic of China (Teng, 1981).

A. *hebraeum* adults and immatures have been reported from a white-throated monitor, *Varanus albigularis,* Smith's plated rock lizard, *Gerrhosaurus validus,* and a puff adder, *Bitis arietans* (Theiler, 1962). Reptiles, however, are atypical hosts for adults of this tick which usually parasitizes large mammals. Nevertheless, both Petney and Horak (1988) and Walker (1991), stated that nymphal A. *hebraeum* often feed on leopard tortoises, *Geochelone pardalis,* in southern Africa. Tortoises develop an acquired, partial immunity to repeated infestations by this tick (Fielden et al., 1992b).

A. *helvolum* (syns., *decoratum, furcosum, quadrimaculatum, tenimberense*) parasitizes lizards, especially monitors, *Varanus* spp. (Anastos, 1950; Auffen-

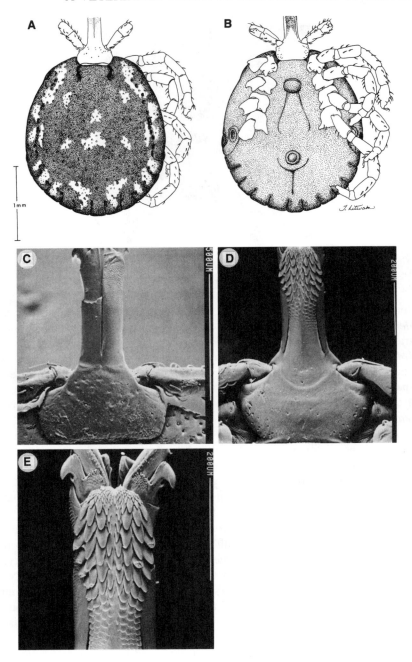

Fig. 81. *Amblyomma glauerti*. **A.** Male, dorsal view showing scutal
ornamentation pattern; **B.** Male, ventral view; **C.** Capitulum of male,
dorsal view; **D.** Capitulum of male, ventral view; **E.** Hypostome of male;

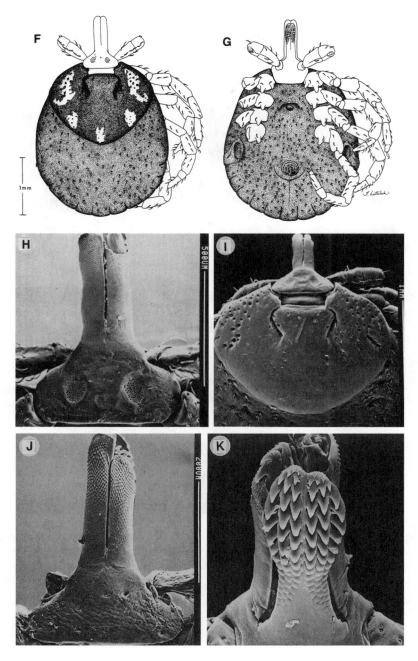

Fig. 81. Continued   **F.** Female, dorsal view; **G.** Female,
ventral view; **H.** Capitulum of female, dorsal view; **I.** Scutum of female;
J. Capitulum of nymph, dorsal view; **K.** Hypostome of nymph;

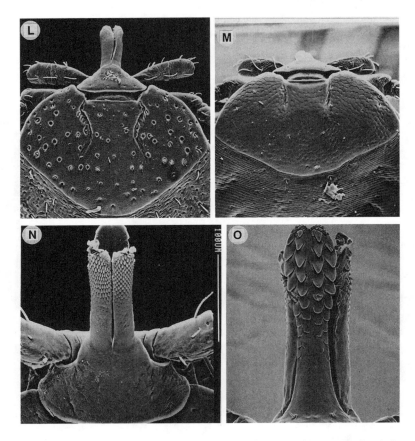

Fig. 81. Continued   **L.** Scutum of nymph; **M.** Scutum of larva; **N.** Capitulum of larva, dorsal view; **O.** Hypostome of larva. (Reproduced with permission from Keirans et al., 1994; copyrighted by the Entomological Society of America).

berg, 1988; Krylov and Said-Aliev, 1964; Petney and Keirans, 1995), and snakes in the genera *Naja, Ophiophagus, Ptyas,* and *Python* (Anastos, 1950; Hoogstraal et al., 1968; Lazell et al., 1991) throughout southeast Asia and the South Pacific (Kohls, 1957; Kolonin, 1995; Wilson, 1969). Auffenberg (1988) stated that in the Philippines, female *A. helvolum* attach preferentially in the axillae or between the front toes of monitor lizards, while male ticks usually attach on the venter of these animals.

A. humerale parasitizes tortoises and, occasionally, turtles of Central and South America (Ernst and Ernst, 1977).

A. javanense usually parasitizes pangolins (Pholidota) in southeast Asia. However, there are a few reptilian records from primarily monitor lizards (e.g., water monitor, *Varanus salvator*) and pythons (e.g., Asiatic rock python, *Python molurus*). The tricarinate hill turtle, *Geoemyda* (= *Melanochelys*) *tricarinata,* also has been reported as a host (Kohls, 1950, 1957).

A. limbatum is exclusively a parasite of Australian reptiles, especially monitor lizards, *Varanus* spp., and various snakes (Roberts, 1970; Sharrad and King, 1981). Chilton et al., (1992a,b) reported the shingle-back skink, *Trachydosaurus rugosus,* to be the preferred host of all stages of this tick in South Australia; attachment to this host was mainly on the ears and lower back. This tick is a vector of the hemogregarine parasite *Hemolivia mariae* to *T. rugosus* (Smallridge and Paperna, 1997).

A. loculosum (Fig. 82) was reported from a Seychelles skink, *Mabuya wrightii* (Hoogstraal et al., 1976). This tick, however, is almost exclusively a parasite of birds on Pacific islands and coastlines (Roberts, 1970).

A. macfarlandi (Figs, 83, 84a–t) is a specific parasite of the Galapagos giant tortoise, *Geochelone elephantopus* (Keirans et al., 1973).

A. marmoreum (Fig. 85) adults and immatures parasitize reptiles, especially the leopard tortoise, *Geochelone pardalis,* in southern Africa (Dower et al., 1988; Fielden et al., 1992a; Ghirotti and Mwanaumo, 1989; Hoffman et al., 1970; Hoogstraal, 1956; Norval, 1975; Petney and Horak, 1988; Rechav and Fielden, 1995; Theiler, 1962; Walker, 1991). Fielden and Rechav (1994) reported that most larvae and nymphs of this tick attach to soft-skinned areas that are protected by the leopard tortoise's carapace anteriorly, while adults attach posteriorly, especially around the tail base and hind legs. This tick is commonly found in fertile growth areas such as forests, but sometimes in arid regions. Immatures also occasionally feed on birds or mammals (Petney and Horak, 1988; Rechav and Fielden, 1995; Walker, 1991). Tortoises develop an acquired, partial immunity to repeated infestations by this tick (Fielden et al., 1992b; Tembo and Kiwanuka, 1997).

A. moreliae infests a variety of lizards and snakes of Australia, but is most common in coastal and subcoastal areas of Queensland and New South Wales (Oliver and Bremner, 1968; Roberts, 1969, 1970; Travassos Santos Dias, 1961a). Lizard hosts include: the spiny tree skink, *Egernia striolata*, and other unspecified *Egernia* species; an unspecified water dragon, *Physignathus* sp.,

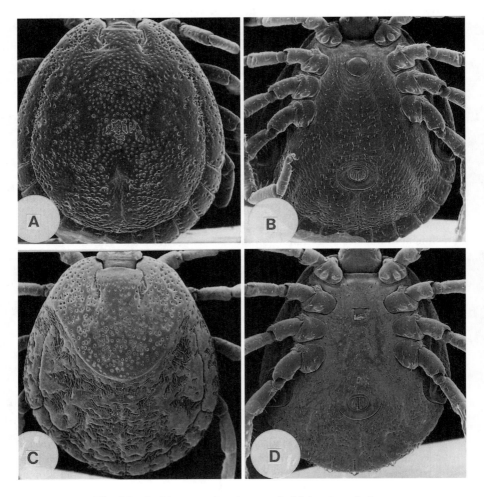

Fig. 82. *Amblyomma loculosum.* **A.** Male, dorsal view;
B. Male, ventral view; **C.** Female, dorsal view; **D.** Female, ventral view.
(Photos courtesy of the U.S. National Tick Collection).

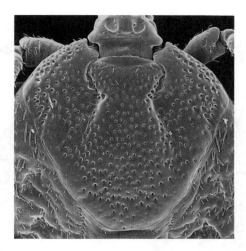

Fig. 83. *Amblyomma macfarlandi.* Scutum and capitulum of female, dorsal view (also see Fig. 84a). (Photo courtesy of the U.S. National Tick Collection).

common blue-tongued skink, *Tiliqua scincoides,* and blotched blue-tongued skink, *T. nigrolutea*; the shingle-back skink, *Trachydosaurus* (= *Tiliqua*) *rugosus*; the lace monitor, *Varanus varius,* and freckled monitor, *V. tristis orientalis.* Snake hosts include: the long-nosed tree snake, *Ahaetulla calligaster,* the black-headed python *Aspidites melanocephalus,* and carpet python, *Python* (= *Morelia*) *spilotes variegatus*; the Australian whip snake, *Demansia textilis,* mainland tiger snake, *Notechis scutatus,* red-bellied black snake, *Pseudechis porphyriacus,* king brown snake, *P. australis,* and taipan *Oxyuranus scutellatus.*

A. *nitidum* (syn., *laticaudae*) parasitizes south Pacific sea snakes in the genus *Laticauda* (Frank, 1981; Kitaoka and Sazuki, 1974; Petney and Keirans, 1995; Telford, 1967; Wilson, 1970; Yamaguti et al., 1971; Zann et al., 1975). Some workers suggest that A. *laticaudae* should be listed as a separate species based principally on differences in hypostomal dentition. Parasitism occurs when these snakes leave the water environment to congregate on beaches by the tens of thousands to breed and again when females lay their eggs. The ticks remain attached to snakes at sea. However, they only reproduce when the snakes come to shore.

A. *nuttalli* (Fig. 86a–h) occurs primarily on African reptiles such as lizards in the genus *Agama* and monitor lizards, *Varanus* spp. Snake hosts include the gaboon viper, *Bitis gabonica,* the puff adder, *B. arietans,* and the African rock python, *Python sebae.* Especially parasitized are tortoises including the Bell's hinge-back tortoise, *Kinixys belliana,* the leopard tortoise, *Geochelone pardalis,*

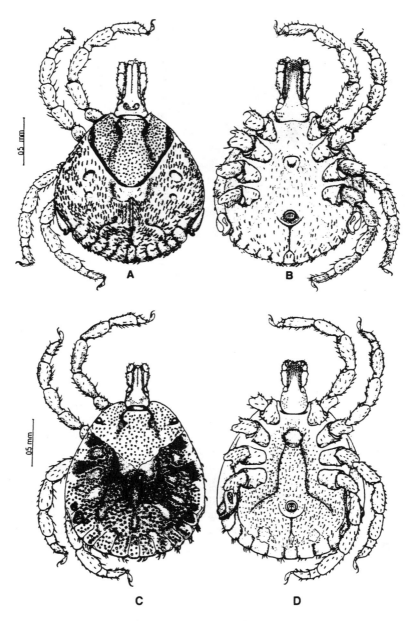

Fig. 84. *Amblyomma macfarlandi*. **A.** Female, dorsal view;
B. Female, ventral view; **C.** Male, dorsal view; **D.** Male, ventral view;

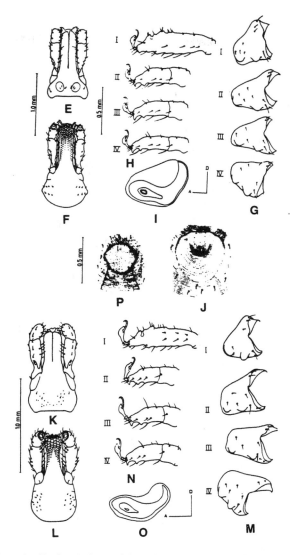

Fig. 84. Continued   **E.** Capitulum of female, dorsal view; **F.** Capitulum of female, ventral view; **G.** Coxae I–IV of female; **H.** Tarsi I–IV of female, lateral view; **I.** Spiracular plate of female (A = out; D = dorsal); **J.** Genital area of female; **K.** Capitulum of male, dorsal view; **L.** Capitulum of male, ventral view; **M.** Coxae I–IV of male; **N.** Tarsi I–IV of male, lateral view; **O.** Spiracular plate of male (A = out; D = dorsal); **P.** Genital area of male;

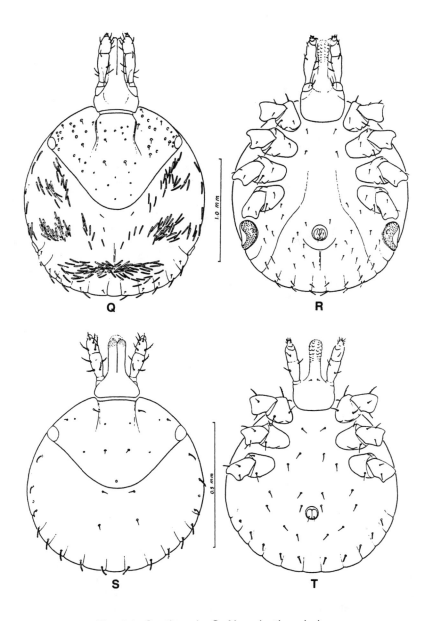

Fig. 84. Continued   **Q.** Nymph, dorsal view;
R. Nymph, ventral view; **S.** Larva, dorsal view; **T.** Larva, ventral view.
(Reproduced with permission from Keirans et al., 1973).

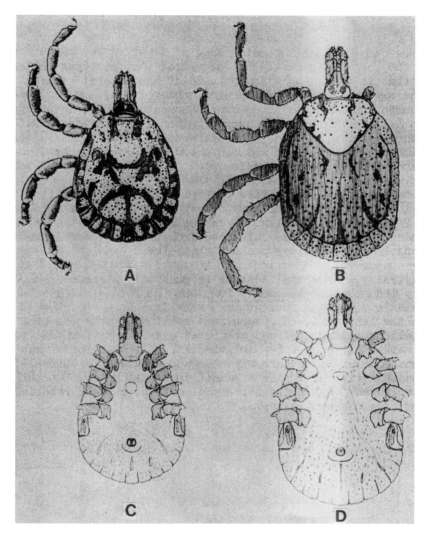

Fig. 85. *Amblyomma marmoreum.* **A.** Male, dorsal view;
B. Female, dorsal view; **C.** Male, ventral view;
D. Female, ventral view. (Reproduced from Hoogstraal, 1956).

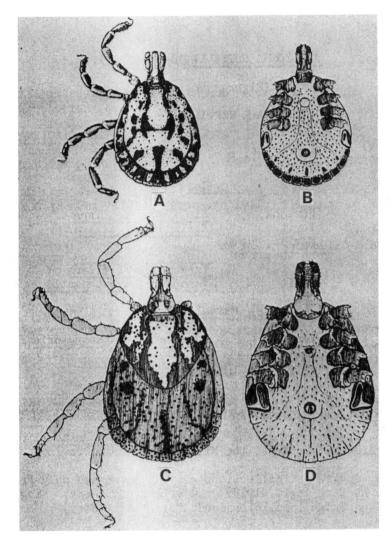

Fig. 86. *Amblyomma nuttalli*. **A.** Male, dorsal view;
B. Male, ventral view; **C.** Female, dorsal view; **D.** Female, ventral view;

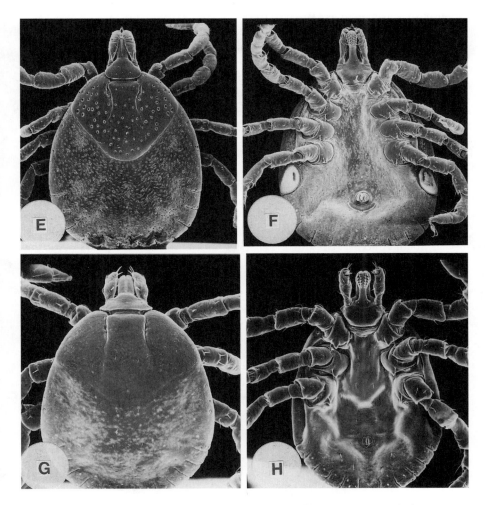

Fig. 86. Continued   **E.** Nymph, dorsal view; **F.** Nymph, ventral view;
G. Larva, dorsal view; **H.** Larva, ventral view. (A-D, reproduced from
Hoogstraal, 1956; E-H, photos courtesy of the U.S. National Tick Collection).

and tortoises in the genus *Pelusios* (Aeschlimann, 1967; Clifford and Anastos, 1962, 1964; Hoogstraal, 1956; Lamontellerie, 1966; Morel, 1978; Morel and Mouchet, 1965; Theiler, 1962; Van der Borght-Elbl, 1977). Immatures also feed on birds and mammals (Walker, 1991).

A. pilosum (Figs. 87, 88a–t) is a specific parasite of the Galapagos giant tortoise, *Geochelone elephantopus* (Keirans et al., 1973).

A. pomposum adults were reported from an African agamid lizard, *Agama* sp., by Theiler (1962), but this tick is mainly a parasite of large mammals (MacLeod, 1970; Matthysse and Colbo, 1987).

A. (formerly *Aponomma*) *quadricavum* (syn., *arianae*) (Fig. 89a–j) parasitizes snakes, especially *Epicrates* spp. in the West Indies, including Cuba, Puerto Rico, Jamaica, and Haiti (Anderson et al., 1981; Keirans and Garris, 1986; Keirans and Klompen, 1996; Travassos Santos Dias, 1993).

A. robinsoni (Fig. 90) parasitizes the Komodo dragon, *Varanus komodoensis,* including specimens retained in captivity (Anastos, 1950; Petney and Keirans, 1995).

A. rotundatum (syn., *agamum*) (Fig. 91a–i) occurs on various reptiles and amphibians, especially the marine toad, *Bufo marinus,* in Mexico, the West Indies, and South America (Becklund, 1968; Jones et al., 1972). Becklund (1968) reported specimens attached to reptiles imported into the United States. Oliver et al. (1993b) showed that this tick is now established in Florida. Snake hosts include: boa constrictors, *Boa constrictor* ssp., Costa Rican lancehead, *Bothrops* (= *Bothriechis*) *lateralis*, green anaconda, *Eunectes murinus,* false yarara,

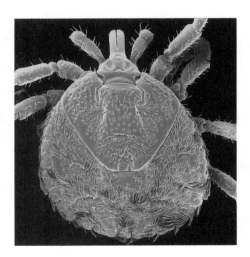

Fig. 87. *Amblyomma pilosum.* Female, dorsal view.
(Photo courtesy of the U.S. National Tick Collection).

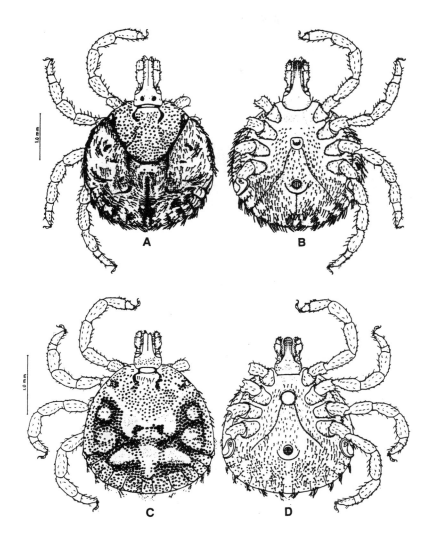

Fig. 88. *Amblyomma pilosum.* **A.** Female, dorsal view;
B. Female, ventral view; **C.** Male, dorsal view; **D.** Male, ventral view;

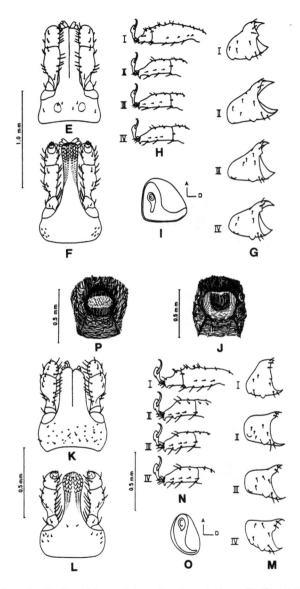

Fig. 88. Continued   **E.** Capitulum of female, dorsal view; **F.** Capitulum of female, ventral view; **G.** Coxae I–IV of female; **H.** Tarsi I–IV of female, lateral view; **I.** Spiracular plate of female (A = anterior; D = dorsal); **J.** Genital area of female; **K.** Capitulum of male, dorsal view; **L.** Capitulum of male, ventral view; **M.** Coxae I–IV of male; **N.** Tarsi I–IV of male, lateral view; **O.** Spiracular plate of male (A = out; D = dorsal); **P.** Genital area of male;

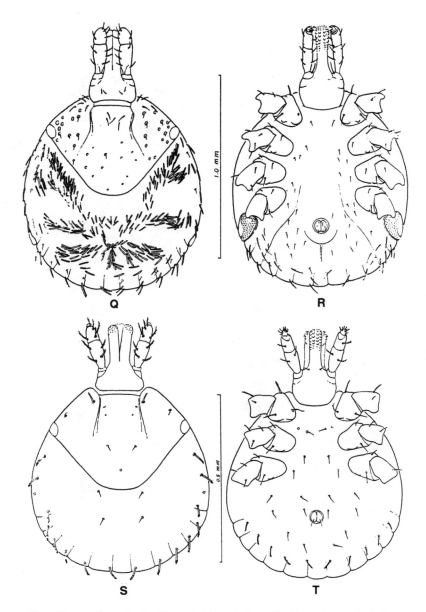

Fig. 88. Continued   **Q.** Nymph, dorsal view; **R.** Nymph, ventral view;
S. Larva, dorsal view; **T.** Larva, ventral view.
(Reproduced with permission from Keirans et al., 1973;
copyrighted by the Entomological Society of America).

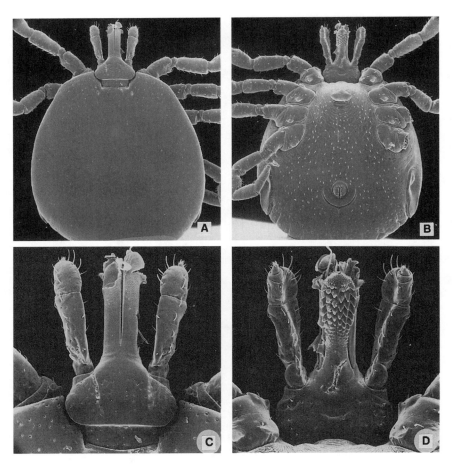

Fig. 89. *Amblyomma quadricavum*. **A.** Male, dorsal view;
B. Male, ventral view; **C.** Capitulum, dorsal view;
D. Capitulum, ventral view;

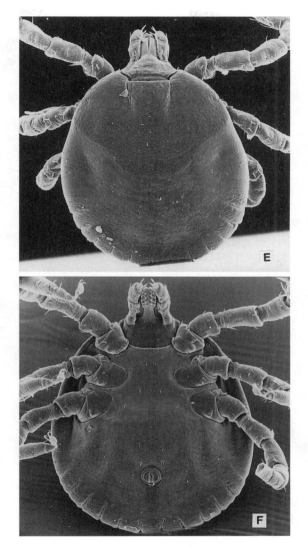

Fig. 89. Continued   **E.** Larva, dorsal view; **F.** Larva, ventral view;

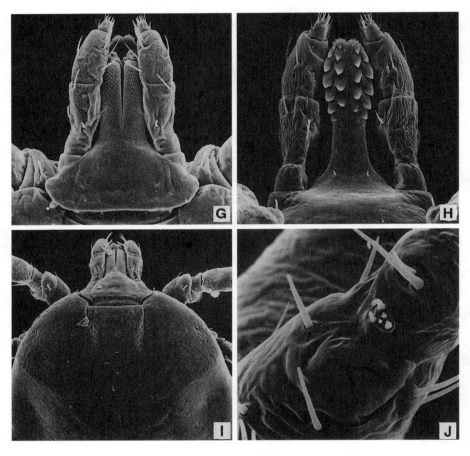

Fig. 89. Continued   **G.** Capitulum of larva, dorsal view; **H.** Hypostome of larva;
I. Scutum of larva; **J.** Haller's organ of larva. (A, B, E, F,
courtesy of the U.S. National Tick Collection; C, D,
reproduced from Keirans and Garris, 1986; G-J,
reproduced with permission from Anderson et al., 1981;
copyrighted by the Entomological Society of America).

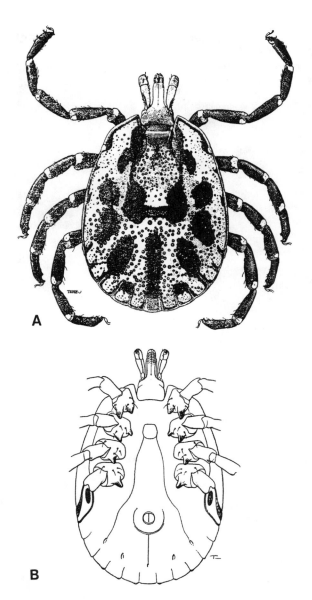

Fig. 90. *Amblyomma robinsoni.* Male. **A.** Dorsal view; **B.** Ventral view.
(Reproduced with permission from Whittick, 1939).

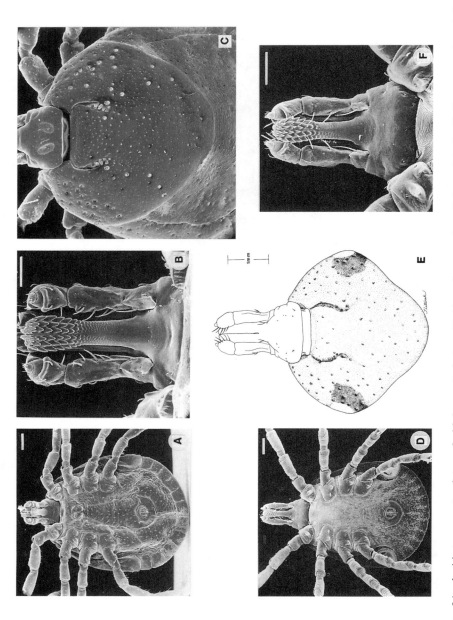

Fig. 91. *Amblyomma rotundatum*. **A.** Male, ventral view; **B.** Hypostome and capitulum of male; **C.** Scutum and capitulum of female; **D.** Nymph, ventral view; **E.** Scutum and capitulum of nymph; **F.** Hypostome and capitulum of nymph;

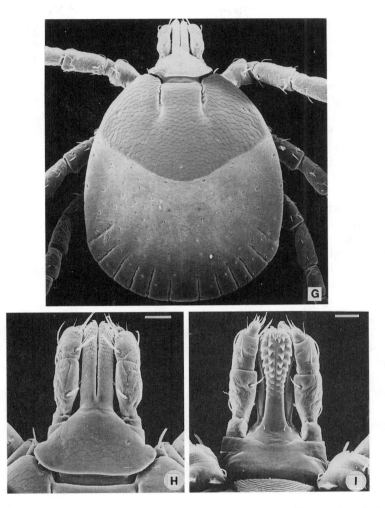

Fig. 91. Continued   **G.** Larva, dorsal view; **H.** Capitulum of larva, dorsal view;
I. Hypostome and capitulum of larva. (A, B, D–F, H, I, Keirans and Oliver, 1993,
reproduced with permission from the Journal of Parasitology;
C, G, courtesy of the U.S. National Tick Collection).

Xenodon merremi, and a coral snake *Micrurus surinamensis.* Only lizards in the genus *Iguana* were reported as hosts for *A. rotundatum.* Turtle hosts include: yellow-foot tortoise, *Geochelone carbonaria,* red-foot tortoise, *G. denticulata,* and furrowed wood turtle, *Rhinoclemmys areolata.* Unfortunately, several reported reptilian hosts could not be traced to current taxonomy and therefore were omitted from this text. *A. rotundatum* is commonly fed on a wide variety of North American snakes in the laboratory.

A. sabanerae infests lizards and turtles of Mexico, Central America, and South America (Fairchild et al., 1966). Ernst and Ernst (1977) reported large numbers of this tick attached to aquatic turtles of the genus *Callopsis* from Belize, Costa Rica, Colombia, Guatemala, Nicaragua, Mexico, Honduras, Surinam, and Panama. Only the green iguana, *Iguana iguana,* has been reported as a lizard host for this tick. Turtle hosts include: brown wood turtle, *Rhinoclemmys annulata,* furrowed wood turtle, *R. areolata,* black wood turtle, *R. funeria,* painted wood turtle, *R. pulcherrima,* other *Rhinoclemmys* spp., American musk or mud turtle, *Kinosteron* sp., common slider, *Pseudemys* (= *Trachemys*) *scripta,* and the Yucatan box turtle, *Terrapene carolina yucatana.*

A. scutatum (syn., *boneti*) (Fig. 92) parasitizes snakes, for example, the boa constrictor, *Boa constrictor,* and the indigo snake, *Drymarchon corais,* and lizards including the jungle runner, *Ameiva ameiva,* spiny-tailed iguanas, *Ctenosaura* spp. and the green iguana, *Iguana iguana,* from Mexico to Brazil and Paraguay (Jones et al., 1972).

A. sparsum adults infest reptiles (Fig. 93) and large mammals of Africa (Frank, 1981; Hoffman et al., 1970; Theiler, 1962; Yeoman and Walker, 1967). Monitor lizards (*Varanus* spp.) are frequently recorded hosts (Böhme et al., 1989; Punyua and Latif, 1990; Wassef et al., 1997), but other reptiles may be parasitized; for example, lizards in the genus *Agama,* the African rock python, *Python sebae,* the puff adder *Bitis arietans,* the Bell's hinge-back tortoise, *Kinixys belliana,* and the leopard tortoise, *Geochelone pardalis* (Walker, 1991). Durden and Kollars (1992) reported this tick from a python, *Python* sp., imported into the United States.

A. squamosum parasitizes the Pacific monitor, *Varanus indicus,* on Guam (Kohls, 1953, 1967).

A. supinoi typically parasitizes turtles in India, Burma (= Myanmar), Thailand, and Vietnam (Kolonin, 1995). These include the spiny turtle, *Heosemys spinosa,* the tricarinate hill turtle, *Melanochelys tricarinata,* and the elongated tortoise, *Testudo* (= *Indotestudo*) *elongata.* However, there are unpublished records of this tick from unspecified monitor lizards, *Varanus* spp. of Burma in the U.S. National Tick Collection.

A. sylvaticum (syns., *devium, latum*) adults infest tortoises of southern Africa (Frank, 1981; Walker, 1991). Typical hosts for all stages are the South African bowsprit tortoise, *Chersina angulata,* beaked cape tortoise, *Homopus areolatus,* and the tent tortoise, *Psammobates tentorius* (Walker, 1991). Theiler (1962),

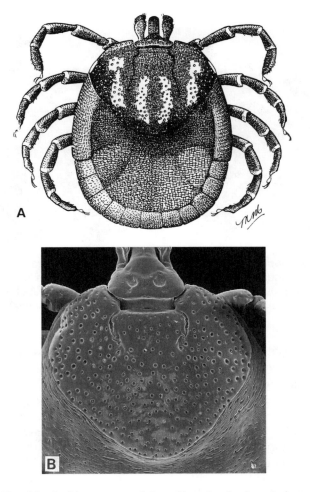

Fig. 92. *Amblyomma scutatum*. Female. **A.** dorsal view;
B. Scutum. (A, reproduced with permission from Whittick,
1939; B, courtesy of the U.S. National Tick Collection).

however, reported adults and nymphs of this tick from a mole snake, *Pseudaspis cana*, and Walker (1991) noted that immature stages also feed on lizards (the spiny agama, *Agama hispida*, and Knox's desert lizard, *Meroles knoxi*), birds, and mammals.

A. testudinarium (syns., *compactum, fallax, infestum*) typically parasitizes large mammals of southeast Asia, but Hoogstraal et al. (1972), Anastos (1950),

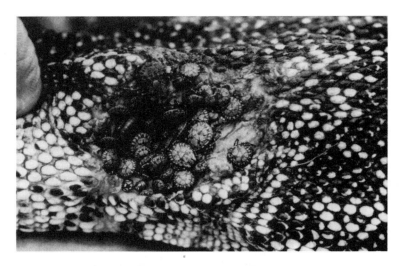

Fig. 93. *Amblyomma sparsum*. Adults concentrated around an old
deep wound on the neck of a Nile monitor, *Varanus niloticus*.
(Reproduced with permission from Punyua and Latif, 1990;
copyrighted by the Entomological Society of America).

and Kohls (1957) have reported a few specimens recovered from reptiles (Asian brown tortoise, *Testudo* [= *Manouria*] *emys,* water monitor, *Varanus salvator,* and reticulated python, *Python reticulatus*).

A. testudinis (syn., *argentinae*) parasitizes various reptiles (e.g., Chaco tortoise, *Geochelone chilensis,* and indigo snake, *Drymarchon corais*) of South America (Becklund, 1968; Lehmann et al., 1969; Robinson, 1926; Travassos Santos Dias, 1958). Laboratory infestations of all stages of *A. testudinis* may cause paralysis in the European grass snake, *Natrix natrix* (Roth and Schneider, 1974).

A. tholloni adults were reported from the leopard tortoise, *Testudo* (= *Geochelone*) *pardalis* (Theiler, 1962; Yeoman and Walker, 1967). Hoogstraal (1956) reported a nymph on the graceful chameleon, *Chamaeleo g. gracilis.* However, these are atypical host records; this tick is almost exclusively a parasite of African elephants (Walker, 1991).

A. torrei (Fig. 94a–f) parasitizes Caribbean iguanas (Cerny, 1967; Keirans, 1985; Keirans and Garris, 1986; Whittick, 1939). It has also been recovered from the curly-tailed lizard, *Leiocephalus macropus* (Maldonado Capriles and Medina-Gaud, 1977) and from a few other lizards such as those in the genera *Iguana* and *Cyclura* (Keirans and Garris, 1986).

A. usingeri (Figs. 95, 96a–t) is a specific parasite of the Galapagos giant tortoise, *Geochelone elephantopus,* although there is a single record from a land iguana (Keirans et al., 1973). MacFarland and Reeder (1974) described tick re-

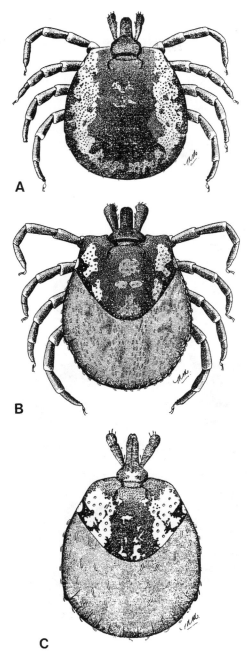

Fig. 94. *Amblyomma torrei.* **A.** Male, dorsal view;
B. Female, dorsal view; **C.** Nymph, dorsal view;

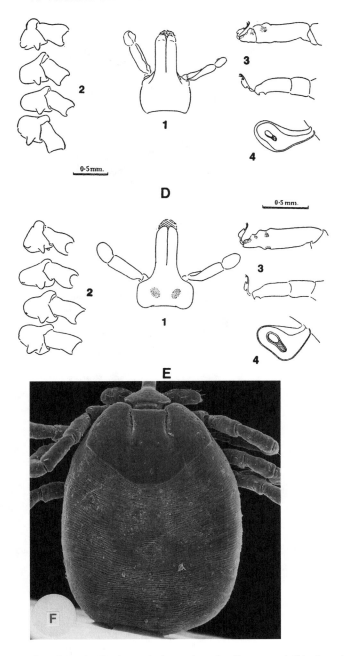

Fig. 94. Continued   **D.** 1–capitulum of male, 2–coxae I–IV of male,
3–tarsi I–IV of male, 4–spiracular plate of male; **E.** 1–capitulum of female,
2–coxae I–IV of female, 3–tarsi I–IV of female, 4–spiracular plate of female;
F. Larva, dorsal view. (A–E, reproduced with permission from
Whittick, 1939; F, courtesy of the U.S. National Tick Collection).

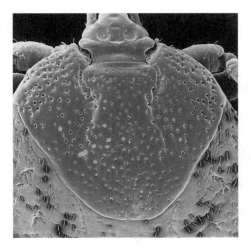

Fig. 95. *Amblyomma usingeri*. Scutum and capitulum of female (also see Fig. 96a). (Photo courtesy of the U.S. National Tick Collection).

moval behavior by Darwin's finches whereby these birds groomed *A. usingeri* from Galapagos giant tortoises.

A. variegatum immatures often parasitize lizards, especially those in the genera *Varanus* and *Chamaeleo* (Brygoo, 1963; Clifford and Anastos, 1964; Hoogstraal, 1956; Lamontellerie, 1966; Morel, 1978; Theiler, 1962), and the puff adder, *Bitis lachesis* (= *arietans*) (Clifford and Anastos, 1964; Theiler, 1962). Adults of this widely distributed African tick parasitize mammals (Walker, 1991).

A. vikirri (Fig. 97a–g) mainly parasitizes the gidgee skink, *Egernia stokesii,* in South Australia (Keirans et al., 1996a). Occasionally, this tick also parasitizes the shingle-back skink, *Trachydosaurus (=Tiliqua) rugosus,* in the same region (Duffield and Bull, 1996a,b). Adult ticks attach mainly on the tail and lower back of this skink, whereas larvae and nymphs typically attach to the ears or between the toes (Keirans et al., 1996a).

A. williamsi (Fig. 98) parasitizes iguanid lizards on the Galapagos islands (Banks, 1924; Hoogstraal and Aeschlimann, 1982).

II. *Aponomma* spp.

Members in the genus *Aponomma* resemble those in the genus *Amblyomma,* with one major exception; *Aponomma* spp. are eyeless. *Aponomma* spp. are about twice as long as wide, and the scutum can be either ornate or inornate. The first palpal segment is shorter than the second one. The palps of the male and female are long,

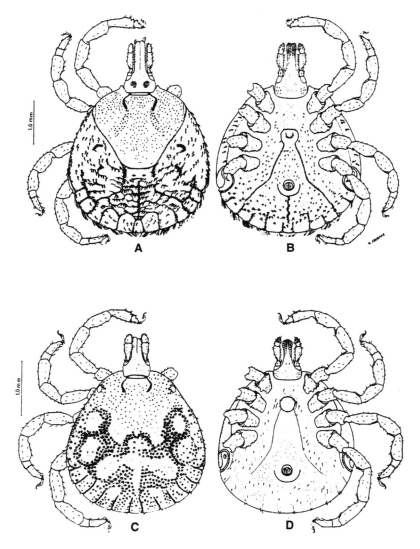

Fig. 96. *Amblyomma usingeri.* **A.** Female, dorsal view; **B.** Female, ventral view; **C.** Male, dorsal view; **D.** Male, ventral view;

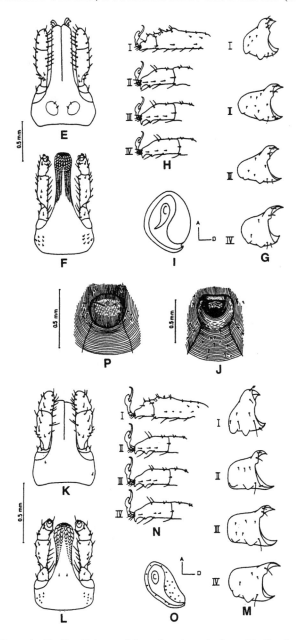

Fig. 96. Continued   **E.** Capitulum of female, dorsal view; **F.** Capitulum of female, ventral view; **G.** Coxae I–IV of female; **H.** Tarsi I–IV of female, lateral view; **I.** Spiracular plate of female (A = anterior; D = dorsal); **J.** Genital area of female; **K.** Capitulum of male, dorsal view; **L.** Capitulum of male, ventral view; **M.** Coxae I–IV of male; **N.** Tarsi I–IV of male, lateral view; **O.** Spiracular plate of male (A = anterior; D = dorsal); **P.** Genital area of male;

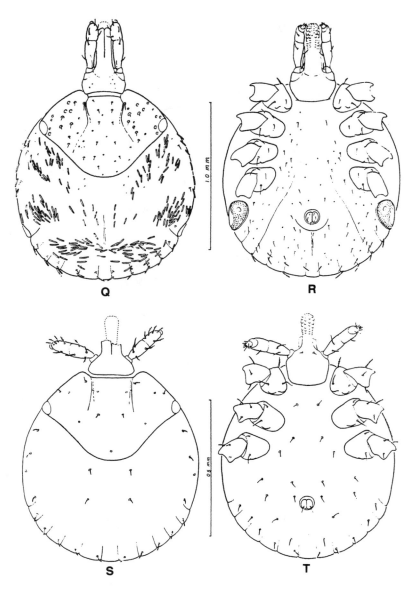

Fig. 96. Continued **Q.** Nymph, dorsal view; **R.** Nymph, ventral view; **S.** Larva, dorsal view; **T.** Larva, ventral view. (Reproduced from Keirans et al., 1973).

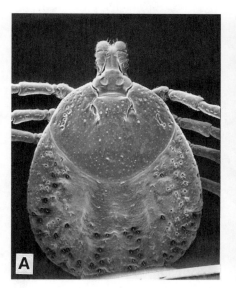

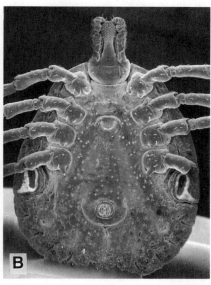

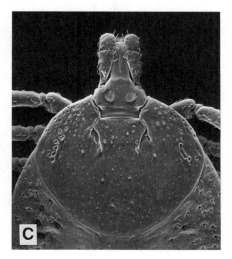

Fig. 97. *Amblyomma vikirri.*
A. Female, dorsal view;
B. Female, ventral view;
C. Scutum and capitulum of female;

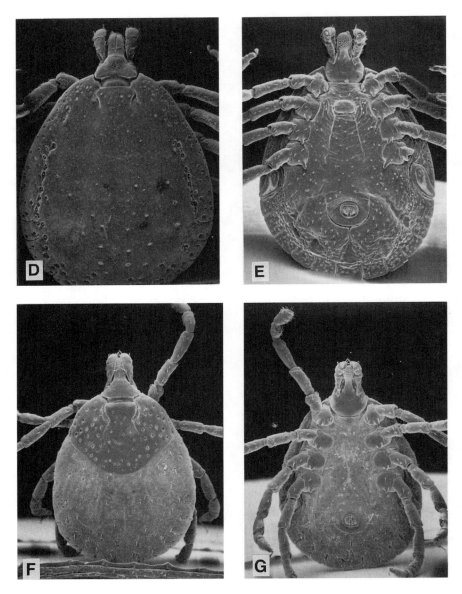

Fig. 97. Continued   **D.** Male, dorsal view; **E.** Male, ventral view;
F. Nymph, dorsal view; **G.** Nymph, ventral view.
(Photos courtesy of the U.S. National Tick Collection).

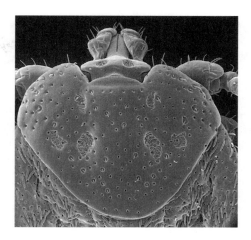

Fig. 98. *Amblyomma williamsi*. Capitulum and scutum of female, dorsal view. (Photo courtesy of the U.S. National Tick Collection).

and these ticks often have a broad and subcircular idiosoma. Festoons are present and there are no adanal shields in the male.

There are approximately 24 species of *Aponomma*. The systematics of this tick genus have been detailed by Kaufman (1972) and Travassos Santos Dias (1993). Unfortunately, the taxonomic interpretations differ slightly in these two mono-graphs. With the exception of two species, which parasitize echidnas and wombats respectively, all members in this genus infest reptiles.

Key to adult *Aponomma* spp. ticks parasitizing reptiles

Adapted from Kaufman (1972), Keirans et al. (1994) and Travassos Santos Dias (1993).

Key to males:

1a   Scutum pilose (with short, stubby setae) and deeply pitted (on Australian monitors, *Varanus glauerti, V. glebopalma*)
. . . . *A. glebopalma*

1b   Scutum not pilose and deeply pitted 2

2a (1b) Lacking anal groove posterior to anus (mainly on African pythons, *Python* spp.). . . . . *A. transversale*

2b   With anal groove posterior to anus 3

3a (2b) Hypostomal dentition 2/2 throughout (mainly on Trans-Pecos rat snake, *Elaphe* [= *Bogertophis*] *subocularis*). . . . . *A. elaphense*

3b   Hypostomal dentition 3/3 or 4/4. 4

4a (3b)	Hypostomal dentition 3/3 distally and 2/2 proximally (on tuatara, *Sphenodon punctatus*) . . . . *A. sphenodonti*	
4b	Hypostomal dentition 3/3 or 4/4. 5	
5a (4b)	Hypostomal dentition 3/3 6	
5b	Hypostomal dentition 4/4 18	
6a (5a)	Coxa I with one spur 7	
6b	Coxa I with two spurs 8	
7a (6a)	Scutum distinctly pitted (on savanna monitor, *Varanus exanthematicus*) . . . . *A. inopinatum*	
7b	Scutum smooth (on African snakes & lizards) . . . *A. flavomaculatum*	
8a (6b)	Scutum inornate. 9	
8b	Scutum ornate 12	
9a (8a)	Coxa I with small internal spur which is sometimes fused with the larger external spur. 10	
9b	Coxa I with both spurs about equal in size 11	
10a (9a)	Cervical pits absent or greatly reduced (on African snakes and lizards). . . . . *A. latum*	
10b	Cervical pits distinct and comma-shaped (mainly on S. Asian snakes) . . . . *A. pattoni*	
11a (9b)	Scutum encircled peripherally with lateral and posterior whitish coloration and with a distinct median inverted Y-shaped whitish area (on Australian snakes and lizards). . . . . *A. decorosum*	
11b	Scutum lacking whitish coloration (on Timor python, *Python timorensis*) . . . . *A. kraneveldi*	
12a (8b)	Scutum with 9 distinct patches of ornamentation (on African reptiles, especially monitor lizards, *Varanus* spp.) . . . . *A. exornatum*	
12b	Scutum with fewer than 9 patches of ornamentation 13	
13a (12b)	With a small patch of ornamentation in each scapular angle extending to the lateral border of the cervical pit 14	
13b	Lacking a small patch of ornamentation in each scapular angle. . . 16	
14a (13a)	Coxa I with both spurs nearly equal in size and slightly separated at their bases (on water monitor, *Varanus salvator*) . . *A. soembawensis*	
14b	Coxa I with spurs distinctly unequal in size. 15	
15a (14b)	Coxa I with internal spur indistinct and sometimes fused with the larger external spur (on S. Asian reptiles). . . . . *A. gervaisi*	
15b	Coxa I with internal spur almost twice as large as external spur (on Komodo dragon, *Varanus komodoensis*). . . . . *A. komodoense*	
16a (13b)	Coxa I with both spurs almost equal in size. 17	
16b	Coxa I with external spur distinctly longer than internal spur (on S. Asian snakes and lizards). . . . . *A. varanensis*	
17a (16a)	Cornua prominent and sharply pointed apically (on Asiatic rock python, *Python molurus*) . . . . *A. fuscolineatum*	

17b	Cornua prominent but bluntly rounded apically (on S.E. Asian snakes and monitor lizards, *Varanus* spp.) . . . . *A. crassipes*	
18a (5b)	Coxa I with 2 spurs (on Australian reptiles) . . . . *A. hydrosauri*	
18b	Coxa I with 1 spur. 19	
19a (18b)	Tarsi II–IV each with a bluntly rounded hump (on S. Asian and Australasian snakes and lizards). . . . . *A. trimaculatum*	
19b	Tarsi II–IV each with a hump that is often concave on the proximal slope (on S.E. Asian, Australasian, and Pacific Island snakes and lizards) . . . . *A. fimbriatum*	

Key to females:

1a	Scutum pilose (with short, stubby setae) and deeply pitted (on Australian monitors, *Varanus glauerti, V. glebopalma*) . . . . *A. glebopalma*
1b	Scutum not pilose and deeply pitted 2
2a (1b)	Lacking anal groove posterior to anus (mainly on African pythons, *Python* spp.). . . . . *A. transversale*
2b	With anal groove posterior to anus. 3
3a (2b)	Coxa I with 1 spur. 4
3b	Coxa I with 2 spurs 9
4a (3a)	Hypostomal dentition 4/4 5
4b	Hypostomal dentition 3/3 or 2/2. 6
5a (4a)	Tarsi II–IV each with a bluntly rounded hump (on S. Asian and Australasian snakes and lizards . . . . *A. trimaculatum*
5b	Tarsi II–IV each with a hump that is often concave on the proximal slope (on S.E. Asian, Australasian, and Pacific Island snakes and lizards. . . . . *A. fimbriatum*
6a (4b)	Scutum ornate. 7
6b	Scutum inornate. 8
7a (6a)	Scutum distinctly pitted (on savanna monitor, *Varanus exanthematicus*) . . . . *A. inopinatum*
7b	Scutum smooth (on African snakes & lizards) . . . *A. flavomaculatum*
8a (6b)	Pits on scutum mostly anterior (mainly on Trans-Pecos rat snake, *Elaphe* [= *Bogertophis*] *subocularis*) . . . . *A. elaphense*
8b	Pits on scutum evenly distributed (on tuatara, *Sphenodon punctatus*) . . . . *A. sphenodonti*
9a (3b)	Hypostomal dentition 4/4 (on Australian reptiles) . . . . *A. hydrosauri*
9b	Hypostomal dentition 3/3 10
10a (9b)	Scutum inornate. 11
10b	Scutum ornate 14
11a (10a)	Coxa I with small internal spur which is sometimes fused with the larger external spur. 12

11b   Coxa I with both spurs about equal in size 13

12a (11a)   Cervical pits absent or greatly reduced (on African snakes and lizards). . . . . *A. latum*

12b   Cervical pits present and comma-shaped (mainly on S. Asian snakes) . . . . *A. pattoni*

13a (11b)   Inner file of hypostomal denticles about equal in size to the 2 outer files of denticles (on Timor python, *Python timorensis*) . . . . *A. kraneveldi*

13b   Inner file of hypostomal denticles very fine and less than one fourth the size of the 2 outer files of denticles (on Australian snakes and lizards) . . . . *A. decorosum*

14a (10b)   Coxa I with both spurs nearly equal in size and slightly separated at their bases. 15

14b   Coxa I with spurs distinctly different in size 17

15a (14a)   Dorsal body surface posterior to scutum evenly covered with setae 16

15b   Dorsal body surface posterior to scutum with setae mostly confined to outer margins (on Asiatic rock python, *Python molurus*) . . . . *A. fuscolineatum*

16a (15a)   Porose areas circular and deep (mainly on water monitor, *Varanus salvator*). . . . . *A. soembawensis*

16b   Porose areas sub-oval and converging posteriorly (on S.E. Asian snakes and monitor lizards, *Varanus* spp.) . . . . *A. crassipes*

17a (14b)   Coxa I with internal spur almost twice as long as external spur (on Komodo dragon, *Varanus komodoensis*). . . . . *A. komodoense*

17b   Coxa I with internal spur distinctly smaller than external spur . . . 18

18a (17b)   Scutum evenly covered with numerous small pits (on African reptiles, especially monitor lizards, *Varanus* spp.) . . . . *A. exornatum*

18b   Scutum evenly covered with a few small-to-large pits 19

19a (18b)   Coxa I with indistinct internal spur which is fused with the external spur (on S. Asian reptiles) . . . . *A. gervaisi*

19b   Coxa I with internal spur smaller than external spur but always distinctly separated from it (on S. Asian snakes and lizards) . . . . *A. varanensis*

A. *Aponomma elaphense* (Fig. 99a–o)

Description   Adult male (Fig. 99a–e): a very small species; body suboval in shape, measuring approximately 2.00 mm long by 1.85 mm wide; ventral surface, except legs, light yellowish-brown with numerous moderate-sized punctations; scutum pale

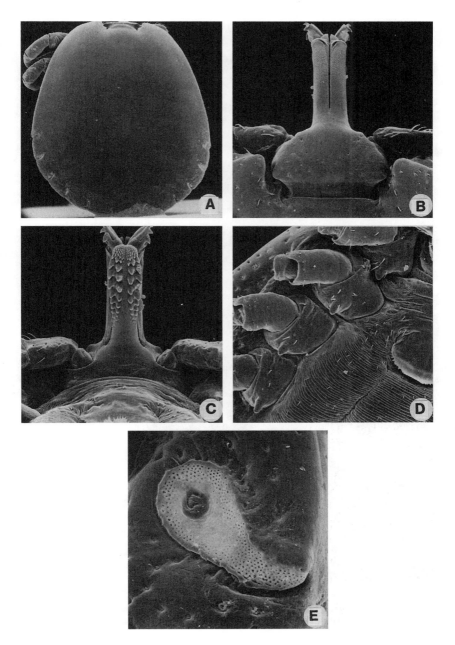

Fig. 99. *Aponomma elaphense.* **A.** Male, dorsal view;
B. Capitulum of male, dorsal view; **C.** Capitulum of male,
ventral view; **D.** Coxae I–IV of male; **E.** Spiracular plate of male;

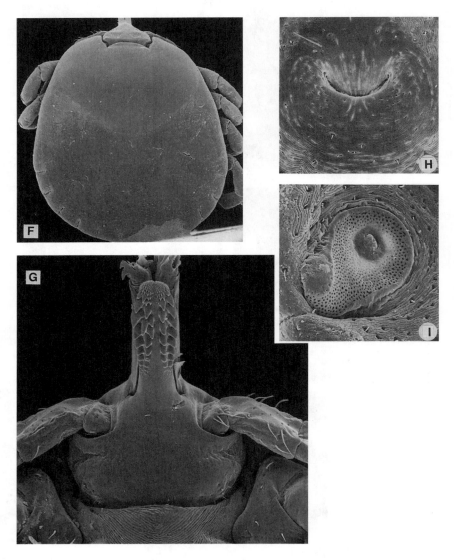

Fig. 99. Continued   **F.** Female, dorsal view; **G.** Capitulum of female, ventral view; **H.** Genital opening of female; **I.** Spiracular plate of female;

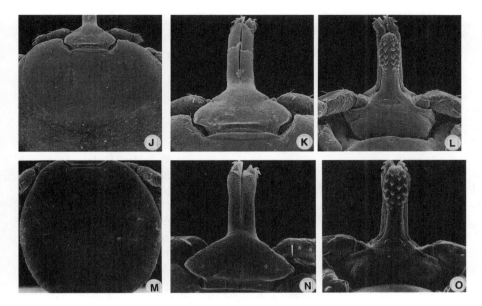

Fig. 99. Continued **J.** Scutum of nymph; **K.** Capitulum of nymph,
dorsal view; **L.** Capitulum of nymph, ventral view;
M. Larva, dorsal view; **N.** Capitulum of larva, dorsal view;
O. Capitulum of larva, ventral view. (A–E, H–O, reproduced
with permission from Keirans and Degenhardt, 1985;
F, G, courtesy of the U.S. National Tick Collection).

yellowish-brown, inornate with short festoons;
basis capituli subtriangular; hypostome (Fig. 99c)
moderately long with 2/2 dentition; legs moderate in length; coxa I short, round, and knoblike,
all coxae with a single triangular spur (Fig. 99d);
spiracular plate (Fig. 99e) long and narrow; genital opening between coxae II and III.

Adult female (Fig. 99f–i): body suboval in shape
without marginal grooves, pale yellowish-brown
in color; unengorged, measures approximately
2.40 mm long by 2.15 mm wide; ventral surface
with closely spaced, fine striations; scutum inornate and pale yellowish-brown in color; basis capituli subtriangular; hypostome (Fig. 99g) moderately long with 2/2 dentition; legs with coxae
as in male; spiracular plate (Fig. 99i) suboval

with short dorsal prolongation; genital opening (Fig. 99h) semicircular and situated between coxae II.

Nymph (Fig. 99j–l): body broadly suboval in shape with inconspicuous transverse striations; about as wide as long, unengorged, body measures 1.63 mm long by 1.48 mm wide; scutum (Fig. 99j) weakly sclerotized with scalelike marking over surface; basis capituli subtriangular; hypostomal dentition 2/2; legs each with a very small bluntly rounded coxal spur; spiracular plate suboval, without dorsal prolongation.

Larva (Fig. 99m–o): body length measures 0.567–0.670 mm, and width 0.549–0.622 mm; suboval in shape with 11 festoons; 13 pairs of dorsal body setae, all minute except SC_1; 15 pairs of ventral body setae; capitulum subtriangular with straight posterior margin; cornua absent; palps and hypostome (Fig. 99o) long; hypostome bluntly rounded apically with 2/2 dentition; scutum inornate, without punctations or cervical grooves; leg coxae each with a small external spur; internal spurs absent.

Host(s)	In nature, Trans-Pecos rat snake, *Elaphe* (= *Bogertophis*) *subocularis*; in captivity, gopher snake, *Pituophis melanoleucus,* black-tailed rattlesnake, *Crotalus molossus,* Texas lyre snake, *Trimorphodon biscutatus vilkinsoni*, and an unspecified rat snake, *Elaphe obsoleta* (Degenhardt and Degenhardt, 1965; Keirans and Degenhardt, 1985; Price, 1958).
Host location	Body surface.
Life cycle	Utilizes three hosts: all stages on snakes, especially the Trans-Pecos rat snake, *Elaphe* (= *Bogertophis*) *subocularis* (Degenhardt and Degenhardt, 1965; Keirans and Degenhardt, 1985). Also see Family Ixodidae above.
Host acquisition	By direct contact with organism.
Symptoms	Heavy infestations may cause anemia, possibly resulting in death (Walker and Bezuidenhout, 1973).

Diagnosis   By demonstration of organism on body surface or
                             cage environment.
Treatment   See Appendix I.

B. Other *Aponomma* spp. affecting reptiles

A. crassipes is native to southeast Asia where it parasitizes the monitor
lizards *Varanus bivittatus* (= *V. salvator bivittatus*), *V. griseus,* and *V. salvator.* Snakes parasitized include the Asiatic rock python, *Python molurus,* the
reticulated python, *P. reticulatus,* and the banded krait, *Bungarus fasciatus*
(Kaufman, 1972; Kolonin, 1995; Petney and Keirans, 1996; Travassos Santos
Dias, 1993).

A. decorosum (syn., *undatum*) is restricted to Australia in coastal and subcoastal regions of Queensland, New South Wales, and Victoria. Hosts are
lizards in the genera *Varanus* and *Tiliqua,* and snakes in the genus *Python.*
This tick also has been recovered from a Komodo dragon, *Varanus komodoensis,* in a zoo (Kaufman, 1972). A specimen of this tick (as *A. undatum*)
was located subdermally in the forelimb of a lace monitor, *Varanus varius*
(Ward, 1989).

A. exornatum (syns., *arcanum, neglectum, rondelliae*) (Fig. 100) is often
called the "monitor lizard tick." Adults parasitize African tortoises, crocodiles,
snakes, and lizards, but the savanna monitor, *Varanus exanthematicus,* and the
Nile monitor, *V. niloticus,* appear to be the preferred hosts (Aeschlimann, 1967;
Arthur, 1962; Clifford and Anastos, 1962, 1964; Hoffman and Lindau, 1971;
Hoogstraal, 1956; Kaufman, 1972; Rousselot, 1953; Theiler, 1962; Travassos
Santos Dias, 1993; Young, 1965). This parasite may be found in the host's nos-
trils, and/or under the scales in the axillae, forelegs, elbows, toes, and cloaca.
Because adults of this tick often attach inside the nasal passages of monitor
lizards, they can suffocate (captive) specimens (Walker, 1991).

A. fimbriatum (syns., *ecinctum, simplex, trabeatum*) is a parasite of lizards
and snakes of Australia, Borneo, New Guinea, Sulawesi, eastern Indonesia,
the Philippines, Guadalcanal, and adjacent islands in the South Pacific (Kaufman, 1972; Kohls, 1957; Oliver and Bremner, 1968; Petney and Keirans,
1996; Roberts, 1964; Sharrad and King, 1981; Wilson, 1969). In Australia, it
has been recorded from coastal and subcoastal regions of all seven mainland
states.

A. flavomaculatum (syns., *halli, pulchrum*) is a widespread tick in west, east,
and central Africa where it parasitizes at least 10 species of snakes and lizards
(Böhme et al., 1989; Hesse, 1985; Kaufman, 1972; Lamontellerie, 1966; Morel,
1978; Morel and Mouchet, 1965; Puhyua and Latif, 1990; Saratsiotis, 1972;
Travassos Santos Dias, 1993). This tick is most frequently found attached to
the savanna monitor, *Varanus exanthematicus,* and the Nile monitor, *V. niloti-*

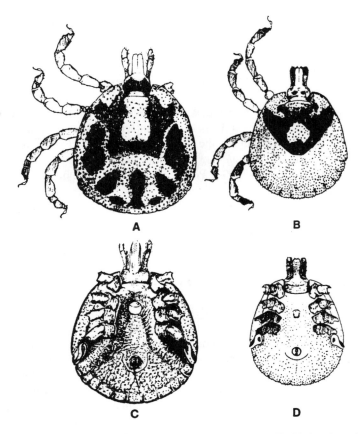

Fig. 100. *Aponomma exornatum.* **A.** Female, dorsal view; **B.** Male, dorsal view; **C.** Female, ventral view; **D.** Male, ventral view. (Reproduced from Hoogstraal, 1956).

cus (Fig. 101), but snakes in the genera *Python* and *Naja* are also commonly parasitized (Punyua and Latif, 1990; Saratsiotis, 1972; Travassos Santos Dias, 1993). Wilson and Barnard (1985) reported this tick from the Nile monitor, *V. niloticus,* imported into the United States.

A. fuscolineatum is known only from India from the rock python, *Python molurus* (Kaufman, 1972).

A. gervaisi (syns., *ophiophilum, patagonicum*) parasitizes lizards and snakes of southern Asia, and the star tortoise, *Testudo* (= *Geochelone*) *elegans* (Auffenberg and Auffenberg, 1990; Bhat and Sreenivasan, 1981; Deraniyasala, 1939; Grokhovskaia and Nguen-Suan-Khoe, 1968; Gupta, 1996; Hoogstraal and Rack, 1967; Hunt, 1957; Kaufman, 1972; Kohls, 1957; Nagar, 1962; Nagar et

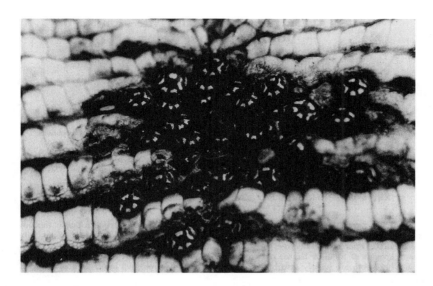

Fig. 101. *Aponomma flavomaculatum.* Males clustered around
the cloaca of a Nile monitor, *Varanus niloticus.*
(Reproduced with permission from Punyua and Latif, 1990;
copyrighted by the Entomological Society of America).

al., 1977; Nguyên, V.-A., 1961; Rao et al., 1973; Seneviratna, 1965; Stephen
and Rao, 1979; Toumanoff, 1941; Travassos Santos Dias, 1993). In Pakistan and
India, female *A. gervaisi* attach preferentially in the axillae of the Bengal monitor, *Varanus bengalensis,* while males attach to the lateral body, tail, and
medioventral depression of this host (Auffenberg and Auffenberg, 1990). *Coxiella burnetii,* the causative agent of Q fever in mammals, has been detected in
A. gervaisi from India (Stephen and Rao, 1979).

    A. glebopalma (Fig. 102a–j) was reported from two Australian rock monitors,
Varanus glebopalma and *V. glauerti,* in the Northern Territory and Kimberly region of Western Australia respectively (Keirans et al., 1994).

    A. hydrosauri (syns., *tachyglossi, trachysauri*) parasitizes a variety of reptiles
throughout the southern regions of Australia (Allman, 1961; Bull and Sara,
1976; Kaufman, 1972; Oliver and Bremner, 1968; Roberts, 1969, 1970; Sharrad and King, 1981; Smith, 1973; Smyth, 1973). The shingle-back skink, *Trachydosaurus* (= *Tiliqua*) *rugosus,* is the most commonly parasitized reptile in
South Australia (Bull et al., 1988).

    A. inopinatum was described from the savanna monitor, *Varanus exanthe-
maticus,* in the Democratic Republic of The Congo (Travassos Santos Dias,
1993).

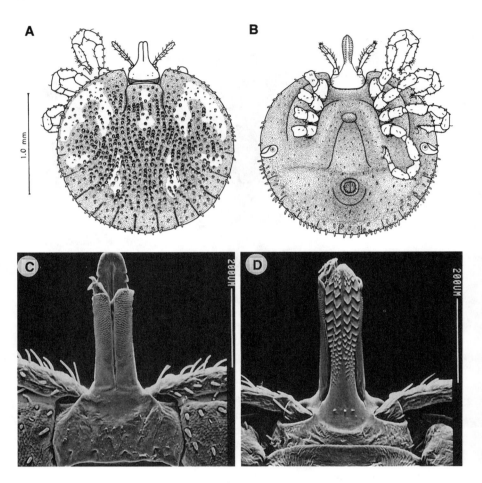

Fig. 102. *Aponomma glebopalma*. **A.** Male, dorsal view; **B.** Male, ventral view; **C.** Capitulum of male, dorsal view; **D.** Capitulum of male, ventral view;

A. komodoense (Fig. 103) parasitizes the Komodo dragon, *Varanus komodoensis,* on the Indonesian islands of Komodo and Flores, and in captivity (Anastos, 1950; Kaufman, 1972; Krylov and Said-Aliev, 1964; Petney and Keirans, 1996). There is also a single record from a water monitor, *V. salvator,* in a zoo in Jakarta, Indonesia.

A. kraneveldi parasitizes the reticulated python, *Python reticulatus,* and the Timor python, *P. timorensis,* on several Indonesian islands including Sumbawa, Flores, and the Sula group (Kaufman, 1972; Petney and Keirans, 1996).

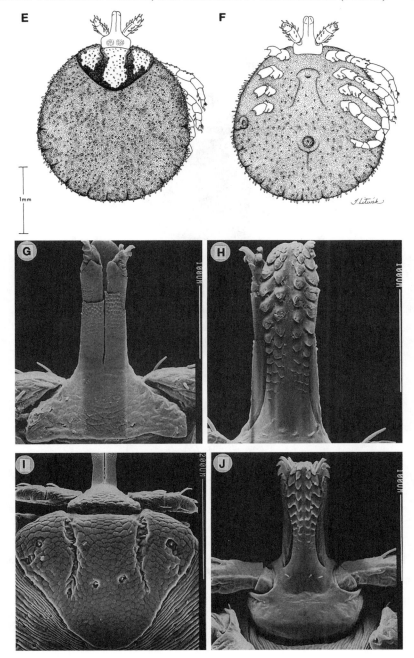

Fig. 102. Continued   **E.** Female, dorsal view; **F.** Female, ventral view;
G. Capitulum of nymph, dorsal view; **H.** Hypostome of nymph; **I.** Scutum of larva;
J. Hypostome of larva. (Reproduced with permission from Keirans et al., 1994;
copyrighted by the Entomological Society of America).

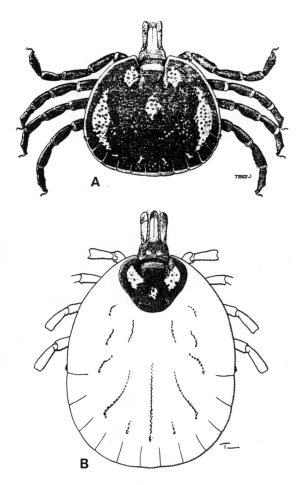

Fig. 103. *Aponomma komodoense.* **A.** Male, dorsal view; **B.** Female, dorsal view. (Reproduced with permission from Whittick, 1939).

A. latum (syns., *falsolaeve, laevatum, laeve, ochraceum*) (Fig. 104) parasitizes several African snakes and lizards. The list of hosts is exhaustive. Common snake hosts include the African rock python, *Python sebae*, ball python *P. regius*, cobras in the genus *Naja*, mambas, *Dendroaspis* spp, snakes in the genera *Boaedon, Dasypeltis,* and *Mehelya,* and lizard hosts in the genus *Varanus*. (Aeschlimann, 1967; Clifford and Anastos, 1964; Frank, 1981; Hoffman et al., 1970; Hoffman and Lindau, 1971; Hoogstraal, 1956; Kamara, 1975; Lamontellerie, 1966; Morel, 1978; Morel and Mouchet, 1965; Saratsiotis, 1972; Theiler, 1962; Travassos Santos Dias, 1963a,b; Walker, 1991; Wilson and Barnard, 1985; Yeoman and Walker, 1967). Both Kaufman (1972) and Travassos Santos Dias (1993) recorded this tick from more than 60 species of reptiles, and from all parts of the Afrotropical region. *Aponomma latum* is often found on pythons exported from Africa; Anderson et al., (1984), Wilson and Barnard (1985), and Durden and Kollars (1992) reported several collections of this tick from such snakes imported into the United States.

A. pattoni (syn., *pseudolaeve*) is widespread but discontinuously distributed in India and southeast Asia. There are no reliable records between India and Thailand, but it is well documented from Laos, Sri Lanka, Thailand, southern China (Yunnan Province), and Vietnam where it parasitizes several species of snakes (Kaufman, 1972; Kolonin, 1995; Travassos Santos Dias, 1993). Reported snake genera include *Bungarus, Coluber, Elaphe, Naja, Ophiophagus, Ptyas, Python,* and *Vipera*. There also are single records from a varanid lizard and a mongoose (Petney and Keirans, 1996).

A. soembawensis has been recovered from the water monitor, *Varanus salvator* (several collections) and the reticulated python, *Python reticulatus* (1 collection) from the Indonesian islands of Sumba, Sumbawa, Sabu, Semau, Timor, and Java (Kaufman, 1972; Petney and Keirans, 1996). King and Keirans (1997) have recently reported collections of this tick from the Timor monitor, *Varanus timorensis,* on several eastern Indonesian islands.

A. sphenodonti is known only from the tuatara, *Sphenodon punctatus,* from New Zealand (Dumbleton, 1943; Kaufman, 1972; Travassos Santos Dias, 1993).

A. transversale (syn., *globulus*) (Fig. 105) adults were found in the eye sockets of the Ball python, *Python regius,* and the African rock python, *P. sebae* (Lamontellerie, 1966; Morel, 1978; Morel and Mouchet, 1965; Theiler, 1962; Yeoman and Walker, 1967). This tick is widely but discontinuously distributed throughout the Afrotropical region (Walker, 1991). In captivity, *A. transversale* may parasitize other reptiles through association with infested African species.

A. trimaculatum infests lizards (*Varanus* spp.) and snakes (*Python* spp. and Amethystine python, *Liasis amethystinus*) of Sri Lanka, Indonesia, New Guinea, the Philippines, Australia (northern Queensland), and adjacent islands (Anastos, 1950; Petney and Keirans, 1996; Roberts, 1964, 1970; Seneviratna, 1965). Travassos Santos Dias (1993) listed collections from 8 species of monitor lizards

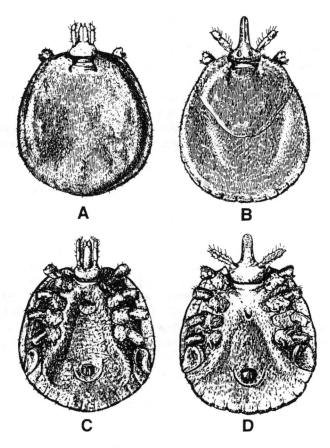

Fig. 104. *Aponomma latum*. **A.** Male, dorsal view; **B.** Female, dorsal view; **C.** Male, ventral view; **D.** Female, ventral view. (Reproduced from Hoogstraal, 1956).

(*Varanus* spp.) and from 3 species of snakes (unspecified). King and Keirans (1997) have recently reported this tick from the Pacific monitor, *Varanus indicus,* from several islands in eastern Indonesia.

A. varanensis (syns., *barbouri, quadratum, lucasi*) (Fig. 106) was reported from varanid lizards and snakes by Anastos (1950), Kolonin (1995) and Petney and Keirans (1996). This parasite has also been reported from the blood python, *Python curtus* (Wilson and Barnard, 1985), the reticulated python, *Python reticulatus* (Hoogstraal et al., 1968), and the brown tortoise, *Manouria emys,* in Burma (= Myanmar) (Frazier and Keirans, 1990). Kaufman (1972) listed at least 10 species of snakes in the genera *Boiga, Bungarus, Elaphe, Eryx, Naja, Ophio-*

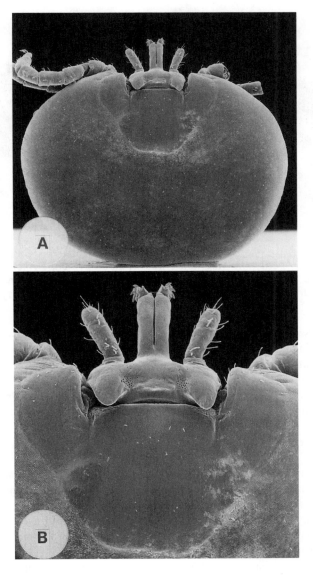

Fig. 105. *Aponomma transversale*. Female. **A.** Dorsal view; **B.** Scutum and capitulum. (Photos courtesy of the U.S. National Tick Collection).

Fig. 106. *Aponomma varanensis* from a blood python, *Python curtus*.
A. Female dorsal view; **B.** Male, dorsal view. (Specimens
courtesy of Nixon Wilson; photos courtesy of Rick E. Perry).

phagus, Ptyas, Python, and *Vipera,* 6 species of varanid lizards of which the valid taxa include *Varanus bengalensis, V. dumerilii, V. indicus, V. rudicollis,* and *V. salvator,* one species of turtle, *Geoemyda spinosa,* and a lizard dubiously named *Lophura amboinensis,* as hosts of *A. varanensis.* He also cited records from several regions and islands from India in the west, to the Philippines and Ternate (Indonesia) in the southeast.

III. *Dermacentor* spp.

Thirty-two species of *Dermacentor* are known with representatives in Eurasia, Africa, and North and Central America. Mammals are typical hosts but immatures of a few species also parasitize birds and, although they are considered atypical host-parasite associations, individuals of a select number of species have been recovered from reptiles. Members of this tick genus are ornate and have short, broad palps; eyes and festoons are present. This genus includes several species that have medical or veterinary importance such as the vectors of the agent of Rocky Mountain spotted fever. The following species have been recorded on reptiles.

A. *D. atrosignatus* adults have been recorded from the water monitor, *Varanus salvator,* and the Asian cobra, *Naja naja,* in peninsular Malaysia

(Hoogstraal and Wassef, 1985b). However, this tick typically parasitizes wild and domestic pigs throughout its range which extends from peninsular Malaysia south and east to Sumatra, Java, Borneo, and the southern Philippines (Hoogstraal and Wassef, 1985b).

B. *D. auratus* adults have been collected from the reticulated python, *Python reticulatus,* in peninsular Malaysia (Hoogstraal and Wassef, 1985a). Adults of this tropical Asian tick normally feed on medium-to-large sized mammals (Hoogstraal and Wassef 1985a).

C. *D. compactus* (one female) was reported from the reticulated python, *Python reticulatus,* in peninsular Malaysia by Hoogstraal and Wassef (1984). Again, this is an atypical host association; adults of this tick normally feed on larger mammals such as pig, buffalo, dog, tiger, civet, human, etc. In nature, this tick occurs in Malaysia, Indonesia, and Borneo (Hoogstraal and Wassef, 1984).

D. *D. marginatus* larvae and nymphs have been reported from the emerald lizard, *Lacerta viridis,* in Europe (Reháček et al., 1961; Lác et al., 1972). However, mammals are the normal hosts of all stages of this tick.

E. *D. reticulatus* (syn: *pictus*) larvae were reported from the emerald lizard, *Lacerta viridis,* in Europe (Lác et al., 1972). However, this is another atypical host association; mammals are the normal hosts of this tick.

F. *D. steini* adults have been recovered from the king cobra, *Ophiophagus hannah,* the water monitor, *Varanus salvator,* and the reticulated python, *Python reticulatus,* in peninsular Malaysia (Wassef and Hoogstraal, 1988). Domestic and wild pigs are the main hosts of this tick which has been recorded from Thailand, Malaysia, Borneo, the Philippines, and New Guinea (Wassef and Hoogstraal, 1988).

IV. *Haemaphysalis* spp.

Approximately 150 species occur worldwide. Two species are native to North America, but this genus of ticks is especially abundant in Asia, Africa, and the East Indies where representatives primarily parasitize mammals and birds. Members of this genus have relatively small bodies, are generally inornate, and lack eyes. The palps of all stages are short and broad, and almost all species have a wedge-shaped second segment. Larval palps have four segments, and there are two marginal setae anterior to each sensilla sagittiformia. Both sexes, as well as the nymphs and larvae, have 11 festoons. Adanal plates are absent in males. The spiracular plates are ovoid in males, and ovoid or comma-shaped in females. *Haemaphysalis* spp. are three-host ticks, with nymphal and larval stages of a few species sometimes infesting reptiles. Walker and Bezuidenhout (1973) reported that infestation by these ticks could cause anemia, possibly resulting in the death of a reptile. Very few *Haema-*

physalis spp. ticks parasitize reptiles and then almost exclusively in the immature stages. The following species have been recorded on reptiles.

A. *H. caucasica* was reported from a racerunner, *Eremias regeli*, and a Schneider's skink, *Eumeces schneideri* in Tajikistan (Starkoff and Said-Aliev, 1968).

B. *H. concinna* is a vector of the causitive agents of both Russian spring-summer encephalitis and Siberian tick typhus. Larval and nymphal stages have been reported from the sand lizard, *Lacerta agilis,* and the emerald lizard, *L. viridis,* of Europe and northern Asia (Hoogstraal, 1966, 1967; Lác et al., 1972; Nosek et al., 1967; Reháček et al., 1961).

C. *H. erinacei taurica* was reported from the Hermann's tortoise, *Testudo hermanni,* in Bulgaria (Zlatanova, 1991).

D. *H. hystricis* (Fig. 107a–j) has been reported from the spiny turtle, *Geoemyda* (= *Heosemys*) *spinosa* in southeast Asia (Anastos, 1950; Hoogstraal et al., 1965).

E. *H. inermis* has been reported from the emerald lizard, *Lacerta viridis,* in Europe (Lác et al., 1972; Reháček et al., 1961).

F. *H. kashmirensis* was reported from an agamid lizard, *Agama tuberculata* in Pakistan (Hoogstraal and McCarthy, 1965).

G. *H. parmata* (Fig. 108) adults were reported from the western forest mole viper, *Atractaspis aterrima,* in southern Africa (Theiler, 1962).

H. *H. parva* (syn., *otophila*) immature stages infest lizards of Egypt (Markov et al., 1964a,b).

I. *H. punctata* is a vector of the rickettsial agent of Siberian tick typhus and of *Babesia bigemina,* the Texas cattle fever (also referred to as bovine piroplasmosis, babesiosis, and red water fever) agent. Reptile hosts include lizards in Europe, northwestern Africa, and southwestern Asia (e.g., the emerald lizard, *Lacerta viridis,* and the sheltopusik, *Ophisaurus apodus*). *Haemaphysalis punctata* also has been reported from the European viper, *Vipera berus* (Hoogstraal, 1967; Lác et al., 1972; Lapage, 1968; Starkoff and Said-Aliev, 1968; Tovornik and Brelih, 1980).

J. *H. sulcata* immatures infest a variety of Asiatic and eastern European reptiles (Berdyev et al., 1974; Filippova, 1959; Hoogstraal, 1959b; Markov et al., 1964a,b; Nemenz, 1967; Ogandzhanian, 1960; Starkoff and Said-Aliev, 1968; Tovornik and Brelih, 1980; Ushakova et al., 1963; Wassef et al., 1997). Valid taxa reported include the Caucasian agama *Agama caucasica,* Himalayan agama, *A. himalayana,* Turkmenian agama, *A. lehmanni,* hardun, *A. stellio,* other *Agama* spp., sun-gazing agamid, *Phrynocephalus helioscopus,* leopard gecko, *Eublepharis maculariús,* geckos in the genus *Gymnodactylus,* racerunners in the genus *Eremias,* emerald lizard, *Lacerta viridis,* sheltopusik, *Ophisaurus apodus,* European snake-eye, *Ophisops elegans,* spiny-tailed agamid, *Uromastyx* sp., desert monitor, *Varanus*

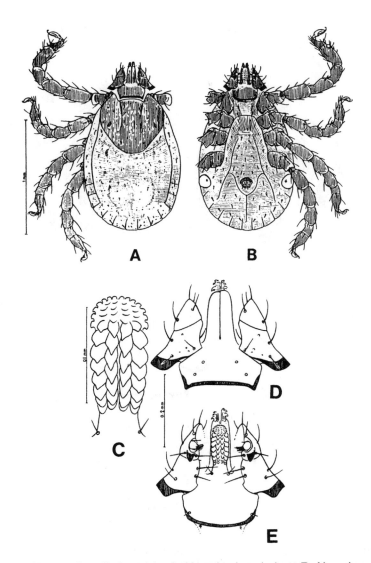

Fig. 107. *Haemaphysalis hystricis.* **A.** Nymph, dorsal view; **B.** Nymph, ventral view; **C.** Hypostome of nymph; **D.** Capitulum of nymph, dorsal view; **E.** Capitulum of nymph, ventral view;

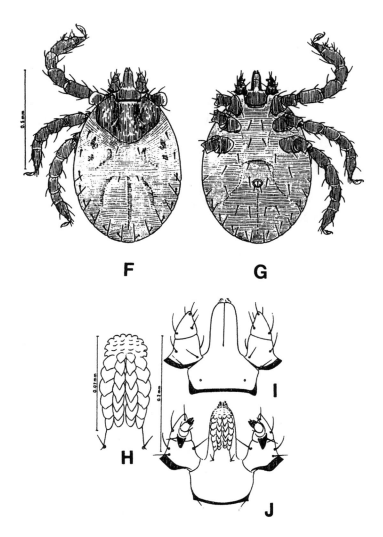

Fig. 107. Continued   **F.** Larva, dorsal view; **G.** Larva, ventral view; **H.** Hypostome of larva; **I.** Capitulum of larva, dorsal view; **J.** Capitulum of larva, ventral view. (Reproduced with permission from Hoogstraal et al., 1965).

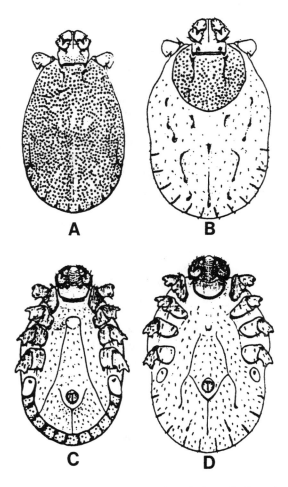

Fig. 108. *Haemaphysalis parmata*. **A.** Male, dorsal view; **B.** Female, dorsal view; **C.** Male, ventral view; **D.** Female, ventral view. (Reproduced from Hoogstraal, 1956).

griseus, variegated racer, *Coluber ravergieri,* and Horsfield's tortoise, *Testudo horsfieldii.*

V. *Hyalomma* spp.

Hyalomma spp. ticks are difficult to identify (Schmidt and Roberts, 1985), partly due to a natural genetic and morphological flexibility and a tendency toward hybridization. Also, there are morphological variations caused by climatic conditions and the lack of food.

Most *Hyalomma* spp. are large ticks, and the scuta are inornate. In some species, ornamentation is confined to the legs which often appear to be banded. Eyes are present and are located away from the scutal margin. They are often raised and protruding. Festoons are present but may be poorly defined and are often partially coalesced. Spiracular plates are comma-shaped in males, and subtriangular in females. Palps and the hypostome are long. Males possess adanal and subanal plates. The palps of the larvae have four segments, and there are 5 setae anterior to each sensilla sagittiformia. Immature stages of *Hyalomma* spp. are difficult to identify, and larvae and nymphs of several species have not been described. Feldman-Muehsam (1948) provided an identification guide to the larvae and nymphs of a few species that feed on reptiles. Rearing immatures to adults is the most reliable method for identification.

Hyalomma spp. are hardy ticks, found in desert conditions in Europe, Africa, and Asia. Generally, they are two-host ticks, although some species utilize three. Their life cycle is presented in Figure 111.

Bites of *Hyalomma* spp. sometimes cause severe wounds that can result in secondary infection including invasion by myiasis-causing maggots. These ticks also can transmit viruses and rickettsiae to their hosts, including humans. The hemogregarine parasite *Hemolivia* (formerly *Hepatozoon*) *mauritanicum* is transmitted to the tortoise, *Testudo graeca,* by *Hyalomma aegyptium* in North Africa (Landau and Paperna, 1997). Except for one species (*H. aegyptium*), only immatures of *Hyalomma* spp. typically feed on reptiles (Hoogstraal and Aeschlimann, 1982).

A. *Hyalomma aegyptium* (Figs. 109a–g, 110)

Also called the "tortoise tick" or "bont-leg tick," it is distributed in southern Europe, the Mediterranean region, and the Middle East. It is a vector of protozoa such as haemogregarines to tortoises (Hoogstraal, 1956).

Description   Adult male (Fig. 109a,b): characteristics same as for female below; also have distinct (unfused) festoons, lack lateral grooves and a caudal depression; with very large adanal shields, and very small or absent subanal shields.

Adult female (Fig. 109c,d): easily distinguished

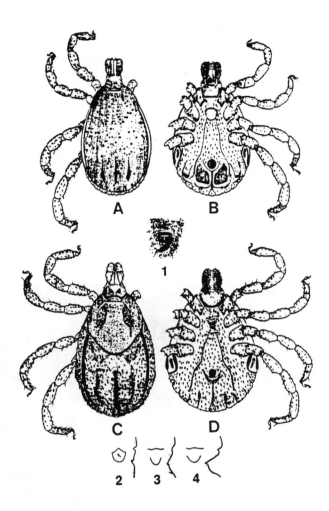

Fig. 109. *Hyalomma aegyptium*. **A.** Male, dorsal view; **B.** male, ventral view; **C.** Female dorsal view; **D.** Female, ventral view; **1.** Genital area; **2.** Unengorged genital apron outline and profile; **3.** Partially engorged genital apron outline and profile; **4.** Fully engorged genital apron outline and profile;

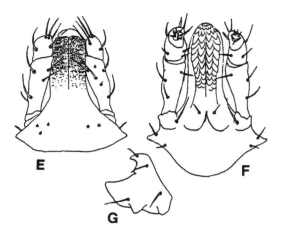

Fig. 109. Continued **E.** Capitulum of nymph, dorsal view; **F.** Capitulum of nymph, ventral view; **G.** First coxa of nymph. (A–D, 1–4, reproduced from Hoogstraal, 1956; E–G, reproduced with permission from Feldman-Muehsam, 1948).

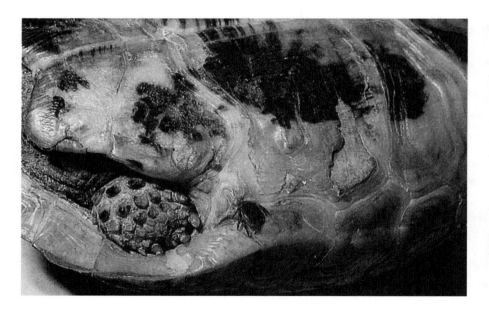

Fig. 110. *Hyalomma aegyptium* feeding on a Greek tortoise, *Testudo graeca*. (Reproduced with permission from Frye, 1991).

from other *Hyalomma* spp. by the presence of two well-separated spurs of equal length on coxa I; scutum smooth and shiny with a few scattered, large, deep punctations.

Nymph (Fig. 109e–g): pale when unfed; lateral edges of basis capituli acutely angled; width of basis same as distance between cervical grooves on scutum; scutum wider than long (0.56 mm by 0.66 mm); palps short; hypostome narrow; coxa I with 2 short spurs; length of unfed nymph 1.4–1.8 mm.

Larva: Incompletely described by Chodziesner (1924) and Senevet (1928). *Hyalomma aegyptium* larva has much stouter terminal setae on palpal article 3 than other species illustrated.

Host(s)	Adults have been reported from chelonians in the genera *Testudo* and *Emys,* and lizards in the genus *Agama* (Berdyev et al., 1974; Feider, 1962; Gina, 1973; Hoogstraal, 1958, 1967; Hoogstraal and Kaiser, 1960b; Kadatskaia and Shirova, 1963; Kaiser and Hoogstraal, 1963; Lapage, 1968; Markov et al., 1964a,b; Nemenz, 1962, 1967; Ogandzhanian, 1960; Sixl, 1971; Starkoff and Said-Aliev, 1968; Sweatman, 1968; Theiler, 1962; Travassos Santos Dias, 1961a; Worms, 1967). This tick, however, usually parasitizes land tortoises (*Testudo* spp.). Immatures also parasitize birds and mammals, and adults sometimes feed on hedgehogs (Hoogstraal and Kaiser, 1960b; Kaiser and Hoogstraal, 1964).
Host location	Body surface (Fig. 110), especially on the back legs and tail of tortoises (Petney and Al-Yaman, 1985).
Life cycle (Fig. 111)	Generally utilizes two hosts: larval and nymphal stages on reptiles, birds or mammals; adults on land tortoises. Also see Family Ixodidae above.
Host acquisition	By direct contact with organism.
Symptoms	Heavy infestations may cause anemia, possibly resulting in death (Walker and Bezuidenhout, 1973).
Diagnosis	By demonstration of organism on body surface or cage environment.
Treatment	See Appendix I.

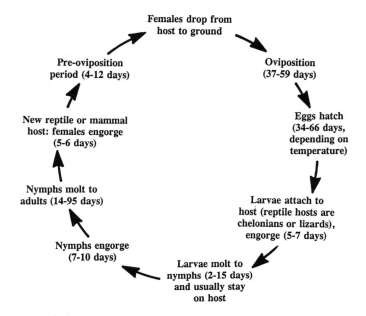

Fig. 111. Generalized life cycle of *Hyalomma* spp. of reptiles.
(Adapted from Soulsby, 1968).

B. Other *Hyalomma* spp. affecting reptiles

H. anatolicum anatolicum was reported from a tortoise, *Testudo* sp., of the Tirane region of Albania (Gina, 1973).

H. anatolicum excavatum immatures were reported from the Hermann's tortoise, *Testudo hermanni*, in Bulgaria (Zlatanova, 1991).

H. detritum (Fig. 112) is an Asiatic tick infesting domestic stock. It is prevalent along the Mediterranean zone of Africa. Kerbabaev (1966) reported immatures from Horsfield's tortoise, *Testudo horsfieldii*.

H. dromedarii (Fig. 113) immatures occasionally infest lizards of Egypt (Hoogstraal and Kaiser, 1958a) and probably elsewhere in North Africa. The principal host is the fringe-fingered lizard, *Acanthodactylus boskians asper*.

H. franchinii larval and nymphal stages often parasitize lizards of North Africa (Hoogstraal and Kaiser, 1958a,b). Hosts include the fringe-fingered lizards, *Acanthodactylus boskianus asper* and *A. scutellatus,* and the desert agama, *Agama mutabilis*. These ticks are found in African desert margins, littoral deserts, and lowland and mountain semi-deserts.

H. impeltatum larval and nymphal stages often infest North African lizards in

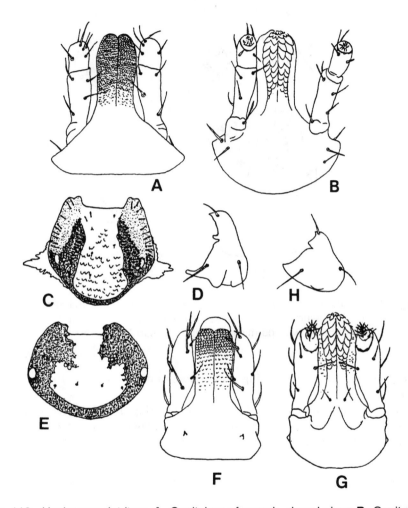

Fig. 112. *Hyalomma detritum*. **A.** Capitulum of nymph, dorsal view; **B.** Capitulum of nymph, ventral view; **C.** Scutum of nymph; **D.** First coxa of nymph; **E.** Scutum of larva; **F.** Capitulum of larva, dorsal view; **G.** Capitulum of larva, ventral view; **H.** First coxa of larva. (Reproduced from Feldman-Muehsam, 1948).

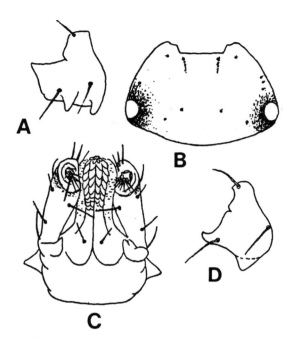

Fig. 113. *Hyalomma dromedarii*. **A.** First coxa of nymph; **B.** Scutum of larva; **C.** Capitulum of larva, ventral view; **D.** First coxa of larva. (Reproduced with permission from Feldman-Muehsam, 1948).

the genus *Acanthodactylus* (Fig. 114) (Hoogstraal and Kaiser, 1958a; Theiler, 1962).

H. marginatum marginatum (syn., *plumbeum*) (Fig. 115) immatures have been reported from tortoises in the Mediterranean region (Gina, 1973; Zlatanova, 1991). Hosts include the Greek tortoise, *Testudo graeca*, and Hermann's tortoise, *T. hermanni*.

VI. *Ixodes* spp.

Of approximately 250 species of *Ixodes* worldwide, 34 species are known from North America, north of Mexico (Durden and Keirans, 1996). Most *Ixodes* spp. are parasites of mammals. Many are small in size and can be missed easily on examination. The palps and hypostome are long. Eyes and festoons are absent, and the scutum is inornate. All stages of *Ixodes* have a distinctive anal groove which curves anteriorly to the anus. Sexual dimorphism is pronounced. Spiracular plates are typically oval in males and circular in females. Figure 116 shows the seta arrangement for larval ticks belonging to the genus *Ixodes*.

Fig. 114. *Hyalomma impeltatum* infesting a fringe-fingered lizard, *Acanthodactylus* sp. (Reproduced with permission from Hoogstraal and Kaiser, 1958; copyrighted by the Entomological Society of America).

Ixodes spp. are three-host ticks with a life cycle essentially identical to that of *Amblyomma* spp. shown in Figure 73. Except for *Ixodes asanumai,* only the immature stages of this tick genus parasitize reptiles. Many ticks of the "*Ixodes ricinus* complex*" (Keirans et al., 1992) feed on a variety of vertebrates, including reptiles, as larvae and nymphs. Examples include *I. ricinus, I. scapularis, I. persulcatus,* and *I. pacificus,* all of which feed on numerous vertebrates. *I. ricinus* complex ticks are efficient vectors of several human pathogens.

A. *Ixodes festai* (syn., *thompsoni*)

Description   Adult female: long setae on dorsal surface; hypostomal dentition 4/4 apically, then 3/3 and 2/2 in proximal half; lateral carinae distinct.
Adult male: very small; posterior and lateral margins of basis capituli straight; cornua distinct and triangular; hypostome with 8 sharp lateral teeth.
Nymph: lateral carinae distinct; prominent cornua (as in Fig. 118 for *I. ricinus*) on basis capituli; hypostomal dentition 3/3 apically, then 2/2.

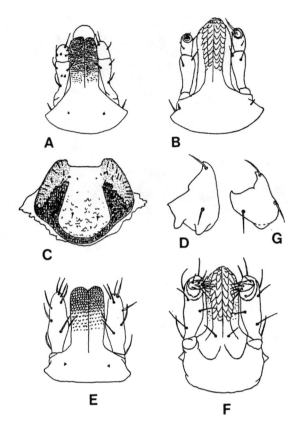

Fig. 115. *Hyalomma marginatum*. **A.** Capitulum of nymph, dorsal view; **B.** Capitulum of nymph, ventral view; **C.** Scutum of nymph; **D.** First coxa of nymph; **E.** Capitulum of larva, dorsal view; **F.** Capitulum of larva, ventral view; **G.** First coxa of larva. (Reproduced with permission from Feldman-Muehsam, 1948).

Larva: Oval-shaped; body setae long, especially on margin; basis capituli triangular with straight posterior and lateral margins; cornua lacking.

Host(s)   Immature stages on various small vertebrates, including lizards in the genera *Agama, Chalcides, Eumeces, Lacerta,* and *Psammodromus* in western Europe (Arthur, 1957, 1958, 1963; Hoogstraal, 1959a, 1960a). Rabbits are typical hosts of adults and nymphs (Arthur, 1963).

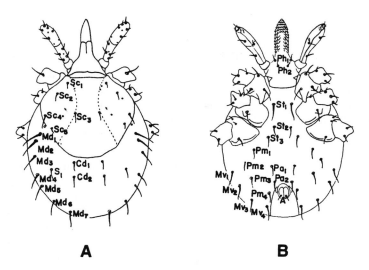

A   **B**

Fig. 116. Setal arrangement of larval *Ixodes* sp. **A.** Dorsal view;
B. Ventral view. **Legend:** A (anal); Cd (central dorsal); Md (marginal
dorsal); Mv (marginal ventral); Pa (preanal); Ph (posthypostomal);
Pm (premarginal); S (supplementary); Sc (scutal); St (sternal).
(Reproduced with permission from Clifford et al., 1961;
copyrighted by the Entomological Society of America).

Host location	Head and axillary regions of body on lizards.
Life cycle	Hoogstraal and Kaiser (1960a) described the following: mating occurs on the host (mainly rabbits) while females feed. Once engorged, females may oviposit for 15–30 days. Eggs hatch in approximately 45–60 days. Depending on the ambient temperature, larvae engorge in 3–7 days, and molting occurs in 21–30 days. Nymphs engorge in 4–9 days (temperature-dependent), and molt 37–38 days later.
Host acquisition	By direct contact with organism in burrows in open dry forests, certain semi-desert areas, and rocky niches.
Symptoms	Heavy infestations may cause anemia, possibly resulting in death (Walker and Bezuidenhout, 1973).
Diagnosis	By demonstration of organism on body surface or cage environment.
Treatment	See Appendix I.

B. *Ixodes pacificus* (Fig. 117a–d)

Also called the "Western blacklegged tick." Adults parasitize deer, cattle, dogs, and other large mammals along the Pacific coast from southern British Columbia to Mexico west of the Cascade Mountains. The bites of *I. pacificus* can cause skin irritation and paralysis in humans, and this tick is a vector of the agents of tularemia and Lyme disease in the western part of the United States (Brown and Lane, 1992; Cheng, 1973; Lane et al., 1991).

Description

Adult female: body measures unfed, 2.64 mm long by 1.14 mm wide, and engorged, up to 9.0 mm long; unfed body nearly elliptical in shape; scutum brown-black in color, slightly longer than wide, reaching approximately half the length of the body in unfed specimens, and measuring 1.26–1.44 mm long by 1.26–1.36 mm wide; cervical grooves present but indistinct; punctations fine and numerous; setae on scutum similar to those on the postscutal area but usually a little longer; capitulum brown-black in color and measuring 0.84 mm long by 0.45 mm wide; basis capituli with an even convex curvature dorsally, lateral margins abrupt, converging posteriorly; cornua absent; palpi long, bluntly rounded apically, flattened on inner faces, and palpal article I with a triangular point; article II longer than III; transverse suture visible; hypostome long, rounded apically, measuring approximately 0.54 mm in length; dentition 4/4 in distal portion, then 3/3, and 2/2 at base; leg tarsi long and tapering with small subapical humps on tarsus I (absent on others); long, spinelike ventral setae on legs; coxae smooth, mildly convex with very long setae; internal spur on coxa I, but absent on II, III, and IV; spiracular plate suboval with the longer axis transverse, and goblet cells moderate in number and size.

Adult male: body oval measuring unfed 2.19 mm long by 1.32 mm wide; scutal surface almost equally convex on both ends and measuring 2.04 mm long by 1.02 mm wide; capitulum surface punctate and measuring 0.48 mm long by

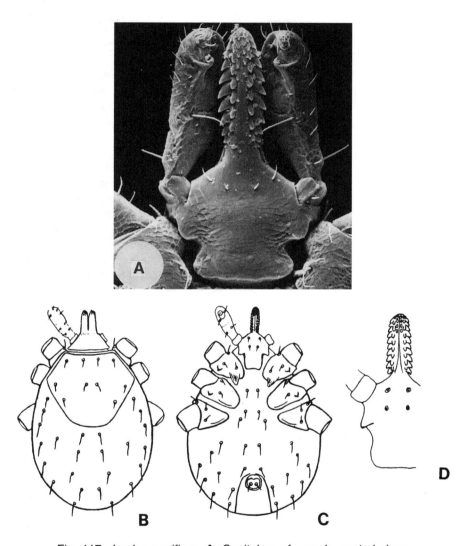

Fig. 117. *Ixodes pacificus.* **A.** Capitulum of nymph, ventral view; **B.** Larva, dorsal view; **C.** Larva, ventral view; **D.** Capitulum of larva, ventral view. (A, courtesy of the U.S. National Tick Collection; B–D, reproduced with permission from Webb et al., 1990).

0.30 mm wide; basis mildly convex; cornua absent; palps broad, rounded apically, with surface depressed at the suture between articles II and III; hypostome measures approximately 0.33 mm long, with large lateral and small median denticles; ventral surface with numerous, fine setae; legs similar to female, but metatarsus on leg I shorter; coxae similar to female, but internal spur on coxa I shorter; spiracular plate oval with longer axis longitudinal; genital aperture at level of coxae III.

Nymph (Fig. 117a): scutum subcircular, slightly wider than long; cervical grooves distinct, but fading before reaching posterolateral margins; scutum with few, small scutal punctations and setae; capitulum length 0.30 mm; basis subtriangular and 0.24 mm wide; in ventral view, basis capituli long, with broadly rounded posterior margin; cornua present but small; palps long, laterally nearly straight, inner edges convex; article I of palp with faint ventral tooth; capitulum with few setae; hypostome rounded apically and measuring approximately 0.19 mm long; dentition 3/3, then 2/2 with lateral teeth pointed and larger; metatarsus on leg I approximately half as long as tarsus; coxae similar to male; spiracular plate subcircular with longer axis transverse; respiratory pore central; goblet cells few and scattered.

Larva (Fig. 117b–d): body length 0.339–0.401 mm, 0.90–0.102 mm in unfed specimens; setae comprise 4 pairs of central dorsals, 7 pairs of marginal dorsals, 1 pair of dorsal supplementaries, 4 pairs of marginal ventrals, and 4 pairs of premarginals; basis capituli with prominent auriculae; hypostomal dentition 3/3 apically, then 2/2; cornua indistinct; coxae I and II with external spurs; coxa I with internal spur.

Host(s)   Larvae and nymphs on reptiles, birds and small mammals. Reptile hosts are garter snakes, *Thamnophis* spp., and North American, Pacific costal region lizards (particularly those in the genus *Sceloporus*) (Arthur and Snow, 1968; Bishopp and Trembly, 1945; Cooley and Kohls, 1943, 1945; Durden and Keirans, 1996; Easton and Goulding, 1974; Gregson, 1935, 1956; Jellison, 1934; Lane, 1990; Lane and Loye, 1989; Manweiler et al., 1990, 1992; Philip and Burgdorfer, 1961; U.S. Dept. of Agriculture, 1965).

Host location
Body surface, especially above forelegs and behind ear orifice in lizards.

Life cycle
Arthur and Snow (1968) reared *I. pacificus* in the laboratory. Females were fed on guinea pigs for 10–11 days. The pre-oviposition period was 11–16 days, and the oviposition period was approximately 33–40 days with 790–1300 eggs being laid per female. Larvae hatched in 53–55 days, and molted to nymphs in 37–38 days. Nymphs fed for 7–11 days, molting to adults in approximately 30 days. *I. pacificus* is a three-host tick. In California, larvae and nymphs of *I. pacificus* each attach for approximately 8 days and 16 days, respectively, to the iguanid lizards *Sceloporus graciosus* and *Uta stansburiana* (Goldberg and Bursey, 1991). Adults parasitize mammals, whereas immatures feed on birds, mammals, or reptiles (Beck, et al., 1963; Bishopp and Trembley, 1945; Brown and Lane, 1992; Gregson, 1935, 1956; Jellison, 1934; Mohr, et al., 1964). Also see Family Ixodidae above.

Host acquisition
By direct contact with organism.

Symptoms
Heavy infestations may cause anemia, possibly resulting in death (Walker and Bezuidenhout, 1973). Dunlop (1993) showed that western fence lizards, *Sceloporus occidentalis,* parasitized with both malaria parasites and *I. pacificus* nymphs, had significantly lower body condition than lizards with one or neither parasite.

Diagnosis
By demonstration of organism on body surface or cage environment.

Treatment
See Appendix I.

C. *Ixodes ricinus* (syns., *reduvius, sanguisugus, fuscus, lacertae*)
(Figs. 118–120).

Also called the "castor-bean tick" or "sheep tick," its bite can cause skin irritation and paralysis in humans. This tick is a vector of the causative agents of tick-borne encephalitis, louping ill, Lyme disease, and babesiosis in Europe and/or Asia (Schmidt and Roberts, 1985; Sonenshine, 1993).

Description

Adult female: body length 3.0–3.9 mm, width 1.6–2.3 mm; scutum more than half body length in unfed specimens; body oval with numerous short setae; basis capituli, scutum and legs brown-black; marginal folds distinct in unfed individuals; posterior margin of basis capituli distinctly concave; cornua lacking; porose areas pear-shaped or oval; palps long, moderately broad and rounded apically; auriculae as small ridges; scutum slightly longer than wide, broadly rounded posteriorly; scapulae well developed and pointed; scutal punctations numerous, small and concentrated posteriorly; all coxae with long setae; long, tapering internal spur on coxa I; internal spurs lacking on coxae II–IV; short external spurs on all coxae; spiracular plate large and oval.

Adult male: body length 2.2–2.6 mm, width 1.2–1.4 mm; body somewhat narrowed anteriorly and broadly rounded posteriorly; dark red-brown to black in color; basis capituli approximately 1.45 mm, longer than broad, surface with few punctations, posterior margin almost straight; cornua absent; auriculae as small lateral prominences connected by a broad ridge; palps short, very broad and apically rounded; hypostome large with 8 distinct lateral teeth; dentition 4/4 on apical half; scutal scapulae long and rounded; scutal punctations numerous, fine, and evenly distributed; numerous fine, long setae and fine punctations on all ventral plates; coxae as in female; spiracular plate large and rounded with numerous goblet cells.

Nymph (Fig. 118): scutum circular, broadly rounded posteriorly; scapulae short and rounded; scutal

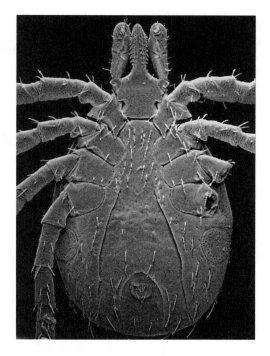

Fig. 118. *Ixodes ricinus.* Nymph, ventral view.
(Photo courtesy of the U.S. National Tick Collection).

Fig. 119. *Ixodes ricinus* larvae and nymphs parasitizing the viviparous lizard,
Lacerta vivipara. (Photo courtesy of Rudolf Malkmus).

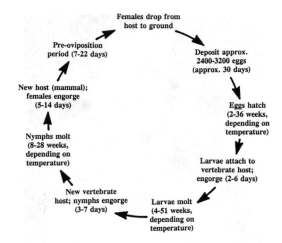

Fig. 120. Life cycle of *Ixodes ricinus*. (Adapted from Soulsby, 1968).

surface smooth with sparse punctations and setae; basis capituli with pointed, posterolaterally directed cornua of moderate size; posterior margin of basis almost straight; palps long and widest at segment III; auriculae large and directed posteriorly; hypostome rounded apically; dentition 3/3 distally, 2/2 proximally; coxae I–IV with small external spurs with that on coxa I being largest; tapering internal spur on coxa I; coxae II–IV lacking internal spurs; spiracular plate subcircular with few goblet cells.

Larva: body oval in unfed specimens; basis capituli with smooth inpunctate surface with almost straight posterior margin; cornua extended laterally; palps long and almost parallel-sided except for slight basal narrowing; auriculae as distinct projections; hypostome relatively short and broad; dentition 3/3 distally, then 2/2; scapulae short and rounded; coxae I–III with distinct external spurs; coxa I with a small internal spur; no internal spurs on coxae II or III.

Host(s)   Larvae and nymphs commonly parasitize lizards (Fig. 119) of Europe, northwestern Asia, and North Africa (Aeschlimann, 1972; Aeschlimann et al., 1965; Bauwens et al., 1983; Feider, 1964; Gina, 1973; Hoogstraal, 1966, 1967; Lác et al., 1972; Lapage, 1962, 1968; Malkmus, 1985, 1995; Markov et al., 1964a,b; Matuschka et al., 1991; Morel et al., 1961; Nosek et al., 1962; Pearson and Tamarind, 1973; Reichenbach-Klinke and Elkan, 1965; Sixl et al., 1971; Tovornik and Brelih, 1980; Turianin, 1963).

Host location	Body folds and surface, especially behind ear orifice and above forelegs in lizards (Fig. 119).
Life cycle (Fig. 120)	Three-host tick: larval and nymphal stages on lizards, birds, or small mammals; adults on domestic and wild mammals. Also see Family Ixodidae above.
Host acquisition	By direct contact with organism.
Symptoms	Heavy infestations may cause anemia, possibly resulting in death (Walker and Bezuidenhout, 1973).
Diagnosis	By demonstration of organism on body surface (Fig. 119) or cage environment.
Treatment	See Appendix I.

D. *Ixodes scapularis* (syns., *dammini, ozarkus*) (Fig. 121a–i)

Also called the "blacklegged tick," it is common to the eastern and south-central part of the United States (Keirans et al., 1996b). It sometimes bites humans and can cause pain and generalized malaise for a short period of time (Schmidt and Roberts, 1985). More importantly, this tick is the principal vector of the causative agents of Lyme disease and human babesiosis in the eastern United States (Anderson and Magnarelli, 1994; Durden and Keirans, 1996; Keirans et al., 1996b). In the laboratory, both southeastern five-lined skinks, *Eumeces inexpectatus,* and green anoles, *Anolis carolinensis,* harbored the Lyme disease bacterium for several days; up to 34% of feeding immature stages of *I. scapularis* were shown to become infected (Levin et al., 1996).

Description	Adult female: body oval in shape, measuring 2.30–2.70 mm long by 1.43–1.89 mm wide when unfed, and engorged up to 10.0 mm long by 7.25 mm wide; scutum brown-black in color, slightly longer than wide, extending slightly more than half the length of the body, measuring 1.38 mm

long by 1.20 mm wide; cervical grooves indistinct and fading before reaching posterolateral margins; scutal setae fine and long, punctations numerous and fine; capitulum brown-black in color, and measuring 0.96 long by 0.51 wide; basis capituli with even curvature dorsally, lateral margins abrupt, converging posteriorly; surface of capitulum smooth with short setae; cornua distinct; palpi long, rounded apically; article II much longer than III; 2 long setae on medial surface of palpal article I; hypostome long, rounded apically, measuring 0.51–0.59 mm in length; apically, dentition 4/4, then 3/3, and 2/2 to hypostome base; legs with small subapical humps; coxae smooth, mildly convex, with long setae; long internal spur on coxa I, tapering and pointed, absent on II, III, and IV; short, external spurs on all coxae; spiracular plate oval, measuring 0.33–0.39 mm long by 0.30–0.33 mm wide; goblet cells numerous.

Adult male: body oval, measuring 1.80–2.24 mm long by 1.14–1.50 mm wide; scutum almost equally convex at both ends, cervical grooves faint, and with numerous, long, fine setae; capitulum punctate; basis capituli flattened, lateral

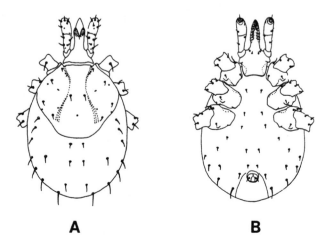

A   **B**

Fig. 121. *Ixodes scapularis.* **A.** Larva, dorsal view; **B.** Larva, ventral view;

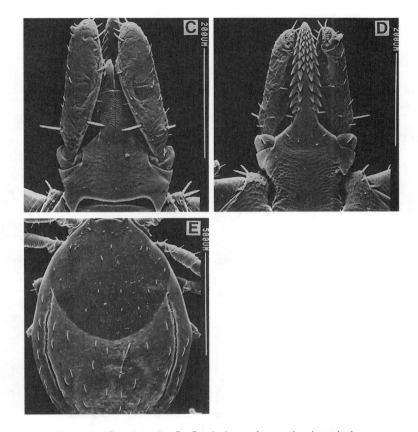

Fig. 121. Continued **C.** Capitulum of nymph, dorsal view;
D. Capitulum of nymph, ventral view; **E.** Scutum of nymph;

margins abrupt, straight and convergent margins
posteriorly; cornua absent; palps short, broad,
rounded apically; hypostome approximately
0.30 mm long; ventral surface with numerous
fine, long setae; legs and coxae similar to female; spiracular plate very large, ellipsoidal,
and goblet cells very numerous.

Nymph (Fig. 121c–e): body length 0.94–1.32 mm,
breadth 0.70–0.98 mm in unfed specimens; scutum longer than wide, broadly rounded posteriorly and measuring 0.63 mm long by 0.57 wide;
cervical grooves shallow, convergent anteriorly,
divergent posteriorly; surface of scutum smooth

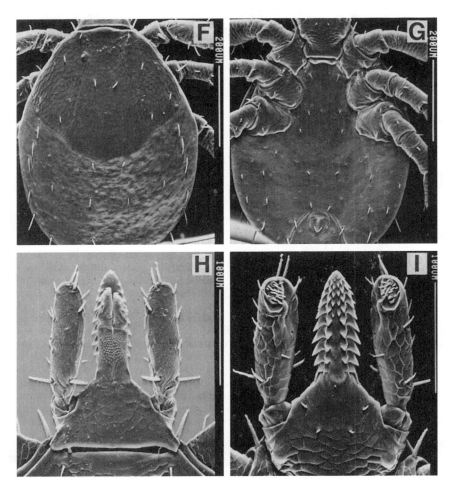

Fig. 121. Continued   **F.** Larva, dorsal view; **G.** Larva, ventral view;
H. Capitulum of larva, dorsal view; **I.** Capitulum of larva, ventral view.
(A, B, reproduced with permission from Clifford et al., 1961; C–E,
reproduced with permission from Keirans et al., 1996b;
copyrighted by the Entomological Society of America;
F–I courtesy of the U.S. National Tick Collection).

with sparse, distinct punctations and no setae; legs similar to those of adults; coxae similar to adults, but with internal spur on coxa I much shorter; spiracular plate subcircular with a few small, scattered goblet cells.

Larva (Fig. 121f–i): body length 0.505–0.601 mm, breadth 0.381–0.479 mm in unfed specimens; 11 pairs of dorsal body setae (3 pairs of central dorsals, 7 pairs of marginal dorsals, 1 pair of supplementaries); 13 pairs of ventral body setae (3 pairs of sternals, 2 pairs of preanals, 4 pairs of premarginals, 4 pairs of marginals) plus 1 pair on anal valves; basis capituli with small auriculae; hypostome 0.099–0.121 mm long; dentition 3/3 apically, then 2/2 to base; scutum broader than long, lacking lateral carinae, with 5 pairs of scutal setae; coxae I–III each with small external spur; coxae II and III each with small internal spur.

Host(s)   Adults parasitize medium-sized to large mammals, whereas immatures feed on a wide variety of lizards, birds, and mammals in eastern North America (Anderson and Magnarelli, 1994; Bishopp and Trembley, 1945; Clymer et al., 1970; Cooley and Kohls, 1945; Eads et al., 1956; Durden and Keirans, 1996; Keirans et al., 1996b; Levine et al., 1997). Lizard hosts include the green anole, *Anolis carolinensis,* six-lined racerunner, *Cnemidophorus sexlineatus,* southeastern five-lined skink, *Eumeces inexpectatus,* five-lined skink, *E. fasciatus,* broad-headed skink, *E. laticeps,* slender glass lizard, *Ophisaurus attenuatus*, eastern glass lizard, *O. centralis,* and eastern fence lizard, *Sceloporus undulatus.*

Host location   On skinks, larvae are usually found between the toes, and larvae and nymphs in leg axillae and just behind the ears; on glass lizards, larvae and nymphs are found along the lateral folds (Apperson et al., 1993; Oliver et al., 1993a).

Life cycle   Three-host tick: larval and nymphal stages on lizards, birds, or small mammals; adults on large mammals. Also see Family Ixodidae above.

Host acquisition By direct contact with organism, primarily in forest habitats.

Symptoms Heavy infestations may cause anemia, possibly resulting in death (Walker and Bezuidenhout, 1973). The absence of an immune response by broad-headed skinks, *Eumeces laticeps,* to parasitism by immature *I. scapularis* has been documented by Galbe and Oliver (1992).

Diagnosis By demonstration of organism on body surface or cage environment.

Treatment See Appendix I.

E. Other *Ixodes* spp. affecting reptiles

I. asanumai is the only *Ixodes* sp. tick known in which all active stages (adults, in addition to larvae and nymphs) typically feed exclusively on reptiles. *Eumeces okadae,* a Japanese skink, is the normal host (Hayashi and Hasegawa, 1984a,b).

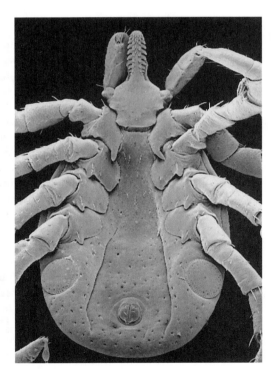

Fig. 122. *Ixodes persulcatus.* Nymph, ventral view.
(Photo courtesy of the U.S. National Tick Collection).

I. kashmiricus was reported from an unspecified lizard of the western Himalayas (Rao et al., 1973). This central Asian tick, however, parasitizes primarily mammals. *Ixodes kashmiricus* belongs to the *I. ricinus* complex (Keirans et al., 1992).

I. nipponensis larvae and nymphs frequently parasitize the Japanese grass lizard, *Takydromus tachydromoides,* in Japan, Korea, and adjacent regions (Fujimoto, 1994a,b; 1996; Fujita and Takada, 1978, 1997; Hayashi and Hasegawa, 1984a; Telford, 1997; Yamaguti et al., 1971). This tick is also a member of the *I. ricinus* complex (Keirans et al., 1992).

I. persulcatus (Fig. 122), another member of the *I. ricinus* complex, frequently parasitizes lizards in eastern Europe, and northern and northwestern Asia. It is especially common in taiga biomes and is often called the "taiga tick." *Ixodes persulcatus* is medically important because it can transmit several pathogens including those that cause tick-borne encephalitis and Lyme disease (Filippova, 1985). Immature stages of this tick typically feed on reptiles (virtually every lizard and tortoise species within its range), birds, or small mammals, while adults usually feed on large mammals including humans.

I. redikorzevi immatures were reported from the emerald lizard, *Lacerta viridis,* by Arthur (1965) who stated that many species of mammals, birds, and reptiles are parasitized by this tick. Pomerantsev (1950) reported immatures from the sheltopusik, *Ophisaurus apodus,* in Russia. The range of this tick extends from southwest Russia west to Bulgaria, Greece, and Egypt (Arthur, 1965).

CHAPTER 5

LABORATORY PROCEDURES FOR THE HERPETOCULTURIST

The laboratory techniques presented in this chapter are suitable for collecting and examining parasitic arthropods. When specimens must be submitted to a diagnostic laboratory, be sure to include the scientific and common names of the host, locality (including state, county, town, road, river, etc.), date the host was obtained, origin of host if it is exotic, where on reptile parasite was found, type of preservative, and the name of the person who collected and/or owns the animal.

EQUIPMENT NEEDED FOR PREPARATION AND EXAMINATION OF ARTHROPODS

Microscopes

A binocular dissecting microscope with magnifications of at least 10X and 20X is suitable for arthropod examinations. Total magnifications of 40X to 80X will easily permit diagnostic structures of ticks to be visualized. It is also useful to have a binocular, compound microscope. Anyone obtaining such a microscope will want to use it for a wide variety of examinations, and therefore it should have total magnifications ranging from 40X to at least 200X.

Lens paper and eyeglass cleaning solution

These items are used to clean microscope oculars, objectives, condenser, and illumination lamp. Although xylene is often used as a cleanser, eyeglass cleaning solution is less damaging to equipment.

Microscope slides, cover glasses, and glass-marking pen

Use any brand of 25 × 75 mm (3 × 1 in.) glass slides, and No. 2 cover glasses. Circular cover glasses of 8 or 12mm in diameter are usually used for slide-mounting small arthropods.

When marking microscope slides and collection containers, use non-water-soluble pens. Slides can be labelled permanently using a diamond marker or gummed labels affixed to one side of the slide onto which data can be inked.

Leak-proof, screw-cap vials or plastic, 35mm, slide film containers, masking tape, paraffin, Parafilm®, clear plastic bags, and rubberbands

With a limited budget, plastic slide film containers may be used for collecting and preserving arthropods, and when sending them to a laboratory for identification.

Masking tape may be used as a substitute for Parafilm® when leak-proof vials are unavailable. Tape may also be used for container labels.

Plastic bags make suitable containers for retaining a dead host until it can be transported to a laboratory for ectoparasite recovery.

Other supplies

Anyone performing arthropod identifications should also have available wide-mouth containers such as beakers (400 ml; 800 ml), cheesecloth, paper towels, clear and brown dropping bottles or suitable substitutes, glass-stoppered bottles, appropriately sized Petri dishes (30 × 10 mm; 60 × 15 mm), straight pins or small sewing needles, and a waste container. It will also be necessary to have a scale that weighs in 0.1-gram increments, Pasteur pipets, and a hot plate.

PREPARING SPECIMENS FOR MAILING

If more than one vial of specimens are being mailed at the same time, be sure to label each one with the host's scientific name (and any other identification necessary to prevent the possibility of errors), the date collected, and the type of preservative used. Be careful not to cross-contaminate samples. A separate collection data sheet, incorporating information for all submitted collections, should also be submitted.

Place arthropods in a vial containing the preservative of choice (see LONG-TERM PRESERVATION below), and cap the vial securely. If the container is not leak-proof, secure the cap with Parafilm® or masking tape. Tape can also serve as the label to identify the sample.

COLLECTING AND KILLING ARTHROPOD SPECIMENS

When collecting arthropods, it is essential not to damage wings, legs, bristles, feeding structures, and other identifying features. Before detaching ticks from a dead reptile, brush the carcass with glycerol or paraffin. This method prevents damage to the hypostome, an important taxonomic structure for identification. Ticks can be collected from living reptiles by following the instructions provided in Appendix I.

Boardman's solution may be the best method for killing ticks because the solution relaxes them so they die with their appendages outstretched. Leave them in the relaxant until they no longer move, then transfer them to a preservative or prepare them (larvae only) for whole mounts. Boardman's solution is prepared by mixing together 97 ml of 20% ethyl alcohol and 3 ml of ether. Live ticks can also be placed directly into a vial of 70% ethanol for both killing and preservation.

When living mosquito larvae and pupae are placed directly in alcohol, they tend to thrash violently, causing the loss of important bristles. When possible, collect these specimens with the water in which they were observed. Slowly heat the water until the insects stop moving. Using this killing technique, larvae maintain a raised head, and pupae their comma shape. Once dead, these specimens can either be placed in an insect preservative or prepared for whole mounts.

To identify larvae of myiasis-producing flies, they should be raised to adults as described below under RAISING MYIASIS-PRODUCING FLIES AND LARVAL IDENTIFICATION. When many larvae are recovered, some may be raised to maturity while the remainder can be killed and mailed to a diagnostic laboratory. The easiest method for killing fly larva is to drop them into water near the boiling point. Next, allow the water to cool, and transfer the larvae to 70–80% ethyl alcohol for shipping. Dropping live larvae directly into a vial of 70% ethanol will also kill them, but they may turn black because of bacterial action. This problem can be avoided by first dropping larvae into boiling water for 5 minutes before placing them in alcohol.

SHORT-TERM PRESERVATION

Alcohol preservation

The simplest and least expensive method for preserving arthropods (except scaled specimens such as adult mosquitoes) is to place them in a 70–80% solution of ethyl alcohol. Specimens preserved in alcohol for prolonged periods can become hard. However, tick specimens have been retained in 70% ethanol for more than 100 years without significant hardening.

To make alcohol solutions, begin with 95% ethyl alcohol. Dilute the 95% alcohol with an amount of distilled water that will give the desired percentage. For example, if 70% alcohol is needed, dilute 70 ml of 95% ethyl alcohol with 25 ml of distilled water. As one can see, 70 + 25 = 95.

Carbon tetrachloride

The coloration of some ticks can be preserved in this reagent. Unfortunately, they become very hard and brittle.

LONG-TERM PRESERVATION

Insect preservative (Meyer and Olsen, 1980)

95% ethyl alcohol . . . . 53 ml
Ethyl acetate . . . . 15 ml
Benzene . . . . 5 ml
Distilled water . . . . 27 ml

Mix reagents together and store in a glass-stoppered bottle.

Kryger's Solution

Matheson (1950) reported that this preservative maintains adult insects in a soft
and pliable condition.

33% acetic acid . . . . 62.5 ml
Mercuric chloride solution (1:1000) . . . . 62.5 ml*
Glycerine . . . . 65.5 ml
95% ethyl alcohol. . . . . 500.0 ml
Distilled water . . . . 312.5 ml

*1 g mercuric chloride powder to 1000 ml distilled water

Mix reagents together and store in a glass-stoppered bottle.

CLEARING AND MOUNTING ARTHROPOD SPECIMENS FOR EXAMINATION

Generally, the cost of preparing arthropods for permanent whole mounts is expensive and time-consuming. Nevertheless, many herpetoculturists enjoy the challenge of such sophisticated techniques of reptile husbandry.

Most engorged or heavily chitinized parasitic arthropods cannot be examined unless they are made transparent. They may have to be treated with an alkaline solution to lighten them. Many immature stages, and already transparent or delicate specimens, do not require an alkaline treatment. In fact, such specimens must occasionally be stained with orange G or acid fuchsin to make the identifying characters more distinct. Other parasitic arthropods that should not be cleared for identification are nymphal and adult ticks, heteropteran bugs, and adult Diptera (flies). Rather, ticks and bugs should be retained in 70% ethanol and briefly dried for low-power microscopical examination and identification before being returned to the ethyl alcohol. Adult Diptera should be pinned or carded as dry specimens. Techniques for clearing specimens and mounting them on microscope slides are as follows:

Clearing

Gently pour the specimen and preservative into an appropriately sized glass Petri dish. While the specimen is still in the preservative, pierce its abdomen with a small needle to allow the clearing agent to penetrate, and to prevent it from collapsing during the clearing and mounting procedures. When working with immature mosquitoes, drain off most of the preservative solution, so the insect sits on the bottom of the Petri dish. Once stable, pass the needle through the pleural membrane of the first abdominal segment. Do not place wings of mosquitoes or other flies in any solutions because scales used for identification purposes may be lost.

Completely drain the preservative from the Petri dish, and replace with distilled water. After 1 or 2 changes of water, replace the water with a 10% solution of potassium hydroxide (KOH). This solution is prepared by dissolving 10 g of potassium hydroxide pellets in 100 ml of distilled water. Depending on the type of arthropod, soak the specimen in KOH, at room temperature, for approximately 12–24 hours, or until it becomes lighter in color (slightly transparent). Although the process can be hastened by warming the KOH solution, chitinous structures may be destroyed if the specimen is not watched carefully. Upon completion of the clearing process, replace the KOH solution with distilled water, and rinse the specimen 2 or 3 times to remove residual alkali. Proceed to the instructions for mounting. Small ectoparasites can be cleared in lactophenol or Nesbitt's solution instead of KOH for a safer, but slower, cleaning procedure. See PREFERRED METHODS FOR PREPARING MICROSCOPE SLIDES OF SMALL ECTOPARASITES below. Specimens to be cleared include fleas and larval ticks. Never attempt to clear nymphal or adult ticks because all diagnostic characters can be seen on their outer surfaces.

Mounting

Before beginning the mounting procedure, prepare microscope slides and cover glasses. Preclean them in a 1:1 solution of 95% ethyl alcohol and acetone and allow them to air-dry. While manipulating the slides, touch only the edges. Oil and grease on the surface of slides may prevent mounting medium from adhering well.

Before placing specimens in mounting medium, they must be dehydrated. This process can be accomplished by either of the two methods described as follows:

Cellosolve method

Drain the water from the Petri dish (from the clearing process) and add Cellosolve (ethylene glycol monoethyl ether). The specimen should be left in Cellosolve for approximately 24 hours to ensure dehydration and clearing, but Benton (1955) reports leaving specimens in the product for 2 weeks without damage. Specimens may be transferred directly from Cellosolve to the mounting medium of choice. The advantage of this method to the one described below is that it reduces the chances of damage to the specimens because they are handled fewer times.

Alcohol/xylene method

Drain the water from the Petri dish (from the clearing process) and proceed with the following series of alcohol baths:

1. 50% ethyl alcohol: soak the specimen for approximately 10 min.; drain and proceed to step 2.
2. 70% ethyl alcohol: soak the specimen for approximately 10 min.; drain and proceed to step 3.
3. 95% ethyl alcohol: soak the specimen for approximately 10 min.; drain and proceed to step 4.
4. 100% ethyl alcohol: soak the specimen for approximately 10 min.; drain, repeat step 4 once more, and proceed to step 5.
5. Xylene: soak the specimen until specimen sinks to bottom of the Petri dish and becomes transparent, (approximately 10 minutes) then proceed to step 6.
6. Draw up specimen in Pasteur pipet (or with a fine-wire loop or needle) and drop onto slide or cover glass. Quickly tip slide or cover glass and touch corner to paper towel to drain off excess xylene. Proceed to step 7.
7. Orient specimen to enhance taxonomic features; maneuver with needles under dissecting microscope, taking care not to allow it to dry out. Proceed to step 8. Note: a specimen that is too dry may develop air bubbles or stick to the slide or cover glass, preventing it from being moved and thereby damaging important structures. On the other hand, if the specimen is too wet, the structures will not stay where they are placed. Orienting specimens properly on slides requires considerable practice.
8. Drop mounting medium (e.g., Canada balsam) onto specimen and affix cover glass.

The best looking mounts are made by choosing the smallest size cover glass that will completely cover the specimen. Specimens should be oriented on a slide to ensure that important taxonomic features can be observed. Orient specimens perpendicular to the long axis of the microscope slide. Specimens that are flattened dorsoventrally should be mounted with the ventor up, facing the cover glass.

When applying a cover glass over a specimen in mountant, be sure the cover does not tilt to one side. It is important to use a proper amount of mounting medium, as too much mountant will cause a specimen to shift when the cover glass is applied. Specimens slide-mounted in this manner can be examined immediately but it is advisable to fully label each slide first. Also, it is advisable to dry slide preparations in a slide oven at 45°C for 1–4 weeks before attempting a detailed examination.

PREFERRED METHODS FOR PREPARING MICROSCOPE SLIDES OF SMALL ECTOPARASITES

Because KOH is a basic corrosive, it can soften and damage some poorly scle-rotized specimens. Also, small specimens are occasionally lost because of the large number of different solutions into which they are placed. While KOH/Canada bal-sam techniques have the advantage of producing permanent slide preparations, the harshness of the KOH and the large number of steps involved are not popular with many workers. Fleas and some dipteran larvae, on the other hand, are heavily scle-rotized and are best cleared in KOH.

The lactophenol/Hoyer's method is used to clear tick larvae. Lactophenol is the clearing agent while Hoyer's medium is the mountant. Nesbitt's fluid can be used in place of lactophenol to clear difficult specimens.

Lactophenol (Krantz, 1978)

Prepare by adding the following in sequence:

Lactic acid . . . . 50 parts
Phenol crystals. . . . . 25 parts
Distilled water . . . . 25 parts

Lactophenol is an acid corrosive and does not tend to soften the exoskeleton of specimens. Therefore, specimens can be left in lactophenol to clear for a week or more without damage. Large or blood-engorged specimens should be punctured with a minute pin to facilitate clearing.

Nesbitt's fluid (Krantz, 1978)

This solution is a more powerful clearing agent and can be used in place of lac-tophenol to clear heavily chitinized specimens or those which have been stored in alcohol for years and do not clear in lactophenol. Prepare as follows:

Chloral hydrate . . . . 40 g
Distilled water . . . . 25 ml
Concentrated hydrochloric acid . . . . 2.5 ml

Hoyer's medium (Krantz, 1978)

Prepare by adding the following in sequence:

Distilled water . . . . 50 ml
Gum arabic (amorphic) . . . . 30 g
Chloral hydrate . . . . 200 g
Glycerin. . . . . 20 ml

When specimens have cleared sufficiently in lactophenol or Nesbitt's fluid, they should be transferred into 2–4 changes of distilled water until the water is no longer cloudy. A drop of Hoyer's medium is then placed in the center of a clean microscope slide. The specimen is transferred into this medium, and covered with a cover slip. The specimen should be labelled and dried in a slide oven at 45°C for 1–4 weeks before examining.

ONE STEP CLEARING AND MOUNTING PROCEDURES

The following procedures allow the clearing and mounting of living or preserved specimens in one step.

Berlese's chloral-gum solution (Meyer and Olsen, 1980)

This medium is recommended for hard-to-clear specimens.

Distilled water . . . . 50 ml
Acacia gum arabic (crystalline) . . . . 40 g
Glycerin. . . . . 20 ml
Chloral hydrate . . . . 50 g
Glacial acetic acid. . . . . 3 ml

Dissolve the gum arabic in the distilled water. Kranz (1978) advises against using powdered gum arabic because minute particles do not wet entirely. Add the glycerin and acetic acid. Place the chloral hydrate in a beaker, and allow it to melt before adding it to the other reagents. Mix thoroughly and strain the solution through several layers of cheesecloth. Store in a glass-stoppered bottle and use as a mounting medium.

Downes Mounting Medium (Matheson, 1950)

This medium is especially useful for mounting mites, mosquito larvae, and adult mosquito parts such as the genitalia.

Dissolve polyvinyl alcohol (PVA powder) in 56 ml of warm distilled water until a thick syrup is produced. To this warm stock solution add 22 ml each of lactic acid and phenol (liquid), and mix until the solution clears. If bubbles form, heat the mixture and allow it to stand until it is clear. Store in a glass-stoppered bottle and use as a mounting medium.

Whole mounts made with this mounting medium can be heated if rapid clearing is desired.

RINGING SPECIMENS MOUNTED IN AQUEOUS MEDIA

Only the KOH/Canada balsam slide preparation technique produces permanent slide mounts. Because all the other mounting media mentioned are aqueous, slide-mounts prepared using them are subject to crystallization, loss of clarity, or worse scenarios such as fungal growth. These occurrences are more common if slides are stored in a humid environment. The "ringing" technique described here can prevent these phenomena from occurring.

The principle behind ringing is to completely encircle the mounting medium/air interface along the edge of the cover slip with an impervious substance. Currently, the most popular and effective agent for ringing slides is Glyptal® which is sold as a waterproofing paint for electrical circuits (Krantz, 1978; Travis, 1978). A circle of Glyptal® should be applied around the cover slip after the slide preparation has oven-dried for 1 week. The slide is typically placed on a turntable. A small artist's brush is used to apply the Glyptal® by holding the brush against the edge of the cover slip while rotating the turntable. Although use of a turntable provides a uniformly circular preparation, the Glyptal® can also be applied using the brush alone. After applying Glyptal® to the slides, replace them in the oven to dry further; for more impervious preparations, a second coat of Glyptal® should be added a week later. The finished slide preparation should then be oven-dried for an additional week before being stored in a slide box.

STORING WHOLE MOUNTS

It is preferable to store whole mounts in a slide box placed in a cool, dark place. Slide boxes should be set on end in such a way that the slides within are in a horizontal position. Although the mounting medium is hard, it is a fluid and specimens will shift over time when they are stored vertically.

RAISING MYIASIS-PRODUCING FLIES AND LARVAL IDENTIFICATION

Place approximately 1 inch of moist sand in a wide-mouth, pint-sized jar to serve as the substrate. Onto the sand, place about 1 teaspoon of canned cat food (dog food may contain too much fat) and a large piece of leafy vegetable. Deposit the maggot(s) into the jar. Cover the jar with several layers of cheesecloth held in place with a rubberband. Set aside in a fly-free, warm room. When the cat food becomes rancid, replace it. It may not be necessary to replace the leafy green, as some fly larvae feed on *decaying* vegetable matter. After the maggot burrows into the sand, remove the food. Check the jar daily for a fly to emerge. In addition to preserving the fly, also preserve the puparium.

Maggots that cannot be reared should either be preserved and mailed to a diagnostic laboratory or prepared for identification by mounting them on microscope slides. Although specific identifications usually cannot be made by larvae, it is possible to determine the family to which they belong. This is achieved by examining the posterior spiracles. The following key to third stage larvae that parasitize reptiles has been modified from Matheson (1950):

1. Larva typically resembling that of housefly (Fig. 123); body slender,
   cylindrical, tapering anteriorly and more or less truncate posteriorly
   2
   Larva large, stout, resembling that of the cattle warble, *Hypoderma* spp.;
   cylindrical or more or less flattened, depressed or pear-shaped (Fig. 124). . . 7
2. Last apparent segment (anal) with a concavity in which are located spiracles
   (see Fig. 7c, Chapter 2); each dorsal cornua of pharyngeal sclerite with deep,
   posterior incision. . . . . Family Sarcophagidae

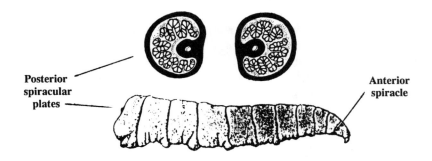

Posterior
spiracular
plates

Anterior
spiracle

Fig. 123. Housefly larva *Musca domestica.* (Reproduced
with permission from Matheson, 1950; courtesy of Cornell University Press).

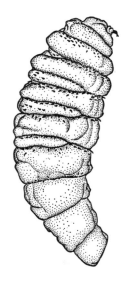

Fig. 124. *Dermatobia hominis.* Larva, full grown.
(Reproduced from Matheson, 1950; courtesy of Cornell University Press).

(*Anolisomyia* spp., *Blaesoxipha* spp., *Cistudinomyia* spp., *Eumacronychia* spp., *Metoposarcophaga* spp.)

Last apparent segment (anal) without a concavity; spiracles more or less flush with posterior face of anal segment; dorsal cornua of pharyngeal sclerite without incision. 3

3. Slits of posterior spiracles long, slender, and nearly parallel to each other (Figs. 125–127) and directed to button area. . Family Calliphoridae (in part) 4

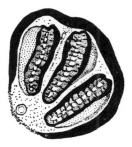

Fig. 125. *Cochliomyia macellaria*. Posterior spiracular plates. (Reproduced with permission from Matheson, 1950; courtesy of Cornell University Press).

Fig. 126. *Calliphora vomitoria*. Posterior spiracular plates. (Reproduced with permission from Matheson, 1950; courtesy of Cornell University Press).

Fig. 127. *Lucilia* (= *Phaenicia*) *sericata*. Posterior spiracular plates. (Reproduced with permission from Matheson, 1950; courtesy of Cornell University Press).

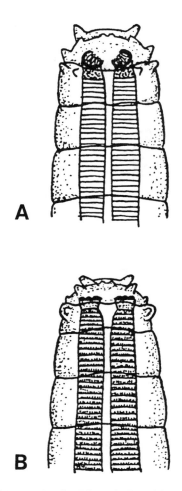

Fig. 128. Posterior end of larva. **A.** *Cochliomyia hominivorax;* **B.** *C. macellaria.*
(Reproduced with permission from Matheson, 1950;
courtesy of Cornell University Press).

Mouth
hooks

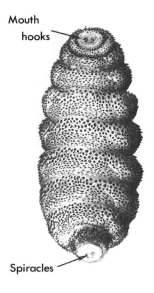

Spiracles

Fig. 129. *Cuterebra* sp. Third stage larva.
(Reproduced with permission from Baird, 1971).

4. Peritreme of posterior spiracles complete and with a distinct button (Figs. 126, 127) . . . . *Calliphora* spp., *Phaenicia* spp.
   Peritreme not complete and button weak, scarcely discernible 5
5. Posterior spiracles lacking a button, not indicated. 6
6. Tracheal trunks extending from posterior spiracles deeply pigmented for some distance (Fig. 128a). The true screwworm of America . . . .
   . . . . *Cochliomyia hominivorax*
   Tracheal trunks extending from posterior spiracles not pigmented
   (Fig. 128b). . . . . *C. macellaria*
7. Each posterior spiracle with numerous small openings but without well-defined slits (Fig. 125) 8
8. Mouth hooks well developed. 9
9. Mouth hooks not stout; body thick with spines or stout scales (Fig. 129); posterior spiracles divided into plates. . . . . *Cuterebra* spp.

APPENDIX I

PARASITICIDES USED IN THE TREATMENT OF TICKS AND FLIES FEEDING ON REPTILES

See table on following pages.

Parasiticides Used in the Treatment of Ticks and Flies Feeding on Reptiles[a]

Therapeutic	Dosage	Reference	Administration	Comments
Ivermectin[b]	0.2 mg/kg	Funk, 1988 Rosskopf, Jr., 1992	IM	Repeat in 2 weeks or, Repeat weekly for 3 doses.
	0.75 mg/kg	Thiruthalinathan et al., 1995	SQ	Single dose.
	0.5 cc (5 mg) per qt water (conc. of 1% sol. Ivomec)	Abrahams, 1992	Spray[c]	Repeated treatments were unnecessary. **DO NOT USE IN CHELONIANS.**
Dichlorvos-impregnated pest strips[d]	6.0 mm per 0.28 cubic meter of cage space	Frye, 1981		Suspend above cage in such a way that reptiles cannot make contact with strip. Use for 5 days and remove for 5 days; repeat cycle 3 to 5 times (Barnard, unpublished). Possible toxicity to small reptiles such as *Anolis* lizards (Marcus, 1981).
Manual removal				With sharply pointed forceps, grasp the tick as close to the skin as possible, and apply a steady, pulling pressure until the tick is removed. Rinse the wound with diluted povidone iodine and apply a topical antibiotic. Note: sharply pointed forceps are preferable to blunt ones

			because they allow close proximity to the skin, decreasing the chance of breaking off the tick's mouthparts.
Fly repellent[e]	As needed	Spray	Apply repellent to reptile's body to help prevent flies from depositing eggs or larvae on animal. Surgical removal of fly larvae is necessary. Debride necrotic tissue, flush cavity with diluted povidone iodine. Note: an application of Derma-Clens ointment will facilitate removal of debris.

[a] For availability, see Appendix II.

[b] Contraindicated in chelonians, or reptiles undergoing diazepam treatment, or those to be treated with diazepam within 10 days after being dosed with ivermectin (Frye, 1991).

[c] Ritchie and Harrison (1994) cautioned that when mixing propylene glycol-based ivermectin in water, the solution should be kept well mixed while using. Propylene glycol precipitates out of water. These authors reported that the water-soluble preparation designed for use in horses is easier to work with. They also warned that ivermectin is environmentally stable and highly toxic to fish and crustaceans. Therefore, the drug or its metabolites should not be allowed to contaminate water courses such as ponds, lakes, streams, or rivers.

[d] Avoid simultaneous administration or exposure to other cholinergic substances or hepatotoxic agents such as arecoline, carbamates, carbon tetrachloride, n-butyl chloride, organophosphates, and tetrachlorethylene (Georgi, 1974).

[e] Observe reptile for possible side effects when using fly repellents. If side effects are observed, change products or discontinue use altogether.

APPENDIX II

PRODUCTS MENTIONED IN TEXT

Product	Manufacturer/Availability*
Acetic acid (glacial)	See suppliers of chemicals and general labware listed below.
Acetone	See suppliers of chemicals and general labware listed below.
Acid fuchsin	See suppliers of chemicals and general labware listed below.
Beakers (200 mL, 400 mL, 800 mL)	See suppliers of chemicals and general labware listed below.
Benzene	See suppliers of chemicals and general labware listed below.
Carbon tetrachloride	See suppliers of chemicals and general labware listed below.
Cellosolve	See ethyl cellosolve below.
Chloral hydrate	See suppliers of chemicals and general labware listed below.
Cover glass forceps	See suppliers of chemicals and general labware listed below.
Derma-Clens ointment	SmithKline Beecham Animal Health 812 Springdale Drive, Exton, PA 19341
Dichlorvos-impregnated pest strips	ACE hardware stores.
Distilled water	Grocery markets and pharmacies; also see suppliers of chemicals and general labware listed below.
Dropping bottles	Select pharmacies; also see suppliers of chemicals and general labware listed below.
Ether	See suppliers of chemicals and general labware listed below.

Product	Manufacturer/Availability*
Ethyl acetate	See suppliers of chemicals and general labware listed below.
Ethyl alcohol (100%)	See suppliers of chemicals and general labware listed below.
Ethyl alcohol (95%)	Available as 180-proof grain alcohol in liquor stores.
Ethyl cellosolve	See suppliers of chemicals and general labware listed below.
Glycerin/glycerol	Select pharmacies; also see suppliers of chemicals and general labware listed below.
Glyptal®	Electrical supply stores.
Gum arabic (amorphic & crystalline)	See suppliers of chemicals and general labware listed below.
Hydrochloric acid (Reagent Grade)	See suppliers of chemicals and general labware listed below.
Ivermectin (Ivomec®)	Merck AgVet Division of Merck & Company, Inc. P.O. Box 2000 Rahway, NJ 07065
Lactic acid	See suppliers of chemicals and general labware listed below.
Lactophenol	See suppliers of chemicals and general labware listed below.
Lens paper	See suppliers of chemicals and general labware listed below.
Mercuric chloride (solution)	See suppliers of chemicals and general labware listed below.
Microscope	See suppliers of chemicals and general labware listed below.
Microscope slides	See suppliers of chemicals and general labware listed below.
Mounting medium	See suppliers of chemicals and general labware listed below.
Orange G	See suppliers of chemicals and general labware listed below.
Parafilm®	See suppliers of chemicals and general labware listed below.
Pasteur pipets	See suppliers of chemicals and general labware listed below.

Product	Manufacturer/Availability*
Petri dishes (35 mm × 10 mm)	See suppliers of chemicals and general labware listed below.
Phenol (crystal; liquid)	See suppliers of chemicals and general labware listed below.
Polyvinyl alcohol (PVA powder)	See suppliers of chemicals and general labware listed below.
Potassium hydroxide (KOH)	See suppliers of chemicals and general labware listed below.
Scale (0.1 g increments)	See suppliers of chemicals and general labware listed below.
Slide forceps	See suppliers of chemicals and general labware listed below.
Test tube brush	See suppliers of chemicals and general labware listed below.
Test tube holder	See suppliers of chemicals and general labware listed below.
Xylene	See suppliers of chemicals and general labware listed below.

*The mention of the products listed in the text, and their availability, does not imply endorsement by the authors. Products and distributors are listed to assist the reader. The list is not intended to be exhaustive; numerous other suppliers exist with equally good products.

SUPPLIERS

Aldrich, 1001 West Saint Paul Ave., Milwaukee, WI 53233

Baxter Scientific, 1430 Waukegan Rd., McGraw Park, IL 60085

BioQuip Products, 17803 LaSalle Ave., Gardena, CA 90248

Carolina Biological Supply Co., 2700 York Rd., Burlington, NC 27215

Cole-Parmer Co., 7425 North Oak Park Ave., Chicago, IL 60648

Edmund Scientific, 101 E. Gloucester Pike, Barrington, NJ 08007

EMD Labs, 4901 W. LeMoyne St., Chicago, IL 60651

Fisher Scientific, 711 Forbes Ave., Pittsburg, PA 15219

Frey Scientific, 905 Hickory Lane, P.O. Box 8101, Mansfield, OH 44901

Hardwood Products Co., Guilford, ME 04443

J. T. Baker, Inc., Phillipsburg, NJ 08865

Markson Sciences, 10201 S. 51st St., Phoenix, AZ 85044

Medical Supply Corporation of New Jersey, Inc., 1900 Adams Ave., Toms River, NJ 08753

Midwest Scientific, 228 Meramec Station Rd., P.O. Box 458, Valley Park, MO 63088

Nasco, 901 Janesville Ave., Fort Atkinson, WI 53538

Nebraska Scientific, 3823 Leavenworth St., Omaha, NE 68105

PGC Scientifics, P.O. Box 7277, Gaithersburg, MD 20898

Research Products International, 410 N. Business Center Dr., Mt. Prospect, IL 60056

Sargent-Welch, 7400 North Linder Ave., P.O. Box 1026, Skokie, IL 60077

Sigma Chemical Co., P.O. Box 14508, St. Louis, MO 63178

Southern Biological Supply, P.O. Box 368, McKenzie, TN 38201

Spectrum Chemical Mfg. Corp., 14422 South San Pedro St., Gardena, CA 90248

Thomas Scientific, Vine Street at Third, P.O. Box 779, Philadelphia, PA 19105

VWR Scientific, P.O. Box 1002, 600C Corporate Court, So. Plainfield, NJ 07080

Wards Natural Science, 5100 West Henrietta Rd., P.O. Box 92912, Rochester, NY 14692

APPENDIX III

SUMMARY OF HOSTS/PARASITES MENTIONED IN TEXT

Host	Parasite
Acanthodactylus boskians asper (fringe-fingered lizard)	*Hyalomma dromedarii* *Hyalomma franchinii*
Acanthodactylus scutellatus (fringe-fingered lizard)	*Hyalomma franchinii*
Acanthodactylus sp. (fringe-fingered lizard)	*Hyalomma impeltatum*
Agama caucasica (Caucasian agama)	*Haemaphysalis sulcata*
Agama himalayana (Himalayan agama)	*Haemaphysalis sulcata*
Agama hispida (spiny agama)	*Amblyomma sylvaticum*
Agama lehmanni (Turkmenian agama)	*Haemaphysalis sulcata*
Agama mutabilis (desert agama)	*Hyalomma franchinii*
Agama stellio (hardun)	*Haemaphysalis sulcata*
Agama tuberculata (agamid lizard)	*Haemaphysalis kashmirensis*
Agama spp. (agamid lizards)	*Amblyomma nuttalli* *Amblyomma pomposum* *Amblyomma sparsum* *Haemaphysalis sulcata* *Hyalomma aegyptium* *Ixodes festai*
Ahaetulla calligaster (long-nosed tree snake)	*Amblyomma moreliae*

Host	Parasite
Amblyrhynchus cristatus (marine iguana)	*Amblyomma darwini* *Ornithodoros darwini* *Ornithodoros galapagensis* *Ornithodoros talaje*
Ameiva ameiva (jungle runner)	*Amblyomma scutatum*
Anolis carolinensis (green anole)	*Anolisimyia blakeae* *Ixodes scapularis*
Asian tortoises	*Amblyomma clypeolatum*
Aspidites melanocephalus (black-headed python)	*Amblyomma moreliae*
Atractaspis aterrima (western forest mole viper)	*Haemaphysalis parmata*
Bitis arietans (puff adder)	*Amblyomma hebraeum* *Amblyomma nuttalli* *Amblyomma sparsum*
Bitis gabonica (gaboon viper)	*Amblyomma nuttalli* *Amblyomma variegatum*
Boa constrictor (boa constrictor ssp.)	*Amblyomma dissimile* *Amblyomma fuscum* *Amblyomma quadricavum* *Amblyomma rotundatum* *Amblyomma scutatum*
Boaedon spp. (house snakes)	*Aponomma latum*
Boiga sp. (mangrove snake)	*Aponomma varanensis*
Bothrops (= *Bothriechis*) *lateralis* (Costa Rican lancehead)	*Amblyomma rotundatum*
Bungarus fasciatus (banded krait)	*Aponomma crassipes* *Aponomma pattoni*
Bungarus spp. (kraits)	*Aponomma varanensis*
Callisaurus draconoides (zebra-tailed lizard)	*Leptoconops californiensis*
Chalcides spp. (barrel skinks)	*Ixodes festai*
Chamaeleo g. gracilis (graceful chameleon)	*Amblyomma tholloni*
Chamaeleo (unspecified)	*Amblyomma variegatum*

Host	Parasite
Chelonia mydas agassizi (Pacific green sea turtle)	*Eumacronychia nigricornis* *Eumacronychia sternalis*
Chelonians	*Aedes aegypti* *Cistudinomyia cistudinis* *Culicoides testudinalis* *Ornithodoros turicata*
Chelonians, sea turtles	*Tabanus* spp.
Chelonians, snapping turtles	*Aedes cinereus*
Chelonians, tortoises	*Amblyomma crassum* *Amblyomma clypeolatum* *Amblyomma falsomarmoreum* *Amblyomma gemma* *Amblyomma geoemydae* *Amblyomma marmoreum* *Amblyomma nuttalli* *Amblyomma sparsum* *Amblyomma sylvaticum* *Aponomma exornatum* *Glossina fuscipes* *Glossina palpalis* *Glossina* spp. *Hyalomma franchinii* *Ornithodoros compactus* *Ornithodoros tartakovskyi*
Chelonians, tortoises (captive)	*Amblyomma clypeolatum*
Chelonians, tortoises (Central and South America)	*Amblyomma humerale*
Chelonians, turtles	*Aedes trivittatus* *Amblyomma sabanerae* *Amblyomma supinoi* *Coquilletidia perturbans* *Eumacronychia* spp.
Chelonians, turtles (Central and South America)	*Amblyomma humerale*
Chersina angulata (South African bowsprit tortoise)	*Amblyomma sylvaticum*
Chinemys reevesii (Reeve's turtle)	*Amblyomma geoemydae*
Chrysemys picta (painted turtle)	*Chrysops callidus*
Cnemidophorus sexlineatus (six-lined racerunner)	*Ixodes scapularis*

Host	Parasite
Cnemidophorus sp. (whiptail lizard)	*Blaesoxipha plinthopyga*
Coluber ravergieri (variegated racer)	*Haemaphysalis sulcata*
Coluber spp. (racers/whipsnakes)	*Aponomma pattoni*
Conolophus pallidus (Galapagos land iguana)	*Ornithodoros darwini* *Ornithodoros galapagensis*
Conolophus subcristatus (Galapagos land iguana)	*Ornithodoros darwini* *Ornithodoros galapagensis*
Crocodiles	*Aponomma exornatum* *Glossina fuscipes* *Glossina longipalpis* *Glossina morsitans* *Glossina palpalis* *Glossina* spp. *Glossina tachinoides* *Tabanus* spp.
Crocodylus johnstoni (Johnston's crocodile)	*Amblyomma* sp.
Crotalus molossus (black-tailed rattlesnake)	*Aponomma elaphense*
Crotalus spp. (rattlesnakes)	*Ornithodoros turicata*
Crotalus viridis abyssus (Grand Canyon rattlesnake)	*Cuterebra* sp.
Ctenosaura spp. (spiny-tailed iguanas)	*Amblyomma scutatum*
Cuora amboinensis (southeast Asian box turtle)	*Amblyomma geoemydae*
Cyclemys dentata (Asian leaf turtle)	*Amblyomma geoemydae*
Cyclura cornuta (rhinoceros iguana)	*Amblyomma cruciferum*
Cyclura spp. (island iguanas)	*Amblyomma albopictum* *Amblyomma cruciferum* *Amblyomma torrei*
Dasypeltis spp. (African egg-eating snakes)	*Aponomma latum*
Demansia textilis (Australian whip snake)	*Amblyomma moreliae*

Host	Parasite
Dendroaspis spp. (mambas)	*Aponomma latum*
Drymarchon corais (indigo snake)	*Amblyomma dissimile* *Amblyomma scutatum* *Amblyomma testudinis*
Egernia spp. (spiny-tailed skinks)	*Amblyomma moreliae*
Egernia stokesii (gidgee skink)	*Amblyomma vikirri*
Egernia striolata (spiny tree skink)	*Amblyomma moreliae*
Elaphe obsoleta (captive) (rat snake)	*Aponomma elaphense*
Elaphe sp. (rat snake)	*Aponomma pattoni* *Aponomma varanensis*
Elaphe (= *Bogertophis*) *subocularis* (Trans-Pecos rat snake)	*Aponomma elaphense*
Emys spp. (European pond turtles)	*Hyalomma aegyptium*
Epicrates cenchria (captive) (rainbow boa)	*Ornithodoros talaje*
Epicrates inornatus (Puerto Rican boa)	*Ornithodoros turicata*
Epicrates spp. (slender boas)	*Amblyomma albopictum* *Amblyomma quadricavum*
Eremias regeli (racerunner)	*Haemaphysalis caucasica*
Eremias spp. (racerunners)	*Haemaphysalis sulcata*
Eryx sp. (sand boa)	*Aponomma varanensis*
Eublepharis macularius (leopard gecko)	*Haemaphysalis sulcata*
Eumeces fasciatus (five-lined skink)	*Ixodes scapularis*
Eumeces inexpectatus (southeastern five-lined skink)	*Ixodes scapularis*
Eumeces laticeps (broad-headed skink)	*Ixodes scapularis*

Host	Parasite
Eumeces okadae (skink)	*Ixodes asanumai*
Eumeces schneideri (Schneider's skink)	*Haemaphysalis caucasica*
Eumeces spp. (skinks)	*Ixodes festai*
Eunectes murinus (green anaconda)	*Amblyomma fulvum* *Amblyomma rotundatum*
Geckos	*Cistudinomyia* sp. *Ornithodoros foleyi*
Geochelone carbonaria (yellow-foot tortoise)	*Amblyomma rotundatum*
Geochelone chilensis (Chaco tortoise)	*Amblyomma testudinis*
Geochelone denticulata (red-foot tortoise)	*Amblyomma rotundatum*
Geochelone elephantopus (Galapagos giant tortoise)	*Amblyomma macfarlandi* *Amblyomma pilosum* *Amblyomma usingeri* *Ornithodoros transversus*
Geochelone pardalis (leopard tortoise)	*Amblyomma falsomarmoreum* *Amblyomma hebraeum* *Amblyomma marmoreum* *Amblyomma nuttalli* *Amblyomma sparsum* *Amblyomma tholloni*
Geoemyda (= *Heosemys*) *spinosa* (spiny turtle)	*Haemaphysalis hystricis*
Geoemyda (= *Melanochelys*) *tricarinata* (tricarinate hill turtle)	*Amblyomma javanense*
Gerrhosaurus validus (Smith's plated rock lizard)	*Amblyomma hebraeum*
Gopherus agassizii (desert tortoise)	*Ornithodoros turicata*
Gopherus polyphemus (gopher tortoise)	*Amblyomma tuberculatum* *Ornithodoros turicata*
Gymnodactylus spp. (geckos)	*Haemaphysalis sulcata*
Heosemys spinosa (spiny turtle)	*Amblyomma geoemydae* *Amblyomma supinoi*

Host	Parasite
Homopus areolatus (beaked cape tortoise)	*Amblyomma sylvaticum*
Homopus spp. (parrot-beaked tortoises)	*Ornithodoros moubata*
Homorelaps sp. (African dwarf garter snake)	*Amblyomma goeldii*
Iguana iguana (green iguana)	*Amblyomma sabanerae* *Amblyomma scutatum*
Iguana pinguis (rock iguana)	*Amblyomma antillorum* *Amblyomma cruciferum*
Iguana spp. (iquanid lizards)	*Amblyomma albopictum* *Amblyomma antillorum* *Amblyomma boulengeri* *Amblyomma cruciferum* *Amblyomma dissimile* *Amblyomma torrei* *Ornithordoros puertoricensis*
Iguanas	*Amblyomma cruciferum* *Amblyomma dissimile* *Amblyomma torrei* *Amblyomma usingeri* *Amblyomma williamsi* *Forcipomyia* sp.
Indotestudo travancorica (= *forstenii*) (travancore tortoise)	*Amblyomma geoemydae*
Kinixys belliana (Bell's hinge-back tortoise)	*Amblyomma falsomarmoreum* *Amblyomma nuttalli* *Amblyomma sparsum*
Kinosternon sp. (musk/mud turtle)	*Amblyomma sabanerae*
Lacerta spp. (Eurasian lizards)	*Ixodes festai*
Lacerta viridis (emerald lizard)	*Haemaphysalis inermis* *Haemaphysalis sulcata* *Ixodes redikorzevi*
Lacerta vivipara (viviparous lizard)	*Ixodes ricinus*
Laticauda spp. (sea kraits)	*Amblyomma nitidum*
Leiocephalus macropus (curly-tailed lizard)	*Amblyomma torrei*
Liasis amethystinus (Amythest python)	*Aponomma trimaculatum*

Host	Parasite
Lizards	*Aedes aegypti*
	Amblyomma albolimbatum
	Amblyomma dissimile
	Amblyomma fuscum
	Amblyomma moreliae
	Amblyomma sylvaticum
	Amblyomma torrei
	Amblyomma variegatum
	Aponomma exornatum
	Aponomma fimbriatum
	Aponomma flavomaculatum
	Aponomma gervaisi
	Aponomma latum
	Aponomma trimaculatum
	Argas brumpti
	Eumacronychia spp.
	Haemaphysalis parva
	Haemaphysalis punctata
	Hyalomma dromedarii
	Hyalomma franchinii
	Hyalomma impeltatum
	Ixodes festai
	Ixodes nipponensis
	Ixodes pacificus
	Ixodes persulcatus
	Ixodes ricinus
	Ixodes scapularis
	Lutzomyia spp.
	Ornithodoros puertoricensis
	Phlebotomus martini
	Sergentomyia spp.
Lizards (Agamidae)	*Ornithodoros foleyi*
Mabuya wrightii (Seychelles' skink)	*Amblyomma loculosum*
Malaclemmys terrapin (diamondback terrapin)	*Metoposarcophaga importuna*
Malacochersus tornieri (pancake tortoise)	*Amblyomma falsomarmoreum*
Malpolon moilensis (Montpellier snake)	*Ornithodoros sonrai*
Manouria emys (brown tortoise)	*Aponomma varanensis*

Host	Parasite
Mehelya spp. (file snakes)	*Aponomma latum*
Melanochelys tricarinata (tricarinate hill tortoise)	*Amblyomma supinoi*
Melanochelys trijuga (Indian black turtle)	*Amblyomma geoemydae*
Meroles knoxi (Knox's desert lizard)	*Amblyomma sylvaticum*
Micrurus surinamensis (coral snake)	*Amblyomma rotundatum*
Naja naja (Asian cobra)	*Dermacentor atrosignatus*
Naja spp. (cobras)	*Amblyomma helvolum* *Aponomma flavomaculatum* *Aponomma latum* *Aponomma pattoni* *Aponomma varanensis*
Natrix natrix (European grass snake)	*Amblyomma testudinis*
Naultinus elegans (green gecko)	*Calliphora stygia*
Notechis scutatus (mainland tiger snake)	*Amblyomma moreliae*
Ophiophagus hannah (king cobra)	*Amblyomma cordiferum* *Amblyomma helvolum* *Aponomma pattoni* *Aponomma varanensis* *Dermacentor steini*
Ophisaurus apodus (sheltopusik)	*Haemaphysalis sulcata* *Ixodes redikorzevi*
Ophisaurus attenuatus (slender glass lizard)	*Ixodes scapularis*
Ophisaurus ventralis (eastern glass lizard)	*Ixodes scapularis*
Ophisops elegans (European snake-eye)	*Haemaphysalis sulcata*
Oplurus fierinensis (Madagascan swift)	*Argas hoogstraali*
Oplurus grandidieri (Madagascan swift)	*Argas hoogstraali*

Host	Parasite
Oplurus quadrimaculatus (Madagascan swift)	*Argas hoogstraali*
Oxyuranus scutellatus (taipan)	*Amblyomma moreliae*
Pelusios spp. (African mud turtles)	*Amblyomma nuttalli*
Phrynocephalus helioscopus (sun-gazing agamid)	*Haemaphysalis sulcata*
Phrynosoma mcalli (flat-tailed horned lizard)	*Leptoconops californiensis*
Physignathus spp. (water dragons)	*Amblyomma moreliae*
Pituophis melanoleucus (gopher snake)	*Aponomma elaphense*
Psammobates tentorius (tent tortoise)	*Amblyomma sylvaticum*
Psammobates spp. (geometric tortoises)	*Ornithodoros moubata*
Psammodromus spp. (sand lizards)	*Ixodes festai*
Pseudaspis cana (mole snake)	*Amblyomma sylvaticum*
Pseudechis australis (king brown snake)	*Amblyomma moreliae*
Pseudechis porphyriacus (red-bellied black snake)	*Amblyomma moreliae*
Pseudemys (= *Trachemys*) *scripta* (common slider)	*Amblyomma sabanerae*
Ptyas spp. (Asian rat snakes)	*Amblyomma helvolum* *Aponomma pattoni* *Aponomma varanensis*
Python curtus (blood python)	*Aponomma varanensis*
Python (= *Morelia*) *spilotes variegatus* (carpet python)	*Amblyomma moreliae*
Python molurus (Asiatic rock python)	*Amblyomma javanense* *Aponomma crassipes* *Aponomma fuscolineatum*
Python regius (ball python)	*Aponomma latum*
Python reticulatus (reticulated python)	*Amblyomma cordiferum* *Amblyomma testudinarium*

Host	Parasite
	Aponomma crassipes
	Aponomma kraneveldi
	Aponomma transversale
	Aponomma varanensis
	Dermacentor auratus
	Dermacentor compactus
	Dermacentor steini
Pythons	*Amblyomma javanense*
	Aponomma decorosum
	Aponomma flavomaculatum
	Aponomma soembawensis
	Aponomma transversale
Python sebae (African rock python)	*Amblyomma nuttalli*
	Amblyomma sparsum
	Aponomma transversale
	Aponomma latum
Python spp. (pythons)	*Amblyomma helvolum*
	Amblyomma sparsum
	Aponomma pattoni
	Aponomma trimaculatum
	Aponomma varanensis
Python timorensis (Timor python)	*Aponomma kraneveldi*
Pyxis arachnoides (spider tortoise)	*Amblyomma chabaudi*
Reptiles	*Aedes atlanticus*
	Aedes canadensis
	Aedes hendersoni
	Aedes sticticus
	Aedes triseriatus
	Aedes vexans
	Amblyomma falsomarmoreum
	Amblyomma limbatum
	Amblyomma marmoreum
	Amblyomma nuttalli
	Amblyomma rotundatum
	Amblyomma sparsum
	Amblyomma testudinarium
	Amblyomma testudinis
	Amblyomma tuberculatum
	Aponomma exornatum
	Aponomma hydrosauri

Host	Parasite
	Argas tragariepinus
	Calliphora spp.
	Chrysops spp.
	Cochliomyia spp.
	Coquilletidia perturbans
	Culex aitkeni
	Culex amazonensis
	Culex apanastasis
	Culex decens
	Culex dunni
	Culex egcymon
	Culex elevator
	Culex erraticus
	Culex invidiosus
	Culex pipiens
	Culex quinquefasciatus
	Culex restuans
	Culex tecmarsis
	Culex territans
	Culicoides spp.
	Culiseta melanura
	Glossina longipennis
	Glossina palpalis
	Glossina spp.
	Glossina tachinoides
	Haemaphysalis concinna
	Haemaphysalis sulcata
	Ixodes asanumai
	Ixodes persulcatus
	Ixodes redikorzevi
	Lucilia (= *Phaenicia*) *sericata*
	Lutzomyia californica
	Lutzomyia stewarti
	Lutzomyia vexator
	Ornithodoros erraticus
	Ornithodoros talaje
	Phlebotomus caucasicus
	Phlebotomus chinensis
	Phlebotomus papatasi
	Psorophora spp.
	Sergentomyia spp.
Reptiles (captive)	*Ornithodoros talaje*

Host	Parasite
Rhinoclemmys annulata (brown wood turtle)	*Amblyomma sabanerae*
Rhinoclemmys areolata (furrowed wood turtle)	*Amblyomma rotundatum*
Rhinoclemmys funeria (black wood turtle)	*Amblyomma sabanerae*
Rhinoclemmys pulcherrima (painted wood turtle)	*Amblyomma sabanerae*
Rhinoclemmys spp. (neotropical wood turtles)	*Amblyomma sabanerae*
Sceloporus graciosus (sagebrush lizard)	*Ixodes pacificus*
Sceloporus occidentalis (western fence lizard)	*Ixodes pacificus*
Sceloporus spp. (fence lizards)	*Ixodes pacificus*
Sceloporus undulatus (eastern fence lizard)	*Amblyomma tuberculatum* *Ixodes scapularis*
Sistrurus spp. (pigmy rattlesnakes)	*Ornithodoros turicata*
Snakes	*Amblyomma albolimbatum* *Amblyomma dissimile* *Amblyomma goeldii* *Amblyomma hainanense* *Amblyomma limbatum* *Amblyomma moreliae* *Amblyomma quadricavum* *Aponomma exornatum* *Aponomma fimbriatum* *Aponomma flavomaculatum* *Aponomma gervaisi* *Aponomma latum* *Aponomma pattoni* *Aponomma trimaculatum* *Aponomma varanensis* *Culex peccator* *Deinocerites* spp. *Glossina fuscipes* *Glossina palpalis* *Glossina* spp. *Ornithodoros turicata* *Uranotaenia sapphirina*

Host	Parasite
Snakes (captive)	*Amblyomma cordiferum*
Sphenodon punctatus (tuatara)	*Aponomma sphenodonti*
Takydromus tachydromoides (Japanese grass lizard)	*Ixodes nipponenis*
Terrapene carolina (wild) (eastern box turtle)	*Lucilia* (= *Phaenicia*) *coeruleviridis* *Ornithodoros turicata*
Terrapene carolina (captive) (eastern box turtle)	*Amblyomma tuberculatum*
Terrapene carolina yucatana (Yucatan box turtle)	*Amblyomma sabanerae*
Terrapene ornata (ornate box turtle)	*Ornithodoros turicata*
Testudo (= *Geochelone*) *elegans* (star tortoise)	*Amblyomma clypeolatum* *Aponomma gervaisi*
Testudo graeca (wild) (Greek tortoise)	*Hyalomma marginatum marginatum*
Testudo graeca (captive) (Greek tortoise)	*Ornithodoros compactus*
Testudo hermanni (Hermann's tortoise)	*Haemaphysalis erinacei taurica* *Hyalomma anatolicum excavatum* *Hyalomma marginatum marginatum*
Testudo horsfieldii (Horsfield's tortoise)	*Haemaphysalis sulcata* *Hyalomma detritum* *Ornithodoros tartakovskyi*
Testudo (= *Pyxis*) *planicauda* (flat-shelled spider tortoise)	*Amblyomma chabaudi*
Testudo (= *Geochelone*) *radiata* (radiated tortoise)	*Amblyomma chabaudi*
Testudo (= *Indotestudo*) *elongata* (Elongate tortoise)	*Amblyomma supinoi*
Testudo (= *Manouria*) *emys* (Asian brown tortoise)	*Amblyomma testudinarium*
Testudo spp. (European tortoises)	*Hyalomma aegyptium* *Hyalomma anatolicum anatolicum* *Hyalomma marginatum marginatum* *Ornithodoros moubata*

Host	Parasite
Thamnophis spp. (garter and ribbon snakes)	*Ixodes pacificus*
Tiliqua nigrolutea (blotched blue-tongued skink)	*Amblyomma moreliae*
Tiliqua spp. (blue-tongued skinks)	*Aponomma decorosum*
Tortoises (see Chelonians)	
Trachydosaurus (= *Tiliqua*) *rugosus* (shingle-back skink)	*Amblyomma albolimbatum* *Amblyomma limbatum* *Amblyomma moreliae* *Amblyomma vikirri* *Aponomma hydrosauri* *Ornithodoros gurneyi*
Trimorphodon biscutatus vilkinsonii (Texas lyre snake)	*Aponomma elaphense*
Tropidurus albemarlensis (lava lizard)	*Ornithodoros galapagensis*
Tropidurus spp. (lava lizards)	*Amblyomma boulengeri*
Turtles (see Chelonians)	
Uma inornata (fringe-toed lizard)	*Leptoconops californiensis*
Uma notata rufipunctata (Colorado fringe-toed lizard)	*Leptoconops californiensis*
Uma scoparia (Mohave fringed-toed lizard)	*Leptoconops californiensis*
Uromastyx sp. (spiny-tailed agamid)	*Haemaphysalis sulcata*
Uta stansburiana (side-blotched lizard)	*Ixodes pacificus*
Varanus albigularis (white-throated monitor)	*Amblyomma hebraeum*
Varanus bengalensis (Bengal monitor)	*Aponomma gervaisi* *Aponomma varanensis*
Varanus bivittatus (= *salvator*) (water monitor)	*Aponomma crassipes*
Varanus dumerilii (Dumeril's monitor)	*Aponomma varanensis*
Varanus exanthematicus (savanna monitor)	*Amblyomma falsomarmoreum* *Aponomma exornatum* *Aponomma flavomaculatum* *Aponomma inopinatum*

Host	Parasite
Varanus giganteus (perentie)	*Amblyomma calabyi*
Varanus glauerti (Kimberly rock monitor)	*Amblyomma glauerti* *Aponomma glebopalma*
Varanus glebopalma (black-palmed monitor)	*Amblyomma glauerti* *Aponomma glebopalma*
Varanus griseus (desert monitor)	*Aponomma crassipes* *Haemaphysalis sulcata* *Ornithodoros erraticus*
Varanus indicus (Pacific monitor)	*Amblyomma squamosum* *Aponomma trimaculatum* *Aponomma varanensis*
Varanus komodoensis (wild) (Komodo dragon)	*Amblyomma robinsoni* *Aponomma komodoense*
Varanus komodoensis (captive) (Komodo dragon)	*Aponomma decorosum* *Aponomma komodoense*
Varanus niloticus (Nile monitor)	*Amblyomma eburneum* *Aponomma exornatum* *Aponomma flavomaculatum*
Varanus rudicollis (black rough-necked monitor)	*Aponomma varanensis*
Varanus salvator (wild) (water monitor)	*Amblyomma geoemydae* *Amblyomma javanense* *Aponomma crassipes* *Aponomma soembawensis* *Aponomma varanensis* *Dermacentor atrosignatus* *Dermacentor steini*
Varanus salvator (captive) (water monitor)	*Amblyomma testudinarium* *Aponomma komodoense* *Aponomma varanensis*
Varanus spp. (monitor lizards)	*Amblyomma helvolum* *Amblyomma javanense* *Amblyomma limbatum* *Amblyomma marmoreum* *Amblyomma nuttalli* *Amblyomma sparsum* *Amblyomma supinoi* *Amblyomma variegatum* *Aponomma decorosum* *Aponomma exornatum*

Host	Parasite
	Aponomma latum
	Aponomma pattoni
	Aponomma trimaculatum
	Aponomma varanensis
	Glossina fuscipes
	Glossina longipalpis
	Glossina morsitans
	Glossina pallidipes
	Glossina palpalis
	Glossina spp.
	Glossina tachinoides
	Ornithodoros moubata
Varanus timorensis (Timor monitor)	*Aponomma soembawensis*
Varanus tristis orientalis (freckled monitor)	*Amblyomma moreliae*
Varanus varius (lace monitor)	*Amblyomma moreliae*
	Aponomma decorosum
Vipera berus (European viper)	*Haemaphysalis punctata*
Vipera sp.	*Aponomma pattoni*
	Aponomma varanensis
Xenodon merremi (false yarara)	*Amblyomma rotundatum*

GLOSSARY

acetic acid (CH₃COOH). A sour, colorless liquid having a sharp odor; it is found in vinegar.

acetone (CH₃ COCH₃). A colorless, volatile liquid used as a solvent.

acidic. Acid-forming.

adanal. Lateral to the anus; adanal plates are used in the taxonomy of some male hard ticks.

alkaline. Having the properties of, or containing an alkali.

ambient temperature. The surrounding temperature.

anemia. Below normal erythrocytes, hemoglobin, or hematocrit.

antenna (antennae, pl.). Either of a pair of moveable, jointed sense organs attached to the head of an insect.

antennomaxillary complex. Pertaining to both the antennae and the maxillae, especially of larval Diptera.

anthrax. An acute, infectious, zoonotic disease of cattle and sheep caused by the bacterium *Bacillus anthracis*.

anticoagulant. Any substance preventing or retarding the clotting of blood.

arbovirus. Any arthropod-borne virus transmitted to a susceptible vertebrate host by a blood-feeding arthropod.

arista. Flagellum-like appendage or bristle on the 3rd antennal segment of a fly of the suborder Brachycera and some members of the suborder Nematocera.

arthropod. Any animal in the phylum Arthropoda (e.g., crustaceans, insects, myriopods, arachnids, etc.).

atria (pl.). Cavities or passages.

babesiosis. A febrile, tick-borne, hemolytic disease of animals (rarely humans) caused by sporozoa in the genus *Babesia*.

basal. The part of an appendage or organ that is closest to the body.

basicostal scale. The second distinct "scale" at the base of the wing of a muscoid fly (i.e., the "scale" after the basal "scale").

basis capituli. The moveable basal portion of the capitulum, attached to the scutum in ticks.

benzene (C₆H₆). A clear, colorless, highly flammable liquid miscible with many organic liquids, used primary as a solvent.

boutonneuse fever. Tick-borne typhus fever caused by the bacterium *Rickettsia conori* and transmitted by ixodid ticks.

brackish (adj.). Slightly salty (e.g., water in marshes near seas).

camerostome. The ventral cavity in the anterior portion of soft ticks into which the mouthparts are recessed.

cannibalistic (adj.). Pertaining to an animal that eats its own kind.

capitulum (capitula, pl.). Also called the gnathosoma: anterior portion of a tick which bears the mouthparts, consisting of the basis capituli, palps, hypostome, and chelicerae.

carapace. The dorsal component of the shell of a turtle.

carnivorous (adj.). Pertaining to an animal that feeds primarily on flesh.

carrion. Decaying flesh of a dead body which may serve as food for scavenging animals.

cc. An abbreviation for cubic centimeter. One cc is equal to one milliliter (ml).

cellosolve $(C_2H_5OCH_2CH_2OH)$. Ethylene glycol monoethyl ether or ethyl cellosove.

cephalopharangeal (adj.). Of or pertaining to the head and pharynx.

cephalothorax. Pertaining to the head and thoracic portion of the body; in arachnids the head and thorax are fused.

cerci (pl.). Appendages or projections, usually sensory, on the eleventh abdominal segment of some insects.

Chagas' disease. A progressive, noncontagious disease caused by the protozoan *Trypanosoma cruzi* and transmitted by a triatomine bug. Sometimes referred to as American trypanosomiasis.

Charleville virus. An Australian arbovirus isolated from sand flies and lizards.

chelicera (chelicerae, pl.). One of the anteriormost pair of appendages in the chelicerate arthropods (e.g., ticks, mites, spiders), usually used for cutting or tearing.

chitin (chitinous, adj.). The structural material of some animals, mainly those in the phylum Arthropoda.

chloral hydrate $[CCl_3CH(OH)_2]$. Water soluble, colorless or white crystals used for rapid anesthesia induction, an anticonvulsant, and as an ingredient of pain-relieving linaments.

cibarium. Part of the pre-oral cavity (between the hypopharynx and labrum in insects; "mouth cavity."

class. A taxonomic category below phylum and above order.

clavate (adj.). Club-shaped.

cloaca (cloacae, pl.). A common chamber for the passage of feces, urine, and reproductive material.

compound eye. The organ of vision formed of several closely grouped prismatic eyes as in most arthropods.

compound microscope. Having a set of lenses built into the objective and another set in the eyepiece.

concave. Hollow and curved like the inside half of a hollow ball.

convex. Curving outward like the outer half surface of a ball.

cornu (cornua, pl.). Projecting posterolateral corner of basis capituli in hard ticks.

Cowdria ruminantium. The rickettsial agent that causes heartwater fever, mainly in southern Africa.

Coxiella burnetti. The species of *Coxiella* which is the causative agent of Q fever.

debride. The cutting away of tissue; the cutting away of dead or contaminated tissue from a wound to prevent infection; chemical agents may be used to achieve similar results.

denticle. A small toothlike projection.

dermatitis. Inflammation of the skin.

dermis. The skin.

dimorphic (adj.). Of or pertaining to living in two distinct structural forms.

dioecious. Having separate sexes.

disc. Circular or platelike structure.

dorsoventral (dorsoventrally, adj.). Extending in a direction from the dorsal surface to the ventral.

dorsum. The back, or the back of any body part (e.g., hand, foot).

edema. Excessive accumulation of fluid in cells, tissues, or cavities of the body resulting in swelling.

elephantiasis. A chronic enlargement and thickening of the cutaneous and subcutaneous tissues as a result of lymphatic obstruction.

emargination. Having a notched margin or tip.

encephalitis. Inflammation of the brain.

encephalomyelitis. Inflammation of the brain and spinal cord.

endemic. Restricted to or constantly present in a particular locality.

enzootic. Affecting animals in a certain area, climate, or season.

enzyme. A catalytic protein manufactured by living cells, having a specific action in bringing about a chemical change (e.g., using water and other materials in a cell to make sugar).

erythrocyte. Red blood cell.

ethanol. Ethyl alcohol.

ether ($C_2H_5)O_2$. A volatile, colorless, highly flammable liquid prepared by the reaction of sulfuric acid and ethyl alcohol; it is used as an anesthetic and a solvent for resins and fats.

ethyl acetate ($CH_3COOC_2H_5$). A colorless liquid, formed from acetic acid and ethyl alcohol, with many uses, including being used as a solvent.

ethyl alcohol (C_2H_5OH). A colorless, volatile liquid used for many purposes in medicine and industry.

ethyl cellosolve. *See* cellosolve.

excreta. Waste matter eliminated (excreted) from the body, especially feces and urine.

exoskeleton. Any hard, external supporting structure of a body.

facultative myiasis. The feeding on either carrion or live hosts by myiasis-producing flies.

facultative parasite. An organism that can live as a parasite or as a free-living form.

festoon. Uniform rectangular areas along posterior border of the dorsum, separated by grooves in hard ticks.

filarial (adj.). Pertaining to parasitic nematodes in the superfamily Filarioidea; adults live in the vertebrate host's circulatory or lymphatic systems, the connective tissues, or serous cavities; larval forms (microfilariae) are found in the blood stream or lymph spaces.

file. Row (*also see* Fig. 42).

genital aperture/opening/pore. A hole or slitlike opening that leads to the genital organs.

glacial acetic acid. A colorless liquid containing not less than 99.4% acetic acid.

glycerin. A commercial term for glycerol.

glycerol ($C_3H_8O_3$). An odorless, colorless, syrupy liquid used widely in industry (e.g., in cosmetics, foods, and medicines).

gnathostoma. Same as capitulum.

gravid. Pregnant.

gum arabic. Acacia; the dried, gummy exudate from the stems and branches of some species of *Acacia* trees.

haemogregarine. A parasitic protozoan organism belonging to the family Haemogregarinidae.

Haller's organ. A depression on the last segment of the first pair of legs of ticks; functions as an olfactory and humidity receptor.

haltere. Knoblike vestigial wing on thorax of a fly in the order Diptera; necessary for balance during flight.

heartwater fever. A disease of ruminants caused by infection with *Cowdria ruminantium.*

hematocrit. The portion of blood cells to the volume of blood.

hematophagous. Feeding on blood; sanguinivorous; sanguivorous.

hemoglobin. The respiratory pigment of red blood cells.

***Hepatozoon* spp.** Blood-borne protozoa, some of which are known to be transmitted by the bite or ingestion of an infected arthropod; occasionally, heavy infections may cause anemia and inanition in reptilian hosts.

heteropteran (adj.). A true "bug" belonging to the insect order Heteroptera.

host. An organism that supports the life of another organism.

humeral pit. A small (blood-borne) depression. In Diptera, this refers to a taxonomically important "polished" pit (depression) on the dorsal surface of the 2nd thoracic segment (wing attachment sites).

hyaline. A clear, structureless, homogeneous, glassy material found normally in the body (e.g., in cartilage matrix, vitreous body, thyroid gland colloid); may also occur pathologically in degeneration of connective tissue and epithelial cells.

hybridization. Cross-breeding.

hydrochloric acid (HCl). A strong, highly corrosive solution of hydrogen chloride gas in water.

hypopleural bristle. One of a row of bristles located on the integument above the mid- and hind leg coxae in Diptera.

hypopygium. The lower plate of the anal opening. In Diptera, this refers to the male genitalia and the terminal segments of the abdomen.

hypostome. Ventral mouthpart, especially of ticks, with recurved teeth or denticles.

idiosoma. Posterior of the two basic parts of the body of a tick (or mite), bearing the legs and most internal organs.

imbibe. To drink.

inanition. A state of starvation.

inflammation. The body's reaction to injury characterized clinically by heat, swelling, redness, and pain.

instar. Any one of the larval or nymphal stages of arthropods.

integument. The skin.

intermediate host. An organism that harbors the asexual or intermediate phases of a parasite.

interocular. Between the eyes (e.g., interocular groove or suture).

kg. An abbreviation for kilogram. One thousand grams (1000 g) or 2.2 pounds.

kilogram (kg). One thousand grams (1000 g) or 2.2 pounds.

lactic acid ($C_3H_6O_3$). A clear or yellowish, syrupy organic acid produced by the fermentation of lactose in milk, or by the action of certain microorganisms on sugar or other carbohydrates.

lactophenol. A mixture of lactic acid and melted phenol crystals used as a clearing agent for the examination of arthropods.

larva (larvae, pl.). The free-living immature form of any animal that changes structurally when it becomes an adult.

larviparous (larviparously, adj.). Producing larvae.

larviposition. The act of depositing larvae.

larvipositor. An organ of many female insects for depositing larvae in a suitable place (often a host).

Leishmania **spp.** Protozoan flagellates transmitted by the bite of certain species in the genus *Phlebotomus,* and causing leishmaniasis in animals, including humans; symptoms of leishmaniasis include a variety of visceral and superficial infections.

leptospirosis. Any infection caused by spirochetal bacteria of the genus *Leptospira.*

life cycle. Stages through which an organism passes, generation after generation.

littoral. The region along the coast (e.g., seashore).

loiasis. A filariasis caused by the filariae *Loa* spp., transmitted by the bite of certain flies in the genus *Chrysops*; it is characterized by transient cutaneous swelling caused by migrating adult worms, often involving the eyes of its host.

louping ill. A form of encephalomyelitis caused by a virus which is transmitted by the tick *Ixodes ricinus* in northern Britain.

maggot. A fly larva, especially one that lives on decaying flesh.

mammilla (mammillae, pl.). A small prominence; papilla; nipple.

mammillated (adj.). Nipplelike projections.

maxilla (maxillae, pl.). One of a pair of oral structures in insects located just behind the mandibles; they function in holding and chewing food.

mercuric chloride. Mercury bichloride.

metastriate ticks. Hard ticks (family Ixodidae) in which the anal groove does not curve anteriorly around the anus. This includes members of all hard tick genera except *Ixodes*.

mg. An abbreviation for milligram. One one-thousandth of a gram (1/1000 g).

milligram (mg). One one-thousandth of a gram (1/1000 g).

milliliter (ml). One one-thousandth of a liter (1/1000 l), and is equal to one cubic centimeter (1 cc).

millimeter (mm). One one-thousandth of a meter (1/1000 m).

ml. An abbreviation for milliliter. One one-thousandth of a liter (1/1000 l), and is equal to one cubic centimeter (1 cc).

mm. An abbreviation for millimeter. One one-thousandth of a meter.

morphometric analysis. Interpretation of the size of different morphological structures.

mounting medium. A substance, such as balsam, used to embed specimens on microscope slides.

myiasis. A condition resulting from the invasion of tissues or organs of humans and other animals by dipterous larvae.

nagana. An infectious disease of animals caused by *Trypanosoma b. brucei* or *T. congolense* and transmitted by the bite of tsetse flies.

nematode. Any worm of the class Nematoda; true roundworms; members of the class are bilaterally symmetrical, unisexual, without a proboscis, and have a body cavity not lined with epithelium.

nymph. Immature stage in the life cycle of an insect or arachnid whereby the wing pads (in winged insects) first appear and the reproductive organs are not yet functional.

obligate myiasis. The feeding on live hosts exclusively by myiasis-producing flies.

occiput. Rear of head.

ocellar bristles. Small setae close to the ocelli.

ocellar triangle. Area delimited by ocelli.

ocelli (pl.). Simple eyes or pigmented spots of invertebrate animals.

oral hook. A hooklike, moveable feeding structure often found in maggots.

oviposit. To deposit eggs.

ovoviviparous. To produce live offspring from eggs that hatched inside the female body.

palp (palpi, pl.). A jointed organ or feeler for touching or tasting.

papilla (papillae, pl.). A small, nipplelike eminence.

parafacial. In Diptera, the side of the "face" below the eyes.

parafrontal. In Diptera, the "front" of the "face."

parascapular (adj.). Beside the scapulae (pointed anterior angles of the scutum in ticks).

parasite. Any organism that lives in or on another organism (host) to obtain some advantage, but contributes nothing useful in return.

parasitologist. Quaint person who seeks truth in strange places; a person who sits on one stool while staring at another.

pathogen (pathogenic, adj.). An organism producing or capable of producing disease.

pecten. A comb or comblike structure.

pedipalp. Appendage of arachnids used for grasping, sensing, fertilizing, etc.

periocular (adj.). Surrounding the eye.

peristaltic contraction. Rhythmic contraction of muscles surrounding a tubular organ such as the gut.

Petri dish. A shallow dish with cover used for many purposes, including culturing microorganisms.

pharyngeal (adj.). Pertaining to the pharynx.

pharynx. Foregut structure into which the mouth opens; often as a well-developed pump.

phenol (C_6H_5OH). A white crystalline compound called carbolic acid in the dilute aqueous form.

phylum. A primary taxonomic division of the animal or vegetable kingdom.

piroplasmosis. Babesiosis.

Plasmodium. A genus of protozoa whose members cause malaria.

plastron. The ventral component of the shell of a turtle.

pleura (plural, adj.). Lateral regions of the thorax.

plumose (adj.). Feathered; feathery.

poikilothermic (adj.). Ectothermic; "cold-blooded."

pollinose. Covered in pollen or appearing to be so.

polygonal. Having many angles.

polyvinal alcohol (PVA). A synthetic, water-soluble polymer of vinyl alcohol used as a preservative and adhesive for mounting mosquito larvae and adult mosquito parts such as the genitalia.

posthumeral bristle. One of (usually) two bristles located close to the wing base in Diptera.

potassium hydroxide (KOH). Caustic potash.

povidone iodine. A water-soluble antiseptic used topically for the prevention of cutaneous infections susceptible to iodine (betadine).

presutural bristle. A bristle, or seta, that inserts on the integument close to a suture line.

proboscis. An elongate structure located at the anterior end of an organism.

prostriate ticks. Hard ticks (family Ixodidae) in which the anal groove curves anteriorly around the anus (members of the genus *Ixodes*).

proteolytic (adj.). The breaking down of proteins to form more simple substances.

protozoa (pl.). Unicellular eukaryotes in the Kingdom Protista.

pteropleural bristle. A bristle, or seta, that inserts laterally on a thoracic segment that bears wings in Diptera.

pubescence. Hairyness (setae).

pulvilli (pl.). Padlike structures on the lower surface of the tarsi; "foot pads."

pupa (pupae, pl.). The nonfeeding stage of an insect occurring between the last larval period and adult form.

puparium. Hardened cuticle of the next-to-last larval instar that encloses a pupa, especially in Diptera.

pupation. To become a pupa.

Q fever. An acute, infectious disease caused by the bacterium *Coxiella burnetti*, acquired by inhalation, handling infected material, drinking contaminated milk, or transmission by a blood-feeding arthropod; it is characterized by a sudden onset of fever, malaise, headache, and interstitial pneumonitis.

relapsing fever. Any acute, infectious disease caused by the spirochetes in the genus *Borrelia* which is transmitted by tick or insect vectors.

reservoir. A living organism that supports the growth of an infectious agent, but suffers little or no effects from that agent; "carrier"; reservoir host.

respiratory trumpet. A lateral "trumpetlike" breathing organ on each side of a mosquito pupa.

rickettsia. A group of bacteria causing the spotted fever group of diseases (e.g., Rocky Mountain spotted fever, Q-fever, murine typhus, epidemic typhus, scrub typhus and rickettsialpox).

saprophagous (adj.). Subsisting on decaying plant matter.

saurian. Reptile in the order Sauria; lizard.

Sauroleishmania spp. Protozoan flagellates transmitted to reptiles by the bite of sand flies (family Psychodidae).

S.C. (= S.Q.). Subcutaneous.

sclerite (sclerotized, adj.). Any well-defined hard plate forming part of the shell-like covering of arthropods.

scute. Scale; any external bony or horny plate.

scutellum. A small, shield-shaped, horny scale or plate.

scutum. A sclerotized plate on the anterodorsal aspect of a hard tick (also, some mites).

sensilla sagittiformia (noun). Specialized sensory or secretory pit often used for identifying tick larvae.

sensillum. Specialized sensory structure, usually a modified pit, peg, or group of setae.

seta (setae, pl.). Hairlike appendage.

setose (adj.). Having bristles.

siphon. A "tube"; often used to describe the respiratory tube attached posteriorly on the abdomen of mosquito larvae.

somite. Body segment, usually in arthropods.

spermatheca (spermathecae, pl.). A small, saclike structure in the female invertebrate (esp. insects) used to receive and store sperm.

spiracle (spiracular, adj.). Any of the small external openings of the tracheal respiratory system in most terrestrial arthropods, usually found along the sides of certain thoracic and abdominal segments.

spiracular plates. Large circular, oval, or elliptical respiratory structures on each side of the idiosoma in nymphal and adult hard ticks.

spirochete. Non-flagellated, spiral-shaped bacterium of the order Spirochaetales, including those that cause disease, are parasitic, and free-living.

sporozoa (pl.). Blood-borne, malaria-producing protozoa transmitted usually by the bites of mosquitoes, now referred to as Apicomplexa.

sternum. The ventral surface, or a ventral plate, of an organism.

stigmal plates. See spiracular plates above.

style. Posterior part of 3rd antennal segment.

subcutaneous (S.C., S.Q.). Under the skin.

substrate. In zoology, the ground or other solid material on which an animal moves or is fastened.

substratum. Same as substrate.

symbiont (symbiotic, adj.). Any organism involved in a parasitic, commensalistic or mutualistic relationship with its "host".

symbiosis. The interaction of organisms whereby one lives on, in, or with another.

symmetrical. Exhibiting corresponding characteristics on opposite sides of a plane.

taiga biome. Swampy, coniferous forests in central Asia.

tarsus (tarsi, pl.). The last segment from the base of an insect or arachnid leg; articulates proximally with the tibia and usually is subdivided into two to five subsegments.

tergite. A large dorsal sclerite on the body of an arthropod.

tessellated. Arranged in a mosaic pattern; chequered.

thorax. The part of the body between the neck and abdomen; the chest.

tibia (tibiae, pl.). Next to the last segment from the base of an arthropod leg.

trachea. Any of the small tubules in the respiratory system of insects and certain other invertebrates, branching throughout the body conducting air.

truncate. Having a square, flattened, or broad end.

trypanosome. Any flagellate protozoan of the genus *Trypanosoma* that lives in the blood of vertebrates and is usually transmitted by the bite or in the feces of an arthropod (or leech).

trypanosomiasis. Any disease caused by a trypanosome.

tularemia. An infection by the organism *Pasturella tularensis* transmitted to humans by the handling of infected mammals and the bite of certain arthropods.

vector. An organism that transfers infective microorganisms from one host to another.

venter. The belly or undersurface of the abdomen.

ventral. Pertaining to the belly or undersurface of the abdomen.

vernacular. Common name, as distinguished from the scientific taxonomic classification.

viviparous. Bearing live offspring.

xylene (C_8H_{10}). A colorless hydrocarbon having the characteristics of benzene, derived from coal or wood tar and petroleum.

zoonosis (zoonotic, zoonotically, adj.). Diseases of animals transmissible to humans, and more recently, also diseases of humans transmissible to animals.

REFERENCES

Abercrombie, J. 1977. Myiasis in the eastern box turtle caused by *Phaenicia coeruleviridis* (Diptera: Calliphoridae). J. Wash. Acad. Sci., 67:155–156.

Abrahams, R. 1992. Ivermectin as a spray for treatment of snake mites. Bull. Assoc. Rept. Amph. Vet., 2:8.

Abreu-Rodriguez, E., and Moya, S. 1995. El culebron de Puerto Rico, *Epicrates inornatus* (Reptilia: Boidae), un nuevo hospedero de *Ornithodoros puertoricensis* (Acari: Argasidae) en Puerto Rico. J. Agr. Univ. Puerto Rico, 79:91–92.

Adeyeye, O.A., and Butler, J.F. 1989. Population structure and seasonal intra-burrow movement of *Ornithodoros turicata* (Acari: Argasidae) in gopher tortoise burrows. J. Med. Ent., 26:279–283.

Adler, S. 1964. *Leishmania.* In: *Advances in Parasitology,* Dawes, B. (Ed.), Vol. 2. Academic Press, New York, NY. pp. 35–96.

Aeschlimann, A.F.J. 1967. Biologie et écologie des tiques (Ixodoidea) de Côte d'Ivoire. Acta Trop., 24:281–405.

Aeschlimann, A.F.J. 1972. *Ixodes ricinis,* Linné, 1758 (Ixodoidea; Ixodidae). Essai préliminaire de synthèse sur la biologie de cette espèce en Suisse. Acta Trop., 29:321–340.

Aeschlimann, A.F.J., Büttiker, W.W.G., Elbl, A., and Hoogstraal, H. 1965. A propos des tiques de Suisse (Arachnoidea, Acarina, Ixodoidea). Rev. Suisse Zool., 72:577–583.

Aldrich, J.M. 1916. *Sarcophaga and Allies in North America.* Vol. 1. Ent. Soc. Am. Thomas Say Foundation, Lafayette, IN. 301 pp.

Allman, S.L. 1961. Medical and veterinary pests. Annual Rep. Ent. Br., Div. Sci. Serv., New South Wales Dept. Agr., 1960–1961:34–35.

Anastos, G. 1950. The scutate ticks, or Ixodidae, of Indonesia. Ent. Am., n.s. 30:1–144.

Anderson, J.F., and Magnarelli, L.A. 1994. Lyme disease: A tick-associated disease originally described in Europe, but named after a town in Connecticut. Am. Ent., 40:217–227.

Anderson, J.F., Magnarelli, L.A., and Keirans, J.E. 1981. *Aponomma quadricavum* (Acari: Ixodidae) collected from an imported boa, *Epicrates striatus*, in Connecticut. J. Med. Ent., 18:123–125.

Anderson, J.F., Magnarelli, L.A., and Keirans, J.E. 1984. Ixodid and argasid ticks in Connecticut, U.S.A.: *Aponomma latum, Amblyomma dissimile, Haemaphysalis leachi* group, and *Ornithodoros kelleyi* (Acari: Ixodidae, Argasidae). Int. J. Acarol., 10:149–151.

Apperson, C.S., Levine, J.F., Evans, T.L., Braswell, A., and Heller, J. 1993. Relative utilization of reptiles and rodents as hosts by immature *Ixodes scapularis* (Acari: Ixodidae) in the coastal plain of North Carolina, USA. Exp. Appl. Acarol., 17:719–731.

Aragao, H. de B. 1936. Ixodidas brasileiros e de alguns paises limitrophes. Mem. Inst. Oswaldo Cruz, 31:759–843.

Arthur, D.R. 1957. Two north African *Ixodes* ticks: *I. kaiseri* sp. nov. from Egyptian desert fox cubs. A redescription of the female and a description of the male of *I. festai* Rondell, 1926 (Ixodoidea, Ixodidae). J. Parasitol., 43: 578–585.

Arthur, D.R. 1958. *Ixodes festai* Rondell 1926 (Ixodoides, Ixodides); redescription de la femelle, description du male et des stades imparfaits et notes sur leur biologie. Arch. Inst. Pasteur Moroc, 5:475–492.

Arthur, D.R. 1962. Some ticks from Mwingi-Garissa region of Kenya. Ann. Mag. Nat. Hist., 5:541–543.

Arthur, D.R. 1963. *British Ticks*. Butterworths, London. 213 pp.

Arthur, D.R. 1965. *Ticks of the Genus Ixodes in Africa*. Athlone Press, University of London, London. 348 pp.

Arthur, D.R., and Snow, K.R. 1968. *Ixodes pacificus* Cooley and Kohls, 1943: Its life-history and occurrence. Parasitology, 58:893–906.

Askew, R.R. 1971. *Parasitic Insects*. American Elsevier Publishing Company, Inc., New York, NY. 316 pp.

Auezova, G., Brushko, Z., and Kubykin, R. 1990. Feeding of biting midges (Leptoconopidae) on reptiles. Abstracts 2nd International Congress of Dipterology, 27 August–1 September 1990, Bratislava, Slovakia.

Auffenberg, T. 1988. *Amblyomma helvolum* (Acarina: Ixodidae) as a parasite of varanid and scincid reptiles in the Philippines. Int. J. Parasitol., 18:937–945.

Auffenberg, W., and Auffenberg, T. 1990. The reptile tick *Aponomma gervaisi* (Acarina: Ixodidae) as a parasite of monitor lizards in Pakistan and India. Bull. Florida. Mus. Nat. Hist., Biol. Ser., 35:1–34.

Ayala, S.C. 1970a. Hemogregarine from sandfly infecting both lizards and snakes. J. Parasitol., 56:387–388.

Ayala, S.C. 1970b. Lizard malaria in California: Description of a strain of *Plasmodium mexicanum,* and biogeography of lizard malaria in western North America. J. Parasitol, 56:417–425.

Ayala, S.C., and Lee, D. 1970. Saurian malaria: Development of sporozoites in two species of Phlebotomine sandflies. Science, 167:891–892.

Baird, C.R. 1971. Development of *Cuterebra jellisoni* (Diptera: Cuterebridae) in six species of rabbits and rodents. J. Med. Ent., 8:615–622.

Balashov, Y.S. 1972. Bloodsucking ticks (Ixodoidea) - vectors of diseases of man and animals. Misc. Publ. Ent. Soc. Am., 8:161–376.

Ball, G.H., Chao, J., and Telford, Jr., S.R. 1969. *Hepatozoon fusifex* sp. n., a hemogregarine from *Boa constrictor* producing marked morphological changes in infected erythrocytes. J. Parasitol., 55:800–813.

Banks, N. 1924. Arachnida of the Williams Galapagos expedition. Zoologica, N.Y. Zool. Soc., 5:93–99.

Baumgartner, D.L. 1988. Review of myiasis (Insecta: Diptera: Calliphoridae, Sarcophagidae) of Nearctic wildlife. Wildl. Rehab., 7:3–46.

Bauwens, D., Strijbosch, H., and Stumpel, A.H.P. 1983. The lizards *Lacerta agilis* and *L. vivipara* as hosts to larvae and nymphs of the tick *Ixodes ricinus.* Holarctic Ecol., 6:32–40.

Beck, D.E., Allred, D.M., and Brinton, E.P. 1963. Ticks of the Nevada test site. Brigham Young University Sci. Bull., Biol. Ser., 4:1–11.

Becklund, W.W. 1968. Ticks of veterinary significance found on imports in the United States. J. Parasitol., 54:622–628.

Belova, E.M. 1971. Reptiles and their importance in the epidemiology of leishmaniasis. Bull. World Health Org., 44:553–560.

Belova, E.M., and Bogdanov, O.P. 1968. Leptomonad infections of snakes in Turkmenian SSR. Med. Parazitol., Moscow, 37:304–306.

Benton, A.H. 1955. A modified technique for preparing whole mounts of Siphonaptera. J. Parasitol., 41:322–323.

Bequaert, J. 1932a. *Amblyomma dissimile* Koch, a tick indigenous to the United States (Acarina: Ixodidae). Psyche, 39:45–47.

Bequaert, J. 1932b. On the ornate nymphs of the tick genus *Amblyomma* (Acarina: Ixodidae). Z. Parasitkd., 4:776–783.

Berdyev, A.S., Atayev, C., Annayev, D., and Ovezmukhammedov, A. 1974. Reptiles of Turkeminstan as the hosts of ixodid ticks. Izvest. Akad. Nauk Turkmen. SSR, s. Biol. Nauk, 6:31–34. (In Russian).

Beron, P. 1966. Contribution à l'étude des acariens parasites des reptiles en Bulgarie. Isvest. Zool. Inst. s Muz., Bulgar. Akad. Nauk Otdel. Biol. Nauk, 22:51–53.

Bhat, H.R., and Sreenivasan, M.A. 1981. Further records of the ticks of some reptilian and mammalian hosts in the Kyasanur Forest Desease area, Karnataka, India. Indian J. Parasitol., 5:207–210.

Bishopp, F.C., and Trembley, H.L. 1945. Distribution and hosts of certain North American ticks. J. Parasitol., 31:1–54.

Blake, D.H. 1955. Note on the rearing of *Anolisimyia blakeae,* a sarcophagid fly from the American chameleon, *Anolis carolinensis* Voigt (Diptera: Sarcophagidae). Proc. Ent. Soc. Wash., 57:187–188.

Blanc, G.M., Delage, B., and Ascione, L. 1962. Étude epidemio-écologique dans la forêt du Cherrat. Arch. Inst. Pasteur Maroc., 6:223–292.

Böhme, W., Jager, U., and Schätti, B. 1989. A new monitor lizard (Reptilia: Varanidae) from Yemen, with notes on ecology, phylogeny and zoogeography. Fauna Saudi Arabia 10:433–448.

Booden, T., Chao, J., and Ball, G.H. 1970. Transfer of *Hepatozoon* sp. from *Boa constrictor* to a lizard, *Anolis carolinensis,* by mosquito vectors. J. Parasitol., 56:832–833.

Boreham, P.F.L., and Snow, W.F. 1973. Further information on the food sources of *Culex (Culex) decens* Theo. (Diptera: Culicidae). Trans. Roy. Soc. Trop. Med. Hyg., 67:724–725.

Borkent, A. 1995a. *Biting midges in the Cretaceous amber of North America (Diptera: Ceratopogonidae).* Backhuys, Leiden, The Netherlands.

Borkent, A. 1995b. Biting midges (Ceratopogonidae: Diptera) feeding on leatherneck turtle in Costa Rica. Brenesia 43–44:25–30.

Brown, R.N., and Lane, R.S. 1992. Lyme disease in California: A novel enzootic transmission cycle of *Borrelia burgdorferi.* Science, 256:1439–1442.

Brygoo, E.R. 1963. Contribution à la connaissance de la parasitologie des caméléons malgaches (2e partie). Ann. Parasitol, 38:525–739.

Bull, C.M., and Sara, G.J. 1976. The population structure of an Australian reptile tick, *Aponomma hydrosauri* (Acari: Ixodidae). I. Evidence from an esterase polymorphism. J. Med. Ent., 13:137–142.

Bull, C.M., Chilton, N.B., and Sharrad, R.D. 1988. Risk of predation for two reptile tick species. Exp. Appl. Acarol., 5:93–99.

Burton, A.N., McLintock, J., and Rempel, J.G. 1966. Western equine encephalitis in Saskatchewan garter snakers and leopard frogs. Science, 154:1029–1031.

Byam, W., and Archibald, R.G. 1921–23. *The Practice of Medicine in the Tropics.* Vols. 1–3, 2550 pp.

Calle, P.P., Rivas, J., Munoz, M., Thorbjarnarson, J., Dierenfeld, E.S., Holmstrom, W., Braselton, W.E., and Karesh, W.B. 1994. Health assessment of free-ranging anacondas (*Eunectes murinus*) in Venezuela. J. Zoo Wildl. Med., 25:53–62.

Carpenter, S.J. 1941. *The Mosquitoes of Arkansas,* 2nd ed. Arkansas State Board of Health. 87 pp.

Cerny, V. 1967. Some results of tick investigations in Cuba. Wiad. Parazytol., 13:533–537.

Cerny, V. 1969. Nuevos conocimientos sobre la Ixodo-fauna Cubana. Torreia, 21:3–8.

Chaniotis, B.N. 1967. The biology of California *Phlebotomus* (Diptera: Psychodidae) under laboratory conditions. J. Med. Ent., 4:221–233.

Chao, J., and Ball, G.H. 1969. Transfer of *Hepatozoon rarefaciens* (Sambon and Seligmann, 1907) from the indigo snake to a gopher snake by a mosquito vector. J. Parasitol., 55:681–682.

Cheng, T.C. 1973. *The Biology of Animal Parasites.* Iowa State Univ. Press, Ames, IA. 965 pp.

Chilton, N.B., Bull, C.M., and Andrews, R.H. 1992a. Niche segregation in reptile ticks: attachment sites and reproductive success of females. Oecologia, 90:255–259.

Chilton, N.B., Bull, C.M., and Andrews, R.H. 1992b. Differences in the attachment site of the Australian reptile tick *Amblyomma limbatum* (Acari: Ixodidae) on two host species. Int. J. Parasitol., 22:783–787.

Chodziesner, M. 1924. Beitrage zur Kenntnis der Zecken mit besonderer Berucksichtigung der Gattung *Hyalomma* Koch. Zool. Jahrb. Jena, Abt. Syst., 47: 505–572.

Christensen, H.A., de Vasquez, A.M., and Boreham, M.M. 1996. Host feeding patterns of mosquitoes (Diptera: Culicidae) from central Panama. Am. J. Trop. Med. Hyg., 55:202–208.

Christopher, S., and Reuben, R. 1971. Studies on the mosquitoes of North Arcot District, Madras State, India. J. Med. Ent., 8:314–318.

Chubkova, A.I. 1960. On questions of the blood-sucking acarine fauna of Erevan and regions of the Sevansk basin. Trudy Armiansk. Protivochum. Stants., 1: 391–401. (In Russian).

Clausen, P.-H., Adeyemi, I., Bauer, B. Breloeer, M., Salchow, F., and Staak, C. 1998. Host preferences of tsetse (Diptera: Glossinidae) based on bloodmeal identifications. Med. Vet. Ent., 12:169–180.

Clifford, C.M., Jr., and Anastos, G. 1962. Ticks. Fasc. (66) Mission (de Witte) (1946–1949) Explor. Parc. Nat. Upemba, 1–45.

Clifford, C.M., Jr., and Anastos, G. 1964. Ticks. Fasc. (44) Mission (H. de Saeger) (1949–1952) Explor. Parc. Nat. Garamba, 3–40.

Clifford, C.M., Jr., and Kohls, G.M. 1962. Description of the female of *Dermacentor latus* Cooley and of *Amblyomma albopictum* Neumann (Acarina-Ixodidae). J. Parasitol., 48:486–489.

Clifford, C.M., Anastos, G., and Elbl, A. 1961. The larval ixodid ticks of the eastern United States (Acarina-Ixodidae). Misc. Pub. Ent. Soc. Am., 2:213–237.

Clymer, B.C., Howell, D.E., and Hair, J. A. 1970. Animal hosts of economically important ticks (Acarina) in east-central Oklahoma. Ann. Ent. Soc. Am., 63: 612–614.

Cooley, R.A., and Kohls, G.M. 1943. *Ixodes californicus* Banks, 1904, *Ixodes pacificus* n. sp., and *Ixodes conepati* n. sp. (Acarina: Ixodidae). Pan-Pacific Ent., 19:139–147.

Cooley, R.A., and Kohls, G.M. 1944a. *The Argasidae of North America, Central America and Cuba.* Am. Mid. Nat., Monograph No. 1. The University Press, Notre Dame, IN. 152 pp.

Cooley, R.A., and Kohls, G.M. 1944b. The genus *Amblyomma* (Ixodidae) in the United States. J. Parasitol., 30:77–111.

Cooley, R.A., and Kohls, G.M. 1945. *The Genus Ixodes in North America.* Natl. Inst. Health Bull. No. 184, U.S. Publ. Health Serv. 246 pp.

Cooney, J.C., and Hays, K.L. 1972. Bionomics of the gopher tortoise tick, *Amblyomma tuberculatum* Marx. J. Med. Ent., 9:239–245.

Darsie, F.R., Jr., and Ward, R.A. 1981. Identification and geographical distribution of the mosquitoes of North America north of Mexico. Mosq. Syst., Suppl., 1:1–313.

Darskaya, N.F., and Besedina, K.P. 1961. On the possibility of fleas (Suctoria) feeding on reptiles. Trudy Nauchno-Issled. Protiv. Inst. Kavk. Zakavk., 5: 33–39. (In Russian).

Davis, G.E. 1936. *Ornithodoros turicata*: The possible vector of relapsing fever in southwestern Kansas. Publ. Health Rept., 51:1719.

DeFoliart, G.R. 1967. *Aedes canadensis* (Theobold) feeding on Blanding's turtle. J. Med. Ent., 4:31.

Degenhardt, W.G., and Degenhardt, P.B. 1965. The host-parasite relationship between *Elaphe subocularis* (Reptilia: Colubridae) and *Aponomma elaphensis* (Acarina: Ixodidae). Southwest. Nat., 10:167–178.

DeGiusti, D.L., and Dobrzechowski, D. 1974. The biology of the chelonian haemoproteid *Haemoproteus metchnikovi* in turtle hosts and in the intermediate host, *Chrysops callidus*. ICOPA III, 1:80–81.

DeGiusti, D.L., Sterling, C.R., and Dobrzechowski, D. 1973. Transmission of the chelonian haemoproteid *Haemoproteus metchnikovi* by a tabanid fly *Chrysops callidus*. Nature, 242:50–51.

Deraniyasala, P.E.P. 1939. *The Tetrapod Reptiles of Ceylon*. Vol. 1. *Testudinates and Crocodilians*. Dulau and Company, London. 412 pp.

Dial, R., and Roughgarden, J. 1996. Natural history observations of *Anolisomyia rufianalis* (Diptera: Sarcophagidae) infesting *Anolis* lizards in a rain forest canopy. Environ. Entomol., 25:1325–1328.

Dinsmore, J.J. 1969. Reptiles of Little Tobago Island, West Indies. Quart. J. Florida Acad. Sci., 32:307–309.

Dodge, H.R. 1955. Sarcophagid flies parasitic on reptiles (Diptera: Sarcophagidae). Proc. Ent. Soc., Wash., 57:183–187.

Doherty, R.L., Carley, J.G., Standfast, H.A., Dyce, A.L., Kay, B.H., and Snowdon, W.A. 1973. Isolation of arboviruses from mosquitoes, biting midges, sandflies and vertebrates collected in Queensland, 1969 and 1970. Trans. Roy. Soc. Trop. Med. Hyg., 67:536–543.

Doherty, R.L., Standfast, H.A., Domrow, R., Wetters, E.J., Whitehead, R.H., and Carley, J.G. 1971. Studies of the epidemiology of arthropod-borne virus infections at Mitchell River Mission, Cape York Peninsula, North Queensland. IV. Arbovirus infections of mosquitoes and mammals, 1967–1969. Trans. Roy. Soc. Trop. Med. and Hyg., 65:504–513.

Dove, W.E., Hall, D.G., and Hull, J.B. 1932. The salt marsh sandfly problem (*Culidoides*). Ann. Ent. Soc. Am., 25:505–527.

Dower, K.M., Petney, T.N., and Horak, I.G. 1988. The developmental success of *Amblyomma hebraeum* and *Amblyomma marmoreum* on the leopard tortoise, *Geochelone pardalis*. Onderstepoort J. Vet. Res., 55:11–13.

Drees, B.M., Butler, L., and Pechnuman, L.L. 1980. *Horse Flies and Deer Flies of West Virginia: An Illustrated Key (Diptera, Tabanidae)*. Bulletin 674. West Virginia University Agricultural and Forestry Experiment Station, Morgantown, WV. 67 pp.

Duffield, G.A., and Bull, C.M. 1996a. Microhabitat choice and its role in determining the distribution of the reptile tick *Amblyomma vikirri*. Aust. J. Ecol., 21:255–263.

Duffield, G.A., and Bull, C.M. 1996b. Host location by larvae of the reptile tick *Amblyomma vikirri* (Acari, Ixodidae). Exp. Appl. Acarol., 20:575–583.

Dumbleton, L.J. 1943. A new tick from the tuatara (*Sphenodon punctatus*). N.Z. J. Sci. Tech., 24:185–190.

Dunlop, K.D. 1993. Effects of nymphal ticks and their interaction with malaria on the physiology of male fence lizards. Copeia 1993:1045–1048.

Dunn, L.H. 1918. Studies on the iguana tick, *Amblyomma dissimile*, in Panama. J. Parasitol., 5:1–10.

Dunn, L.H. 1933. Observations on the host selection of *Ornithodoros talaje* Guern., in Panama. Am. J. Trop. Med., 13:475–483.

Durden, L.A., and Keirans, J.E. 1996. *Nymphs of the Genus Ixodes (Acari: Ixodidae) of the United States: Taxonomy, Identification Key, Distribution, Hosts, and Medical/Veterinary Importance.* Ent. Soc. Am., Lanham, MD. 95 pp.

Durden, L.A., and Kollars, T.M. 1992. An annotated list of the ticks (Acari: Ixodoidea) of Tennessee, with records of four exotic species for the United States. Bull. Soc. Vector Ecol., 17:125–131.

Durden, L.A., Klompen, J.S.H., and Keirans, J.E. 1993. Parasitic arthropods of sympatric opossums, cotton rats, and cotton mice from Merritt Island, Florida. J. Parasitol., 79:283–286.

Dyar, H.G. 1923. The mosquitoes of the United States. Proc. U.S. Natl. Mus., 62:1–119.

Eads, R.B., Menzies, G.C., and Hightower, B.G. 1956. The ticks of Texas, with notes on their medical significance. Texas J. Sci., 8:7–24.

Easton, E.R., and Goulding, R.L., 1974. Ectoparasites in two diverse habitats in western Oregon. I. *Ixodes* (Acarina: Ixodidae). J. Med. Ent., 11:413–418.

Edman, J.D. 1974. Host-feeding patterns of Florida mosquitoes, IV. *Deinocerites*. J. Med. Ent., 11:105–107.

Emerton, J.H. 1904. A dipterous parasite of the box turtle. Psyche, 11:34.

Endris, R.G., Keirans, J.E., Robbins, R.G., and Hess, W.R. 1989. *Ornithodoros (Alectorobius) puertoricensis* (Acari: Argasidae): redescription by scanning electron microscopy. J. Med. Ent., 26:146–154.

Ernst, C.H., and Ernst, E.M. 1977. Ectoparasites associated with Neotropical turtles of the genus *Callopsis* (Testudines, Emydidae, Batagurinae). Biotropica, 9:139–142.

Fairchild, G.B. 1943. An annotated list of the bloodsucking insects, ticks and mites known from Panama. Am. J. Trop. Med., 23:569–591.

Fairchild, G.B., Kohls, G.M., and Tipton, V.J. 1966. The ticks of Panama. In: *Ectoparasites of Panama,* Wenzel, R. L. and Tipton, V. J. (Eds.). Field Museum of Natural History, Chicago, IL. pp. 167–219.

Feider, Z. 1962. Caracterele sexuale la nimfa de Ixodide. Stud. Cercet. Ştiint., Acad. Repub. Pop. Romine, 13:305–310.

Feldman-Muehsam, B. 1948. On larvae and nymphs of some species of Palestinian *Hyalomma.* Parasitology, 39:138–147.

Fielden, L.J., and Rechav, Y. 1994. Attachment sites of the tick *Amblyomma marmoreum* on its tortoise host, *Geochelone pardalis.* Exp. Appl. Acarol., 18: 339–349.

Fielden, L.J., Magano, S., and Rechav, Y. 1992a. Laboratory studies on the life cycle of *Amblyomma marmoreum* (Acari: Ixodidae) on two different hosts. J. Med. Ent., 29:750–756.

Fielden, L.J., Rechav, Y., and Bryson, N. R. 1992b. Acquired immunity to larvae of *Amblyomma marmoreum* and *A. hebraeum* by tortoises, guinea-pigs and guinea-fowl. Med. Vet. Ent., 6:251–254.

Filippova, N.A. 1959. On the fauna of the ticks (Parasitiformes, Ixodidae) infesting terrestrial vertebrates in the vicinity of the Lake Issyk-kul. Parazitol. Sborn. Zool. Inst., Akad. Nauk SSR, 18:110–119. (In Russian).

Filippova, N.A. 1985. *Taiga Tick, Ixodes persulcatus Schulze (Acarina, Ixodidae). Morphology, Systematics, Ecology, Medical Importance.* Akad. Nauk. SSSR, Inst. Evol. Morf. Ekol. Zhiv. im A.N. Severtsova, Leningrad. 416 pp. (In Russian).

Flynn, R.J. 1973. *Parasites of Laboratory Animals.* Iowa State Univ. Press, Ames, IA. 884 pp.

Fowler, M.E. 1986. *Zoo and Wild Animal Medicine.* W. B. Saunders Co., Philadelphia, PA. 1127 pp.

Fox, I., Fox, R.I., and Bayone, I.G. 1966. Fleas feed on lizards in the laboratory in Puerto Rico. J. Med. Ent., 2:395–396.

Francis, E., and Mayne, B. 1922. Experimental transmission of tularaemia by flies of the species *Chrysops discalis.* U.S. Pub. Hlth. Serv., Hyg. Lab. Bull., 130: 8–16.

Frank. W. 1981. Ectoparasites. In: *Diseases of the Reptilia,* Cooper, J. E. and Jackson, O. F. (Eds.), Vol. 1. Academic Press, NY. pp. 359–383.

Frazier, J.G., and Keirans, J.E. 1990. Ticks (Acari: Ixodidae) collected on chelonians (Reptilia) from India and Myanmar. J. Bombay Nat. Hist. Soc., 87: 247–249.

Frye, F.L. 1981. *Biomedical and Surgical Aspects of Captive Reptile Husbandry.* Veterinary Medicine Publishing Company, Lawrence, KS. 456 pp.

Frye, F.L. 1991. *Biomedical and Surgical Aspects of Captive Reptile Husbandry.* Krieger Publishing Company, Malabar, FL. 653 pp.

Fujimoto, K. 1994a. Effect of photoperiod on host-seeking activity and development of the larvae and nymphs of *Ixodes nipponensis* Kitaoka and Saito (Acari: Ixodidae). Jap. J. Sanit. Zool., 45:63–69.

Fujimoto, K. 1994b. Effect of age on the host-feeding activity of *Ixodes nipponensis* nymphs (Acarina: Ixodidae) exposed to short-day photoperiods. Jap. J. Sanit. Zool., 45:159–161.

Fujimoto, K. 1996. Behavioral diapause of *Ixodes nipponensis* adults (Acari: Ixodidae). Med. Entomol. Zool., 47:175–178.

Fujita, H., and Takada, N. 1978. Studies on ixodid fauna in northern part of Honshu, Japan. 3. Preliminary notes on *Ixodes nipponensis* (Ixodoidea; Ixodidae) found on the small reptile *Takydromus tachydromoides*. Jap. J. Sanit. Zool., 29:269–271.

Fujita, H., and Takada, N. 1997. Collection records of immature *Ixodes nipponensis* and *Ixodes persulcatus* ticks found on the small reptile *Takydromus tachydromoides* in the northern part of Honshu, Japan. Med. Entomol. Zool., 48: 123–125. (In Japanese).

Funk, R.S. 1988. Herp health hints and husbandry: Parasiticide dosages for captive amphibians and reptiles. Bull. Chicago Herp. Soc., 23(2):30.

Galbe, J., and Oliver, J.H., Jr. 1992. Immune response of lizards and rodents to larval *Ixodes scapularis* (Acari: Ixodidae). J. Med. Ent., 29:774–783.

Garnham, P.C.C. 1954. A haemogregarine in *Argas brumpti*. Riv. Parasitol., 15: 425–435.

Garnham, P.C.C. 1971. The genus *Leishmania*. Bull. World Health Org., 44: 477–489.

Garrigues, R.M. 1965. A *Cuterebra* (Diptera: Cuterebridae) infestation in the Grand Canyon rattlesnake, *Crotalus viridis abyssus,* with a list of those recorded from other hosts. Trans. Kansas Acad. Sci., 67:689–692.

Gebhardt, L.P., Stanton, G.J., and de St. Jear, S. 1966. Transmission of WEE virus to snakes by infected *Culex tarsalis* mosquitoes. Proc. Soc. Expl. Biol. Med., 123:233–235.

Gebhardt, L.P., Stanton, G.J., Hill, D.W., and Collett, G.C. 1964. Natural overwintering hosts of the virus of western equine encephalitis. New Eng. J. Med., 271:172–177.

Georgi, J.R. 1974. *Parasitology for Veterinarians.* W.B. Saunders Company, Philadelphia, PA. 386 pp.

Ghirotti, M., and Mwanaumo, B. 1989. *Amblyomma marmoreum* on tortoises of Southern Province, Zambia. J. Wildl. Dis., 25:634–635.

Gina, A. 1973. Të dhëna faunistike mbi rignat e familjes Ixodidae në rethin e Tiranës. Bull. i Shken. Natyr., 27:73–86.

Godsden, H., and Guerra, G. 1991. Los acaros ectoparasitos de *Amblyrhynchus cristatus* Bell (Sauria: Iguanidae) como trazadores zoogeograficos, en las Islas Galapagos, Ecuador. Folia Ent. Méxicana, 83:183–197.

Goldberg, S.R., and Bursey, C.R. 1991. Duration of attachment by mites and ticks on the iguanid lizards *Sceloporus graciosus* and *Uta stansburiana*. J. Wildl. Dis., 27:719–722.

Goodwin, J.T., Mullens, B.A., and Gerhardt, R.R. 1985. The Tabanidae of Tennessee. Univ. Tenn. Ag. Exp. Sta., Knoxville. Bull. 642.

Gorham, J.R. (Ed.). 1991. *Insect and Mite Pests in Food,* Vols. 1 & 2. USDA Agr. Hdbk. No. 655. 767 pp.

Graham-Jones, O. 1961. Notes on the common tortoise. IV. Some clinical conditions affecting the North African tortoise ("Greek" tortoise) *Testudo graeca*. Vet. Rec., 73:317–321.

Gregson, J.D. 1935. A preliminary report of the lizard-tick relationship on the British Columbia coast. Proc. Ent. Soc. Brit. Columbia, 31:17–21.

Gregson, J.D. 1956. The Ixodoidea of Canada. Can. Dept. Agr., 930:1–92.

Grokhovskaià, I.M., and Nguen-Suan-Khoe. 1968. On the study of ixodid ticks (Ixodidae) of the Democratic Republic of Viet-Nam (Russian text). Med. Parazitol. Parazit. Bolenzni, 37:710–715.

Gunter, G. 1958. A sarcophagid fly larva parasitic in *Anolis carolinensis*. Copeia, 1958:336.

Gupta, B.K. 1996. On the tick *Aponomma gervaisi* in *Varanus bengalensis* and *V. griseus*. Hamadryad, 21:43–44.

Harbison, C.F. 1937. The adobe tick on *Gopherus agassizii*. Herpetologica, 1:80.

Harris, P., Riordan, D.F., and Cooke, D. 1969. Mosquitoes feeding on insect larvae. Science, 164:184–185.

Hayashi, F., and Hasegawa, M. 1984a. Selective parasitism of the tick *Ixodes asanumai* (Acarina: Ixodidae) and its influence on the host lizard *Eumeces okadae* in Miyake-jima, Izu islands. Appl. Ent. Zool., 19:181–191.

Hayashi, F., and Hasegawa, M. 1984b. Infestation level, attachment site and distribution pattern of the lizard tick *Ixodes asanumai* (Acarina: Ixodidae). Appl. Ent. Zool., 19:299–305.

Hayes, J. 1965. New host record for *Aedes canadensis*. Mosq. News, 25:344.

Henderson, B.E., and Senior, L. 1961. Attach rate of *Culex tarsalis* on reptiles, amphibians and small mammals. Mosq. News, 21:29–32.

Hesse, G.H. 1985. Interstadial competition for sites of attachment to hosts in a one-host reptile tick in Senegal. Acarologia, 26:355–360.

Ho, T.M., and Ismail, S. 1984. Life cycle of the tick *Amblyomma cordiferum* Neumann under laboratory conditions. Malayan Nature J., 38:73–77.

Hoare, C.A. 1931. Studies on *Trypanosoma grayi*. III. Life cycle in the tsetse fly and in the crocodile. Parasitology, 23:449–484.

Hoare, C.A. 1932. On protozoal blood parasites collected in Uganda with an account of the life cycle of the crocodile haemogragarine. Parasitology, 24:210–224.

Hoffman, G., and Lindau, M. 1971. Zecken an Nutz- und Wildtieren in Niger. Ztschr. Ang. Ent., 69:72–82.

Hoffman, G., Köhler, G., and Sachs, R. 1970. Beitrag zur Kenntnis der Zeckenfauna der Wildtiere der Serengeti. Acta Trop., 27:193–207.

Hoogstraal, H. 1956. *African Ixodoidea. I. Ticks of the Sudan (with special reference to Equatoria Province and with preliminary reviews of the genera Boophilus, Margaropus, and Hyalomma)*. Dept. Navy, Bur. Med. Surg., Washington, D.C. 1101 pp.

Hoogstraal, H. 1959a. *Ixodes festai* Rondelli, 1926 (Ixodoidea, Ixodidae) of the Western Mediterranean area: A review. Arch. Inst. Pasteur Maroc, 5:710–713.

Hoogstraal, H. 1959b. Biological observation on certain Turkish *Haemaphysalis* ticks (Ixodoidea, Ixodidae). J. Parasitol., 45:227–232.

Hoogstraal, H. 1964. Ergebnisse der zoologischen Nubien-Expedition 1962. Teil XXVII. Ticks and parasitic mites. (Zecken und parasitischen Milben). Ann. Naturh. Mus. Wein, 67:627–629.

Hoogstraal, H. 1966. Ticks in relation to human diseases caused by viruses. Ann. Rev. Ent., 11:261–308.

Hoogstraal, H. 1967. Ticks in relation to human diseases caused by *Rickettsia* species. Ann. Rev. Ent., 12:377–420.

Hoogstraal, H. 1973. Acarina (ticks). In: *Viruses and Invertebrates,* Gibbs, A.J. (Ed.). North-Holland Publishing Company, Amsterdam. pp. 83–103.

Hoogstraal, H. 1985. Argasid and nuttalliellid ticks as parasites and vectors. Adv. Parasitol., 24:135–238.

Hoogstraal, H., and Aeschlimann, A. 1982. Tick-host specificity. Mitt. Schweiz. Ent. Ges., 55:5–32.

Hoogstraal, H., and Kaiser, M.N. 1957. Results of the NAMRU-3 southeastern Egypt expedition, 1954. 3. *Argas brumpti* Neumann, 1907, and *Ornithodoros foleyi* Parrot, 1928 (Ixodoidea, Argasidae) in Egypt. Bull. Zool. Soc. Egypt, 13:29–40.

Hoogstraal, H., and Kaiser, M.N. 1958a. Observations on Egyptian *Hyalomma* ticks (Ixodoidea, Ixodidae). I. Parasitism of lizards by nymphs. Ann. Ent. Soc. Am., 51:7–12.

Hoogstraal, H., and Kaiser, M.N. 1958b. Observations on Egyptian *Hyalomma* ticks (Ixodoidea, Ixodidae). 4. Identity, distribution, and hosts of *H. franchinii* Tonelli-Rondelli (new combination). Systematic status of *H. tunesiacum* Sc. & Sc. and its subspecies. Ann. Entomol. Soc. Am., 51:397–400.

Hoogstraal, H., and Kaiser, M.N. 1960a. Observations on ticks (Ixodoidea) of Libya. Ann. Ent. Soc. Am., 53:445–457.

Hoogstraal, H., and Kaiser, M.N. 1960b. Some host relationships of the tortoise tick, *Hyalomma* (*Hyalommasta*) *aegyptium* (L.) (Ixodoidea, Ixodidae) in Turkey. Ann. Ent. Soc. Am., 53:457–458.

Hoogstraal, H., and Kohls, G.M. 1966. *Argas* (*Microargas*) *transversus* Banks (new subgenus) (Ixodidae, Argasidae), a diminutive parasite of the Galapagos giant tortoise: Redescription of the holotype male and description of the larva. Ann. Ent. Soc. Am., 59:247–252.

Hoogstraal, H., and McCarthy, V.C. 1965. Hosts and distribution of *Haemaphysalis kashmirensis* with descriptions of immature stages and definition of the subgenus *Herpetobia* Canestrini (resurrected). J. Parasitol., 51:674–679.

Hoogstraal, H., and Rack, G. 1967. Ticks (Ixodidae) collected by Deutsche Indien-Expedition, 1955–1958. J. Med. Ent., 4:284–288.

Hoogstraal, H., and Wassef, H.Y. 1984. *Dermacentor* (*Indocentor*) *compactus* (Acari: Ixodoidea: Ixodidae): wild pigs and other hosts and distribution in Malaysia, Indonesia, and Borneo. J. Med. Entomol., 21:174–178.

Hoogstraal, H., and Wassef, H.Y. 1985a. *Dermacentor (Indocentor) auratus* (Acari: Ixodoidea: Ixodidae): hosts, distribution, and medical importance in tropical Asia. J. Med. Entomol., 22:170–177.

Hoogstraal, H., and Wassef, H.Y. 1985b. *Dermacentor (Indocentor) atrosignatus* (Acari: Ixodoidea: Ixodidae): hosts and distribution in the Malay Peninsula, Indonesia, Borneo, and southern Philippines. J. Med. Entomol., 22:644–647.

Hoogstraal, H., Clifford, C.M., and Keirans, J.E. 1973. *Argas (Microargas) transversus* (Ixodoidea: Argasidae) of Galapagos giant tortoises: Description of the female and nymph. Ann. Ent. Soc. Am., 66:727–732.

Hoogstraal, H., Santana, F.J., and van Peenen, P.F.D. 1968. Ticks (Ixodoidea) of Mt. Sontra, Danang, Republic of Vietnam. Ann. Ent. Soc. Am., 61:722–729.

Hoogstraal, H., Trapido, H., and Kohls, G.M. 1965. Studies on Southeast Asian *Haemaphysalis* ticks (Ixodoidea, Ixodidae). The identity, distribution, and hosts of *H. (Kaiseriana) hystricis* Supino. J. Parasitol., 51:467–480.

Hoogstraal, H., Lim, B.L., Nadchatram, M., and Anastos, G. 1972. The Gunong Benom expedition 1967. 8. Ticks (Ixodidae) of Gunong Benom and their altidutinal distribution, hosts and medical relationships. Bull. Brit. Mus. (Nat. Hist.), Zool., 23:167–186.

Hoogstraal, H., Wassef, H.Y., Converse, J.D., Keirans, J.E., Cifford, C.M., and Feare, C.J. 1976. *Amblyomma loculosum* (Ixodoidea: Ixodidae): Identity, marine bird and human hosts, virus infection, and distribution in southern oceans. Ann. Ent. Soc. Am., 69:3–14.

Hubbard, H.G. 1894. The insect guests of the Florida land tortoise. Insect Life, 6:302–315.

Hunt, T.J. 1957. Notes on diseases and mortality in Testudines. Herpetologica, 13:19–23.

Irby, W.S., and Apperson, C.S. 1988. Hosts of mosquitoes in the Coastal Plain of North Carolina. J. Med. Ent., 25:85–93.

Jackson, C.G., Jr., Jackson, M.M. and Davis, J. D. 1969. Cutaneous myiasis in the three-toed box turtle, *Terrapene carolina triunguis*. Bull. Wildl. Dis. Assoc., 5:114.

Jacobson, E. 1986. Parasitic diseases. In: *Zoo and Wild Animal Medicine,* Fowler, M. E. (Ed.). W. B. Saunders Company, Philadelphia, pp. 162–186.

James, M. T. 1947. *The Flies that Cause Myiasis in Man.* United States Dept. of Agr., Misc. Publ. No. 631. U.S. Gov. Printing Ofc., Wash., D.C.

Jansen, J., Jr., and van den Broek, E. 1966. Parasites of zoo-animals in the Netherlands and of exotic animals II. Bijdr. Dierk., K. Zool. Genootsch. Natura Artis Magistra Amsterdam, (36):65–68.

Jäth, H. 1952. Beobachtungen zur lebensweise der Flöhe (Insecta, Siphonaptera). Z. Hyg. Zool., 40:133–137.

Jellison, W.L. 1934. The parasitism of lizards by *Ixodes ricinus californicus* (Banks). J. Parasitol., 20:243.

Jones, E.K., Clifford, C.M., Keirans, J.E., and Kohls, G.M. 1972. The ticks of

Venezuela (Acarina: Ixodoidea) with a key to the species of *Amblyomma* in the Western Hemisphere. Brigham Young Univ. Sci. Bull., Biol. Ser., 17:1–40.

Kadatskaia, K.P., and Shirova, L.F. 1963. Ixodid ticks and fleas in a tularemia focus of the Nakhichevan ASSR. Dokl. Akad. Nauk Azerbaidzhan SSR, 19: 79–83. (In Russian).

Kaiser, M.N., and Hoogstraal, H. 1963. The *Hyalomma* ticks (Ixodoidea, Ixodidae) of Afghanistan. J. Parasitol., 49:130–139.

Kaiser, M.N., and Hoogstraal, H. 1964. The *Hyalomma* ticks (Ixodoidea: Ixodidae) of Pakistan, India and Ceylon, with keys to subgenera and species. Acarologia, 6:257–286.

Kamara, J.A. 1975. Some parasites of wild animals in Sierra Leone. Bull. Anim. Health Prod. Africa, 23:265–268.

Kaufman, T.L. 1972. A revision of the genus *Aponomma* Neumann, 1899 (Acarina: Ixodidae). Ph.D. diss., University of Maryland. 389 pp.

Keirans, J.E. 1972. Redescription of *Amblyomma fulvum* Neumann 1899 (Acarina: Ixodidae), a parasite of the giant anaconda in northern South America. J. Med. Ent., 9:138–139.

Keirans, J.E. 1985. *Amblyomma antillorum* Kohls, 1969 (Acari: Ixodidae): Description of the immature stages from the rock iguana, *Iguana pinguis* (Sauria: Iguanidae) in the British Virgin Islands. Proc. Ent. Soc. Wash., 87:821–825.

Keirans, J.E. 1992. Systematics of the Ixodida (Argasidae, Ixodidae, Nuttalliellidae): An overview and some problems. In: *Tick Vector Biology: Medical and Veterinary Aspects,* Fivaz, B., Petney, T., and Horak, I. (Eds.). Springer-Verlag, Berlin. pp. 1–21.

Keirans, J.E., and Degenhardt, W.G. 1985. *Aponomma elaphense* Price, 1959 (Acari: Ixodidae): Diagnosis of the adults and nymph with first description of the larva. Proc. Biol. Soc. Wash., 98:711–717.

Keirans, J.E., and Garris, G.I. 1986. *Amblyomma arianae* n. sp. (Acari: Ixodidae), a parasite of *Alsophis portoricensis* (Reptilia: Colubridae) in Puerto Rico. J. Med. Ent., 23:622–625.

Keirans, J.E., and Klompen, J.S.H. 1996. *Amblyomma quadricavum* (Schulze) (new combination), and *Amblyomma arianae* Keirans and Garris, a new junior synonym of *Amblyomma quadricavum* (Acari: Ixodidae). Proc. Ent. Soc. Wash., 98:164–165.

Keirans, J.E., and Oliver, J.H., Jr. 1993. First description of the male and redescription of the immature stages of *Amblyomma rotundatum* (Acari: Ixodidae), a recently discovered tick in the U.S.A. J. Parasitol., 79:860-865.

Keirans, J.E., Bull, C.M., and Duffield, G.A. 1996a. *Amblyomma vikirri* n. sp. (Acari: Ixodida: Ixodidae), a parasite of the gidgee skink *Egernia stokesii* (Reptilia: Scincidae) from South Australia. Syst. Parasitol., 34:1–9.

Keirans, J.E., Clifford, C.M., and Hoogstraal, H. 1980. Identity of the nymphs and adults of the Galapagos iguanid lizard parasites, *Ornithodoros* (*Alectorobius*) *darwini* and *O.* (*A.*) *galapagensis* (Ixodoidea: Argasidae). J. Med. Ent., 17:427–438.

Keirans, J.E., Dennis, R.K., and Sharrad, R.D. 1994. *Aponomma* (*Bothriocroton*) *glebopalma,* n. subgen., n. sp., and *Amblyomma glauerti* n. sp. (Acari: Ixodida: Ixodidae), parasites of monitor lizards (Varanidae) in Australia. J. Med. Ent., 31:132–147.

Keirans, J.E., Hoogstraal, H., and Clifford, C.M. 1973. The *Amblyomma* (Acarina: Ixodidae) parasitic on giant tortoises (Reptilia: Testudinidae) of the Galapagos Islands. Ann. Ent. Soc. Am., 66:673–688.

Keirans, J.E., Hutcheson, H.J., Durden, L.A., and Klompen, J.S.H. 1996b. *Ixodes* (*Ixodes*) *scapularis* (Acari: Ixodidae): Redescription of all active stages, distribution, hosts, geographical variation, and medical and veterinary importance. J. Med. Ent., 33:297–318.

Keirans, J.E., Oliver, J.H., Jr., and Needham, G.R. 1992. The *Ixodes ricinus/persulcatus* complex defined. In: Proc. and Abstracts, First Int. Conf. Tick-borne pathogens at the host-vector interface: An agenda for Res. University of Minnesota, St. Paul. p. 32.

Kepner, W.A. 1912. The larva of *Sarcophaga,* a parasite of *Cistudo carolina,* and the history of its respiratory apparatus. Biol. Bull. Mar. Biol. Lab. Woods Hole, 22:163–172.

Kerbabaev, E.B. 1966. On the ecology of *Hyalomma detritum* P. Schulze, 1919 in Turkmenia. Izvest. Akad. Nauk Turkmen. SSR, s. Biol. Nauk, 3:60–65. (In Russian).

King, D.R., and Keirans, J.E. 1997. Ticks (Acari: Ixodidae) from varanid lizards (Reptilia: Varanidae) in eastern Indonesia. J. W. Aust. Mus., 18:329–330.

King, W.V., and Griffo, J.V., Jr. 1958. A box turtle fatality apparently caused by *Sarcophaga cistudinis* larvae. Florida Ent., 41:44.

King, W.V., Bradley, G.H., Smith, C.N., and McDuffie, W.C. 1960. *A Handbook of the Mosquitoes of the Southeastern United States.* USDA Agr. Hdbk. No. 173. 188 pp.

Kitaoka, S., and Suzuki, H. 1974. Reports of Medico-Zoological investigations in the Nansei Islands. Part 2. Ticks and their seasonal prevalences in southern Amami-Oshima. Eisei Dobutsu, Japan. J. San. Zool., 25:21–26. (In Japanese).

Klein, T.A., Young, D.G., and Telford, S.R. 1987. Vector incrimination and experimental transmission of *Plasmodium floridense* by bites of infected *Culex* (*Melanoconion*) *erraticus*. J. Am. Mosquito Control Assoc., 3:165–175.

Klein, T.A., Young, D.G., Greiner, E.C., Telford, Jr., S.R., and Butler, J.F. 1988. Development and experimental transmission of *Schellackia golvani* and *Schellackia occidentalis* by ingestion of infected blood-feeding arthropods. Int. J. Parasitol., 18:259–267.

Klompen, J.S.H., and Oliver, J.H., Jr. 1993. Systematic relationships in the soft ticks (Acari: Ixodida: Argasidae). Syst. Ent., 18:313–331.

Knipling, E.F. 1937. The biology of *Sarcophaga cistudinis* Aldrich (Diptera), a species of Sarcophagidae parasitic on turtles and tortoises. Proc. Ent. Soc., Wash. D.C., 39:91–101.

Kohls, G.M. 1950. *Ticks (Ixodoidea) of the Philippines*. Natl. Inst. Health Bull., No. 192. 28 pp.

Kohls, G.M. 1953. Notes on the ticks of Guam with the description of *Amblyomma squamosum* n. sp. (Acarina: Ixodidae). J. Parasitol., 39:264–267.

Kohls, G.M. 1957. Ticks (Ixodoidea) of Borneo and Malaya. Malaysian Parasites, 28:65–94.

Kohls, G.M. 1969. New records of ticks from the Lesser Antilles. Studies Fauna Curacao and Carib. Is. (Wagenaar Hummelinck, P.), 28:126–134 (Natuurrwetensch. Studiek. Suriname en Nederlandse Antillen, No. 53).

Kohls, G.M., Clifford, C.M., and Hoogstraal, H. 1969. Two new species of *Ornithodoros* from the Galapagos Islands (Acarina: Argasidae). J. Med. Ent., 6:75–78.

Kohls, G.M., Sonenshine, D.E., and Clifford, C.M. 1965. The systematics of the subfamily Ornithodorinae (Acarina: Argasidae). II. Identification of the larvae of the Western Hemisphere and descriptions of three new species. Ann. Ent. Soc. Am., 58:331–364.

Kolonin, G.V. 1995. Review of the ixodid tick fauna of Vietnam. J. Med. Ent., 32:276–282.

Krantz, G.W. 1978. *A Manual of Acarology*. Oregon State University Book Stores, Inc., Corvallis, OR. 509 pp.

Krylov, M.V., and Said-Aliev, S.A. 1964. Blood parasites of the family Haemogregarinidae from *Varanus komodoensis* (Russian text). Izvest. Akad. Nauk Tadzhiksk. SSR, Otdel. Biol. Nauk, 2:96–97.

Kulakova, Z.G. 1964. Feeding habits of the flea *Xenopsylla gerbilli capica* Ioff and some other fleas. Ectoparasites. Fauna, Biology and Practical Significance, Moscow State University, 4:205–220. (In Russian).

Lác, J., Cyprich, D., and Kiefer, M. 1972. Zeckenartige (Ixodidae) als Parasiten von Eidechsen unter den ökologischen Bedingungen der Slowakei. Zool. Listy, 21:133–144.

Lainson, R., and Shaw, J.J. 1969. A new haemosporidian of lizards, *Saurocytozoon tupinambi* gen. nov., sp. nov., in *Tupinambus nigropunctatus* (Teiidae). Parasitology, 59:159–162.

Lainson, R., Landau, I., and Shaw, J.J. 1974. Further parasites of the family Garniidae (Coccidiida: Haemosporidiidea) in Brazilian lizards. *Fallisia effusa* gen. nov., sp. nov. and *Fallisia modesta* gen. nov., sp. nov. Parasitology, 68:117–125.

Lamontellerie, M. 1966. Tiques (Acarina, Ixodoidea) de Haute-Volta. Bull. Inst. Fond. Afrique Noire, S. A., 28:597–642.

Landau, I., and Paperna, I. 1997. The assignment of *Hepatozoon mauritanicum,* a tick-transmitted parasite of tortoise, to the genus *Hemolivia.* Parasite-Journal de la Societé Francaise de Parasitologie, 4:365–367.

Lane, R.P. 1993. Sandflies (Phlebotominae). In: *Medical Insects and Arachnids,* Lane, R. P., and Crosskey, R. W. (Eds.). Chapman and Hall, London. pp. 78–119.

Lane, R.S. 1990. Susceptibility of the western fence lizard (*Sceloporus occidentalis*) to the Lyme borreliosis spirochete (*Borrelia burgdorferi*). Am. J. Trop. Med. Hyg. 42:75–82.

Lane, R.S., and Loye, J.E. 1989. Lyme disease in California: Interrelationship of *Ixodes pacificus* (Acari: Ixodidae), the western fence lizard (*Sceloporus occidentalis*), and *Borrelia burgdorferi.* J. Med. Ent., 26:272–278.

Lane, R.S., Piesman, J., and Burgdorfer, W. 1991. Lyme borreliosis: Relation of its causative agent to its vectors and hosts in North America and Europe. Ann. Rev. Ent., 36:587–609.

Lapage, G. 1962. *Mönning's Veterinary Helminthology and Entomology.* Williams and Wilkins, Baltimore, MD. 600 pp.

Lapage, G. 1968. *Veterinary Parasitology.* Oliver and Boyd, London. 1182 pp.

Laurence, W., Quate, S.H. 1967. Pacific insects: A monograph of Papuan Psychodidae, including *Phlebotomus* (Diptera). Monograph 15:1–216. Bernice P. Bishop Museum, Honolulu, HI.

Lawler, A.R. 1977. Notes on sarcophagids from the new host *Romalea microptera,* and from *Terrapene carolina carolina.* Gulf Res. Rept., 6:69–70.

Lazell, J.D., Keirans, J.E., and Samuelson, G.A. 1991. The Sulawesi black racer,

Coluber (Ptyas) dipsas, and a remarkable ectoparasitic aggregation. Pac. Sci., 45:355–361.

Lehmann, H.D., Roth, B., and Schneider, C.C. 1969. Die Zecke *Amblyomma testudinis* (Conil, 1877), ihre Entwicklung und ihre Wirkung auf den Wirt. Ztschr. Tropenmed. Parasitol., 20:247–259.

Lent, H., and Wygodzinsky, P. 1979. Revision of the Triatominae (Hemiptera: Reduviidae), and their significance as Vectors of Chagas' disease. Bull. Am. Mus. Nat. Hist., 163:125–520.

Levin, M., Levin, J.F., Yang, S., Howard, P., and Apperson, C.S. 1996. Reservoir competence of the southeastern five-lined skink (*Eumeces inexpectatus*) and the green anole (*Anolis carolinensis*) for *Borrelia burgdorferi*. Am. J. Trop. Med. Hyg., 54:92–97.

Levine, J.F., Apperson, C.S., Howard, P., Washburn, M., and Braswell, A.L. 1997. Lizards as hosts for immature *Ixodes scapularis* (Acari: Ixodidae) in North Carolina. J. Med. Entomol., 34:594–598.

Littig, K.S., and Stojanovich, C.J. 1965. Mosquitoes. Characteristics of anophelines and culicines. In: *Pictorial Keys to Arthropods, Reptiles, Birds and Mammals of Public Health Significance.* CDC, Atlanta, GA. p. 134.

Lopes, H. de S. 1982. On *Eumachronychia sternalis* Allen (Diptera, Sarcophagidae) with larvae living on eggs and hatchlings of the East Pacific green turtle. Rev. Bras. Biol., 42:425–429.

Lopes, H. de S. and Tibana, R. 1988. On Johnsoniini (Diptera, Sarcophagidae), with *Notochaetisca* new name, and descriptions of eight new species. Rev. Bras. Biol., 48:315–332.

Maa, T.C., and Kuo, J.S. 1966. Catalogue and bibliography of ticks and mites parasitic on vertebrates in Taiwan. Quart. J. Taiwan Mus. 19:373–413.

MacFarland, C.G., and Reeder, W.G. 1974. Cleaning symbiosis involving Galapagos tortoises and two species of Darwin's finches. Z. Tierpsychol., 34:464–483.

MacLeod, J. 1970. Tick infestation patterns in the Southern Province of Zambia. Bull. Ent. Res., 60:253–274.

Maldonado Capriles, J., and Medina-Gaud, S. 1977. The ticks in Puerto Rico (Arachnida: Acarina). J. Agr. Univ. Puerto Rico, 61:402–404.

Malkmus, R. 1985. Zecken (*Ixodes ricinus*) an einer Zauneidechse (*Lacerta agilis*). Nachr. Naturwiss. Mus. Aschaffenburg, 93:69–73.

Malkmus, R. 1995. Starker Befall einer Bergeidechse (*Lacerta vivipara* Jacquin, 1787) durch die Zecke *Ixodes ricinus* L., 1758 (Rept.: Sauria; Arachn.: Acari). Nachr. Naturwiss. Mus. Aschaffenburg, 102:33–36.

Manweiler, S.A., Lane, R.S., and Tempelis, C.H. 1992. The western fence lizard

Sceloporus occidentalis: Evidence of field exposure to *Borrelia burgdorferi* in relation to infestation by *Ixodes pacificus* (Acari: Ixodidae). Am. J. Trop. Med. Hyg., 47:328–336.

Manweiler, S.A., Lane, R.S., Block, W.M., and Morrison, M.L. 1990. Survey of birds and lizards for ixodid ticks (Acari) and spirochetal infection in northern California. J. Med. Ent., 27:1011–1015.

Marchette, N.J. 1966. Rickettsioses (tick typhus, Q-fever, urban typhus) in Malaya. J. Med. Ent., 2:339–371.

Marcus, L.C. 1981. *Veterinary Biology and Medicine of Captive Amphibians and Reptiles.* Lea and Febiger, Philadelphia, PA. 239 pp.

Markov, G.S., Lukina, G.P., Markova, L.I., and Mozgina, A.A. 1964a. Parasites of reptiles in the northern Caucasus. Uchen. Zapiski Volgograd. Gosudarstv. Pedagog. Inst. im. A. S. Serafimovich. Kafedry Zool., Fiziol. i Morfol., 16:99–105. (In Russian).

Markov, G.S., Ivanov, V.P., Kryuchkov, B.P., Luk'yanova, Z.H.F., Nikulin, V.P., and Chernobay, V.F. 1964b. Protozoa and Acarina parasitizing reptiles of the Caspian Sea region. Uchen Zapiski Volgograd. Gosudarstv. Pedagog. Inst. im. A. S. Serafimovich, Kafedry Zool., Fiziol. i Morfol., 16:106–110. (In Russian).

de Marmels, J. 1994. *Cistudinomyia* (Dipt., Sarcophagidae) causing myiasis in a Venezuelan gecko (Sauria, Geckonidae). Ent. Mon. Mag., 130:223–225.

Marshall, J.F. 1938. *The British Mosquitoes.* British Museum (Natural History), London. 341 pp.

Matheson, R. 1950. *Medical Entomology*, 2nd ed. Comstock Publishing Associates, Ithaca, NY. 612 pp.

Matthysse, J.G., and Colbo, M.H. 1987. *The Ixodid Ticks of Uganda Together With Species Pertinent to Uganda Because of Their Present Known Distribution.* Ent. Soc. Am., College Park, MD. 426 pp.

Matuschka, F.R., Fischer, P., Musgrave, K., Richter, D., and Spielman, A. 1991. Hosts on which nymphal *Ixodes ricinus* most abundantly feed. Am. J. Trop. Med. Hyg., 44:100–107.

McIver, S.B. 1968. Host preferences and discrimination by the mosquitoes *Aedes aegypti* and *Culex tarsalis* (Diptera: Culicidae). J. Med. Ent., 5:422–428.

Means, R.G. 1968. Host preferences of mosquitoes (Diptera: Culicidae) in Suffolk County, New York. Ann. Ent. Soc. Am., 61:116–120.

van der Merwe, S. 1968. Some remarks on the "tampans" of the *Ornithodoros moubata* complex in southern Africa. Zool. Anz., 181;280–289.

Meyer, M.C., and Olsen, O.W. 1980. *Essentials of Parasitology.* Wm.C. Brown Co. Publishers, Dubuque, IA. 266 pp.

Mohiuddin, A. 1959. The behavior of *Leishmania adleri* in various lizards. E. African Md. J., 36:171–176.

Morh, C.O., Beck, D.E., and Brinton, E.P. 1964. Observations on host-parasite relationships and seasonal history of ticks in San Mateo County, California. Great Basin Nat., 24:1–6.

Morel, P.C. 1967. Les tiques des animaux sauvages des Antilles (Acariens, Ixodoidea). Acarologia, 9:341–352.

Morel, P.C. 1978. Tiques d'animaux sauvages en Haute-Volta (Acariens, Ixodidae). Rev. Elev. Med. Vet. Pays Trop., 31:69–78.

Morel, P.C., and Mouchet, J. 1965. Les tiques du Cameroun (Ixodidae et Argasidae) (2e note). Ann. Parasitol. Hum. Comp., 40:477–496.

Morel, P.C., Chabaud, A.G., Campana-Rouget, Y., and Callot, J. 1961. Station expérimentale de parasitologie de Richelieu (Indre-et-Loire). Contribution à la faune parasitaire régionale. Chapter II. Liste des parasites par ordre sytématique. R. Ixodidés). Ann. Parasitol. Hum. Comp., 36:337–340.

Moreno, E., and Bolanos, R. 1977. Hemogregarinas en serpientes de Costa Rica. Rev. Biol. Trop., 25:47–57.

Mullen, G.R., Trauth, S.E., and Sellers, J.C. 1984. Association of a miltogrammine fly, *Eumacronychia nigricornis* Allen (Diptera: Sarcophagidae), with the brood burrows of *Sceloporus undulatus* (Latrielle) (Reptilia: Lacertilia). J. Georgia Ent. Soc., 19:1–6.

Mullens, B.A., Barrows, C., and Borkent, A. 1997. Lizard feeding by *Leptoconops* (*Brachyconops*) *californiensis* (Diptera; Ceratopogonidae) on desert sand dunes. J. Med. Entomol., 34:735–737.

Muller, J.F. 1921. Notes on the habits of the soft-shell turtle *Amyda mutica*. Am. Midl. Nat., 7:180–184.

Nagar, S.K. 1962. A faunistic survey of the ticks (Ixodidae) from Delhi State with a revision of the genus *Hyalomma* Koch reported from India. Bull. Ent. Madras, 3:58–61.

Nagar, S.K., Raizada, R.N., and Saxena, V.K. 1977. Observations on the prevalence of babesiosis, and the composition and ecology of ixodid ticks in Delhi. Ind. J. Anim. Sci., 47:654–663.

Nemenz, H. 1962. Zecken aus der Türkei und dem Karakorum (Acari, Ixodidae). Z. Parasitenk., 22:111–113.

Nemenz, H. 1967. Zecken aus der Türkei (Acari, Ixodidae). Zool. Anz., 178: 191–195.

Neumann, L.G. 1899. Révision de la famille des Ixodidés. Mém. Soc. Zool. de France, 12:107–294.

Newstead, R., Evans, A.M., and Potts, W.H. 1924. *Guide to the Study of Tsetse Flies.* School of Trop. Med. Mem., n.s. No. 1, University of Liverpool Press, Liverpool, and Hodder and Stroughton, London.

Ngumbi, P.M., Lawyer, P.G., Johnson, R.N., Kiilu, G., and Asiago, C. 1992. Identification of phlebotomine sandfly bloodmeals from Baringo district, Kenya by direct enzyme-linked immunosorbent assay (ELISA). Med. Vet. Ent., 6:385–388.

Nguyên, V.-A. 1961. Services pratiques. Rap. Ann. Fonction Techn. Inst. Pasteur Vietnam., 1960:115–219.

Nolan, M.P., Jr., Moussa, M.A., and Hayes, D.E. 1965. *Aedes* mosquitoes feeding on turtles in nature. Mosq. News, 25:218–219.

Norval, R.A.I. 1975. Studies on the ecology of *Amblyomma marmoreum* Koch 1844 (Acarina: Ixodidae). J. Parasitol., 61:737–742.

Nosek, J. 1971. The ecology, bionomics, and behaviour of *Haemaphysalis (Aboimisalis) punctata* tick in central Europe. Ztscher. Parasitenk., 37:198–210.

Nosek, J., Lichard, M., and Sztankay, M. 1967. The ecology of ticks in the Tribĕc and Hronský Inovec Mountains. Bull. World Health Org., 36:49–59.

Nosek, J., Reháček, J., Ernek, E., and Grĕsikova, M. 1962. Importance of small vertebrates as reservoirs of the tick-borne encephalitis virus in a natural focus in the region of Zlaté Moravce. Ceskoslov. Epidemiol., Mikrobiol., Immunol., 11:381–385. (In Czechoslovakian).

O'Connor, P. 1966. Diseases of snakes. In: *Current Veterinary Therapy: Small Animal Practice,* 1966–1967, Kirk, R.W. (Ed.). W.B. Saunders, Philadelphia, PA. pp. 582–585.

Ogandzhaniaǹ, A.M. 1960. Rodents, birds and reptiles as hosts of ixodid ticks in conditions of Armenian SSR and contiguous regions of Azerbaidzhan. Trudy Armianski. Protivochum. Stants, 1:81–86. (In Russian).

Oliver, J.H., Jr. 1989. Biology and systematics of ticks (Acari: Ixodidae). Ann. Rev. Ecol. Syst., 20:397–430.

Oliver, J.H., Jr., and Bremner, K.C. 1968. Cytogenics of ticks. III. Chromosomes and sex determination in some Australian hard ticks (Ixodidae). Ann. Ent. Soc. Am., 61:837–844.

Oliver, J.H., Jr., Cummins, G.A., and Joiner, M.A. 1993a. Immature *Ixodes scapularis* (Acari: Ixodidae) parasitizing lizards from the southeastern U.S.A. J. Parasitol., 79:684–689.

Oliver, J.H., Jr., Hayes, M.P., Keirans, J.E., and Lavender, D.R. 1993b. Establishment of the foreign parthenogenetic tack *Amblyomma rotundatum* (Acari: Ixodidae) in Florida. J. Parasitol., 79:786–790.

Osimani, J.J. 1942. *Haemogregarina triatomae* n. sp. from a South American lizard *Tupinambis teguixin* transmitted by the reduviid *Triatoma rubrovaria*. J. Parasitol., 28:147–154.

Packard, A.S. 1882. Bot fly maggots in a turtle's neck. Ent. Notes, Am. Nat., 16:598.

Papadopoulos, B., Büttiker, W., Morel, P.C., and Aeschliman, A. 1991. Ticks (Acarina, Fam. Argasidae and Ixodidae) of Oman. Fauna of Saudi Arabia, 12:200–208.

Pape, T. 1994. *The World Blaesoxipha Loew, 1861 (Diptera: Sarcophagidae)*. Ent. Scand. Soc., Suppl., 45. Scan. Soc. Ent. 247 pp.

Pearson, A.D., and Tamarind, D.L. 1973. Acarine parasites of the lizard *Lacerta vivipara* Jacquin. British J. Herp., 5:352–353.

Pegram, R.G. 1976. Ticks (Acarina, Ixodoidea) of the northern regions of the Somali Democratic Republic. Bull. Ent. Res., 66:345–363.

Peters, J.A. 1948. A box turtle as a host for dipterous parasites. Am. Midl. Nat., 40:472–474.

Petit, G., Landau, I., Boulard, Y., Gomes, A., and Touratier, L. 1983. Sporogonie de *Plasmodium agamae* chez *Culicoides nebeculosus* au laboratorie: I. Experimentation et description du cycle. Protistologica, 19:537–541.

Petney, T.N., and Al-Yaman, F. 1985. Attachment sites of the tortoise tick *Hyalomma aegyptium* in relation to tick density and physical condition of the host. J. Parasitol., 71:287–289.

Petney, T.N., and Horak, I.G. 1988. Comparative host usage by *Amblyomma hebraeum* and *Amblyomma marmoreum* (Acari, Ixodidae), the South African vectors of the disease heartwater. J. Appl. Ent., 105:490–495.

Petney, T.N., and Keirans, J.E. 1995. Ticks of the genera *Amblyomma* and *Hyalomma* from South-east Asia. Trop. Biomed., 12:45–56.

Petney, T.N., and Keirans, J.E. 1996. Ticks of the genus *Aponomma* (Acari: Ixodidae) in South-east Asia. Trop. Biomed., 13:167-172.

Philip, C.B., and Burgdorfer, W. 1961. Arthropod vectors as reservoirs of microbial disease agents. Ann. Rev. Ent., 6:391–412.

Pomerantsev, B.I. 1950. Fauna of the USSR. Vol. IV. No. 2. Arachnida. Ixodid ticks (Ixodidae). Academy of Sciences USSR, Moscow. 224 pp. (In Russian).

Porter, C.H., and Young, D.G. 1986. A new species of phlebotomine sand fly (Diptera: Psychodidae) from Guatemala. J. Med. Ent., 23:236–243.

Pratt, H.D., and Stojanovik, C.J. 1965. Mosquitoes: Pictorial key to United States genera of adults (female). In: *Pictorial Keys to the Arthropods, Reptiles, Birds and Mammals of Public Health Significance*. CDC, Atlanta, GA. p. 148.

Price, M.A. 1958. A new species of tick from the Trans-Pecos region of Texas. J. Parasitol., 44:649–651.

Punyua, K.K., and Latif, A.A. 1990. Ticks (Acari: Ixodidae) of the Nile monitor on Rusinga Island, Kenya. J. Med. Ent., 27:313–315.

Rainey, D.G. 1953. Death of an ornate box turtle parasitized by dipterous larvae. Herpetologica, 9:109–110.

Rao, T.R., Dhanda, V., Bhat, H.R., and Kulkarni, S.M. 1973. A survey of haema-tophagous arthropods in Western Himalayas, Sikkim and Hill Districts in West Bengal. A general account. Indian J. Med. Res., 61:1421–1461.

Rechav, Y., and Fielden, L.J. 1995. Seasonal abundance of the tortoise tick *Amblyomma marmoreum* (Acari: Ixodidae) on the leopard tortoise, *Geochelone pardalis*. J. Med. Ent., 32:161–165.

Reháček, J., Nosek, J., and Gresikova, M. 1961. Study of the relationship of the green lizard (*Lacerta viridis* Laur.) to natural foci of tick-borne encephalitis. J. Hyg., Epidemiol., Microbiol. and Immunol., 5:366–372.

Reichenbach-Klinke, H., and Elkan, E. 1965. *Principal Diseases of Lower Vertebrates: Diseases of Reptiles*. T.F.H. Publications, Inc., Neptune City, NJ. 600 pp.

Reinhard, H.J. 1965. Review of the miltogrammid genus *Eumacronychia* (Sarcophagidae: Diptera). Can. Ent., 97:337–350.

Rendel, J.M. (Chairman). 1962. Divisions of Animal Genetics and Animal Health. Annual Rep. Anim. Res. Lab., Commonwealth Scientific and Industrial Research Organization, Melbourne, 1961–1962:19–104.

Ritchie, B.W., and Harrison, G.J. 1994. Formulary. In: *Avian Medicine: Principles and Application,* Ritchie, B.W., Harrison, G.J., and Harrison, L.R. Wingers Publishing, Inc., Lake Worth, FL. p. 464.

Roberts, F.H.S. 1953. The Australian species of *Aponomma* and *Amblyomma*. Australian J. Zool., 1:111–161.

Roberts, F.H.S. 1963. *Amblyomma calabyi* n. sp. from Western Australia (Acarina: Ixodidae). Parasitology, 53:177–181.

Roberts, F.H.S. 1964. Further observations on the Australian species of *Aponomma* and *Amblyomma* with descriptions of the nymphs of *Amblyomma moreliae* (L. Koch) and *Amb. loculosum* Neumann (Acarina: Ixodidae). Australian J. Zool., 12:288–313.

Roberts, F.H.S. 1969. The larvae of Australian Ixodidae (Acarina: Ixodidae). J. Australian Ent. Soc., 8:37–78.

Roberts, F.H.S. 1970. *Australian Ticks.* Commonwealth Scientific and Industrial Research Organization, Melbourne. 267 pp.

Robinson, L.E. 1926. *Ticks, a Monograph of the Ixodoidea.* Part IV. The Genus *Amblyomma.* Cambridge University Press, London. 302 pp.

Rosskopf, W.J., Jr. 1992. Ivermectin as a treatment for snake mites. Bull. Assoc. Rept. and Amph. Vet., 2:7.

Roth, B., and Schneider, C.C. 1974. The histo-pathological picture of the skeletal muscle of snakes after paralysis by ticks. Proc. 3rd Int. Congr. Parasitol. (Munich, Aug. 1974), 3:1667–1668 (Abstract).

Rousselot, R. 1953. *Notes de parasitologie tropicale.* Tome II. *Ixodes.* A.O.F., A.E.F. Paris. 135 pp.

Ryckman, R.E. 1954. Lizards: A laboratory host for Triatominae and *Trypanasoma cruzi* Chagas. Trans. Am. Microsc. Soc., 73:215–218.

Ryckman, R.E., and Kohls, G.M. 1962. The desert tortoise, *Gopherus agassizii,* a host for the tick *Ornithodoros turicata* in California. J. Parasitol., 48: 502–503.

Sabrosky, C.W. 1986. *North American Species of Cuterebra, the Rabbit and Rodent Bot Flies (Diptera: Cuterebridae).* Thomas Say Monogr. No. 11, Ent. Soc. Am., College Park, MD. 240 pp.

Saratsiotis, A. 1972. Contribution a l'étude morphologique et biologique du genre *Aponomma* Neumann, 1899 (Acariens, Ixodidea). Acarologia, 13:476–495.

Schmidt, G.D., and Roberts, L.S. 1985. *Foundations of Parasitology,* 3rd ed. Times Mirror/Mosby College Publishing, St. Louis, MO. 775 pp.

Schofield, C.J. 1994. *Triatominae: Biology and Control.* Eurocommunica, Bognor Regis, UK. 80 pp.

Schofield, C.J., and Dolling, W.R. 1993. Bedbugs and kissing-bugs (bloodsucking Hemiptera). In: *Medical Insects and Arachnids,* Lane, R. P. and Crosskey, R. W. (Eds.). Chapman and Hall, London. pp. 483–516.

Schwardt, H.H., and Hall, D.G. 1930. *Preliminary Studies on Arkansas Horse-flies.* Agricultural Experiment Station, University of Arkansas, Bulletin No. 256. 27 pp.

Scott, H.G., and Borom, H.R. 1961. Kissing bugs. Pictorial key to some common species in the United States. In: *Pictorial Keys to Arthropods, Reptiles, Birds and Mammals of Public Health significance.* CDC, Atlanta, GA. p. 95.

Senevet, G. 1928. Clé pour la détermination des larves d'Ixodidés trouvées sur les bovins en Algérie. Arch. Inst. Pateur d'Algérie, 6:42–46.

Seneviratna, P. 1965. The Ixodoidea (ticks) of Ceylon. Parts II and III. Ceylon Vet. J., 13:28–54.

Sharrad, R.D., and King, D.R. 1981. The geographical distribution of reptile ticks in Western Australia. Aust. J. Zool., 29:861–873.

Sixl, W. 1971. Faunistische Nachrichten aus Steiermark (XVI/9): *Hyalomma aegyptium* L.—eine eingeschleppte Zeckenart (Arachnida, Acari). Mitt. Naturw. Ver. Steiermark, 100:453–454.

Sixl, W., Riedl, H., and Schmeller, E. 1971. Heimische Zecken (Arachnida, Acari). 2. Mitteilung. Mitt. Naturw. Ver. Steiermark, 100:391–393.

Smallridge, C., and Paperna, I. 1997. The tick-transmitted haemogregarinid of the Australian sleeply lizard *Tiliqua rugosa* belongs to the genus *Hemolivia*. Parasite-Journal de la Societe Francaise de Parasitologie, 4:359–363.

Smith, K.G.V. 1973. *Insects and Other Arthropods of Medical Importance*. British Museum (Natural History), London. 561 pp.

Smith, T.G. 1996. The genus *Hepatozoon* (Apicomplexa: Adeleina). J. Parasitol., 82:565–585.

Smith, T.G., Desser, S.S., and Martin, D.S. 1994. The development of *Hepatozoon sipedon* sp. nov. (Apicomplexa, Adeleina, Hepatozoidae) in its natural host, the northern water snake (*Nerodia sipedon sipedon*), in the culicine vectors *Culex pipiens* and *C. territans,* and in an intermediate host, the northern leopard frog (*Rana pipiens*). Parasitology Research, 80:559–568.

Smyth, M. 1973. The distribution of three species of reptile ticks, *Aponomma hydrosauri* (Denny), *Amblyomma albolimbatum* Neumann, and *Amb. limbatum* Neumann. I. Distribution and hosts. Australian J. Zool., 21:91–101.

Sonenshine, D.E. 1993. *Biology of Ticks*. Vol. II. Oxford University Press, Oxford. 488 pp.

Sonenshine, D.E., Clifford, C.M., and Kohls, G.M. 1966. The systematics of the subfamily Ornithodorinae (Acarina: Argasidae). III. Identification of the larvae of the Eastern Hemisphere. Ann. Ent. Soc. Am., 59:92–122.

Soulsby, E.J.L. 1968. *Helminths, Arthropods and Protozoa of Domesticated Animals*. Williams and Wilkins Co., Baltimore, MD. 824 pp.

Southgate, B.A. 1967. Studies in the epidemiology of East African leishmaniasis. 5. *Leishmania adleri* and natural immunity. J. Trop. Med. Hyg., 70:33–36.

Starkoff, O.A., and Said-Aliev, S.A. 1968. Ixodid ticks (Ixodidae), the parasites of some reptile species in Tadjikistan. Dokl. Akad. Nauk Tadzhiksk. SSR, 11:64–66. (In Russian).

Stephen, S., and Rao, K.N.A. 1979. Q fever in South Kanora district: Natural occurrence of *Coxiella burnettii* in the tick (*Aponomma gervaisi*)—preliminary report. Indian J. Med. Res., 69:244–246.

Steyskal, G.C., Murphy, W.L., and Hoover, E.M. (Eds.). 1986. *Insects and Mites: Techniques for Collection and Preservation.* USDA Misc. Pub. No. 1443. 103 pp.

Stone, A. 1930. The bionomics of some Tabanidae (Diptera). Ann. Ent. Soc. Am., 23:262–304.

Strickland, R.K., Gerrish, R.R., Hourigan, J.L., and Schubert, G.O. 1976. *Ticks of Veterinary Importance.* USDA Agriculture Handbook No. 485. 122 pp.

Sweatman, G.K. 1968. Temperature and humidity effects on the oviposition of *Hyalomma aegyptium* ticks of different engorgement weights. J. Med. Ent., 5:429–439.

Telford, S.R., Jr. 1967. Studies on the parasites of oriental reptiles. I. Parasitology of the seasnake, *Laticauda semifasciata,* in the vicinity of Amami Island, Japan. Japan J. Exper. Med., 37:245–256.

Telford, S.R., Jr. 1997. *The Ecology of a Symbiotic Community. Vol. II. The Component Symbiote Community of the Japanese Lizard Takydromus tachydromoides (Schlegel) (Lacertidae).* Krieger Publishing Company, Malabar, FL. 170 pp.

Tembo, S.D., and Kiwanuka, A. 1997. Aquisition of protective immunity in *Geochelone pardalis* against *Amblyomma marmoreum* (Acari, Ixodidae) nymphal ticks. Onderstepoort J. Vet. Res., 64:1–4.

Tempelis, C.H., and Galindo, P. 1970. Feeding habits of five species of *Deinocerites* mosquitoes collected in Panama. J. Med. Ent., 7:175–179.

Tempelis, C.H., and Galindo, P. 1975. Host-feeding patterns of *Culex* (*Melanoconian*) and *Culex* (*Aedinus*) mosquitoes collected in Panama. J. Med. Ent., 12:205–209.

Teng, K.F. 1981. A new species of *Amblyomma* from Hainan Island, China (Acarina: Ixodidae). Acta Zootaxon. Sinica, 6:399–401.

Theiler, G. 1962. *The Ixodoidea Parasites of Vertebrates in Africa South of the Sahara (Ethiopian region).* Report to the Director of Veterinary Services, Onderstepoort. 255 pp.

Thiruthalinathan, R., Pannerselvam, N., and Swaminathan, D. 1995. Efficacy of ivermectin against ticks on snakes. J. Vet. Parasitol., 9:37–39.

Thomas, L.A., Eklund, C.M., and Rush, W.A. 1958. Susceptibility of garter snakes (*Thamnophis* spp.) to western equine encephalomyelitis virus. Proc. Soc. Exp. Biol. Med., 99:698–700.

Toumanoff, C. 1941. Une espèce de tique du genre *Aponomma* non encore signalée en Indochine. Rev. Med. Franc. Extreme-Orient., 19:1072–1074.

Tovornik, D., and Brelih, S. 1980. Ixodid ticks, the parasites of lizards (Lacertidae) in the Karst and other districts of Yugoslavia. Scopolia, 3:1–21. (In Yugoslavian).

Townsend, C.H. 1917. New genera and species of American muscoid Diptera. Proc. Biol. Soc, Wash., 30:43–50.

Trauth, S.E., and Mullen, G.R. 1990. Additional observations on sarchophagid fly infestations of *Sceloporus undulatus* (Sauria: Iguanidae) egg clutches in Arkansas. Southwest. Nat., 35:97–98.

Travassos Santos Dias, J.A. 1958. Notas ixodologicas. V. Acerca de alguns ixodideos do Museo de Hamburgo. Mem. e Estud. Mus. Zool. Univ. Coimbra, 253:1–32.

Travassos Santos Dias, J.A. 1961a. Mais alguns ixodideos do Museu de Hamburgo. An. Serv. Vet. e Indust. Animal, Mocambique, 1955–1959 (7):229–235.

Travassos Santos Dias, J.A. 1961b. Contribuicao ao estudo da fauna do Afganistao. 30. Ixodoidea. Mem. e. Estud. Mus. Zool. Univ. Coimbra, (267):1–18.

Travassos Santos Dias, J.A. 1963a. Nova contribuicao para o conhecimento Colhides por uma Missao de estudo do Museu de Hamburgo. An. Serv. Vet. e Indust. Animal, Mocambique, 1961(9):79–98.

Travassos Santos Dias, J.A. 1963b. Sobra uma pequena coleccao ixodologica proveniente do Congo (ex-Belga). An. Serv. Vet. e Indust. Animal, Mocambique, 1961(9):99–103.

Travassos Santos Dias, J.A. 1993. *Contribucao Para o Estudo da Sistematica e Taxonomia das Especies do Genero Aponomma Neumann, 1899 (Acarina-Ixodoidea)*. Est. Ens. Doc. Lisboa, No. 157. 240 pp.

Travis, B.V. 1968. Glyptal - a useful slide ringing compound. J. Med. Ent., 5:24.

Tucker, A.D. 1995. First record of parasitism by a tick on an Australian freshwater crocodile. Mem. Qld. Mus., 38:686.

Turianin, N.I. 1963. Vertebrate animals fed on by ticks of the genus *Ixodes* in the Soviet Carpathians. In: *Trudy 4. Nauch. Konf. Parazitol., USSR*. pp. 402–404. (In Russian).

Uilenberg, G., Hoogstraal, H., and Klein, J.M. 1979. *Les Tiques (Ixodoidea) de Madagascar et Leur Rôle Vecteur*. Arch. Inst. Pasteur Madagascar. 153 pp.

U.S. Department of Agriculture. 1965. *Manual on Livestock Ticks*. USDA, ARS 91–49.

Ushakova, G.V., Busalaeva, N.N., and Peteshev, V.M. 1963. Contribution to the fauna and distribution of the *Ixodes* ticks of the Syr-Darya left bank. Trudy Inst. Zool. Akad. Nauk Kazakhsk. SSR, 19:173–179. (In Russian).

Van der Borght-Elbl, A. 1977. Ixodid ticks (Acarina, Ixodidae) of Central Africa. Vol. V. The larval and nymphal stages of the more important species of the genus *Amblyomma* Koch, 1844. Ann. K. Mus. Midden-Africa, Tervuren, s. 8, Zool. Wetensch. 158 pp.

Varma, M.G.R. 1973. Ticks (Ixodidae) of British Honduras. Tr. Roy. Soc. Trop. Med. Hyg., 67:92–102.

Vasil'eva, I.S. 1976. Habitats of *Ornithodoros tartakovskyi* Ol. (Argasidae) populations in Southern Tajikistan. Report 2. Distribution of *O. tartakovskyi* along the pathways of burrows in summer. Med. Parazitol. Parazit. Bolezni, 45: 204–209. (In Russian).

Vogt, R.C. 1981. Turtle egg (*Graptemys*: Emydidae) infested by fly larvae. Copeia, 1981:457–459.

Walker, J.B. 1974. *The Ixodid Ticks of Kenya. A Review of Present Knowledge of Their Hosts and Distribution.* Commonwealth Institute of Entomology. 220 pp.

Walker, J.B. 1987. The tick vectors of *Cowdria ruminantium* (Ixodoidea, Ixodidae, genus *Amblyomma*) and their distribution. Onderstepoort J. Vet. Res., 54:353–379.

Walker, J.B. 1991. A review of the ixodid ticks (Acari, Ixodidae) occurring in southern Africa. Onderstepoort J. Vet. Res., 58:81–105.

Walker, J.B., and Bezuidenhout, J.D. 1973. Treatment of tick-infested tortoises. J. S. African Vet. Med. Assoc., 44:381.

Walton, G.A. 1962. The *Ornithodoros moubata* superspecies problem in relation to human relapsing fever epidemiology. Symp. Zool. Soc. Lond., 6: 83–156.

Ward, D.L. 1989. Subdermal infestation of a monitor lizard by *Aponomma undatum* (Fabricius) (Acarina: Ixodidae). Australian Ent. Mag., 16:78.

Wassef, H.Y., and Hoogstraal, H. 1988. *Dermacentor* (*Indocentor*) *steini* (Acari: Ixodoidea: Ixodidae): hosts, distribution in the Malay Peninsula, Indonesia, Borneo, Thailand, the Philippines, and New Guinea. J. Med. Entomol., 25: 315–320.

Wassef, H.Y., Büttiker, W., and Gallagher, M.D. 1997. Further records of ticks (Acari: Argasidae and Ixodidae) from the Arabian Peninsula. Fauna of Saudi Arabia, 16:63–88.

Webb, J.L., and Wells, R.W. 1924. Horse-flies; biologies and relation to western agriculture. Dept. Bull. No. 1218, U.S. Dept. Agr. 36 pp.

Webb, J.P. Jr., Bennett, S.G., and Challet, G.L. 1990. The larval ticks of the genus *Ixodes* Latreille (Acari: Ixodidae) of California. Bull. Soc. Vector Ecol., 15:73–124.

Wheeler, W.M. 1890. The supposed bot-fly parasite of the box turtle. Psyche, 5:403.

Whittick, R.J. 1939. On some ticks belonging to the genera *Aponomma* and *Amblyomma*. Parasitology, 31:435–441.

Whitworth, R.J., and Wangberg, J.K. 1985. Parasitization of the Texas spotted whiptail lizard (*Cnemidophorus gularis*) by a sarcophagid fly (*Blaesoxipha plinthopyga*): A new host record. Southwest. Nat., 30:160–164.

Wilson, N. 1966. Variation in two species of *Amblyomma* (Metastigmata: Ixodidae). Proc. Ent. Soc. Wash., 68:222–224.

Wilson, N. 1969. Ticks (Metastigmata: Ixodidae) collected by the Noona Dan expedition to the Philippine and Bismarck Archipelagos. Ent. Meddel., 37: 285–288.

Wilson, N. 1970. New distributional records of ticks from Southeast Asia and the Pacific (Metastigmata: Argasidae, Ixodidae). Oriental Insects, 4:37–46.

Wilson, N., and Barnard, S.M. 1985. Three species of *Aponomma* (Acari: Ixodidae) collected from imported reptiles in the United States. Florida Ent., 68: 478–480.

Wilson, N., and Kale, H.W. 1972. Ticks collected from Indian River County, Florida (Acari: Metastigmata: Ixodidae). Florida Ent., 55:53–57.

Wilson, N., and Southgate, B.A. 1979. Lizard *Leishmania*. In: *Biology of the Kinetoplastida*. Lumsden, W.H.R. and Evans, D. A. (Eds.), Vol. 2, Academic Press, New York, N.Y. pp. 241–268.

Wirth, W.W., and Hubert, A.A. 1962. The species of *Culicoides* related to *piliferus* Root and Hoffman in eastern North America (Diptera: Ceratopogonidae). Ann. Entomol. Soc. Am., 55:182–195.

Wirth, W.W., and Hubert, A.A. 1989. The *Culicoides* of Southeast Asia (Diptera: Ceratopogonidae). Mem. Am. Ent. Inst., 44:1–508.

Worms, M.J. 1967. Parasites in newly imported animals. J. Inst. Anim. Tech., 18:39–47.

Wozniak, E.J., and Telford, S.M., Jr. 1991. The fate of *Hepatozoon* spp. naturally infecting Florida black racers and watersnakes in potential mosquito and soft tick vectors, and histological evidence of pathogenicity in unnatural host species. Int. J. Parasitol., 21:511–516.

Wright, R.E., and DeFoliart, G.R. 1970. Associations of Wisconsin mosquitoes and woodland vertebrate hosts. Ann. Ent. Soc. Am., 63:777–786.

Yamaguti, N., Tipton, V.J., Keegan, H.L., and Toshioka, S. 1971. Ticks of Japan, Korea, and the Ryukyu Islands. Brigham Young Univ. Sci. Bull., Biol. Ser., 15:1–226.

Yeoman, G.H., and Walker, J.B. 1967. *The Ixodid Ticks of Tanzania. (A Study of the Zoogeography of the Ixodidae of an East African Country).* Commonwealth Institute of Entomology, London. 215 pp.

Young, D.E., and Perkins, P.V. 1984. Phlebotomine sand flies of North America (Diptera: Psychodidae). Mosquito News, 44:263–304.

Young, E. 1965. *Aponomma exornatum* (Koch) as a cause of mortality among monitors. J. S. African Vet. Med. Assoc., 36:579.

Yuill, T.M. 1969. Mosquitoes for drawing blood from small reptiles. Trans. Roy. Soc. Trop. Med. Hyg., 63:407.

Zann, L.P., Cuffey, R.J., and Kropach, C. 1975. Fouling organisms and parasites associated with the skin of sea snakes. In: *The Biology of Sea Snakes,* Dunson, W. A. (Ed.). University Park Press, Baltimore, MD. pp. 251–265.

Zlatanova, V.D. 1991. Ixodid ticks (Parasitiformes, Ixodidae) of tortoises (Reptilia, Testudinidae) in Bulgaria. Acta Zool. Bulgaria, 41:77–79. (In Bulgarian).

Zumpt, F. 1965. *Myiasis in Man and Animals in the Old World: A Textbook for Physicians, Veterinarians and Zoologists.* Butterworths, London. 247 pp.

INDEX